BLUEPRINTS

RICHARD HELLER

Richard Heller

to Cherri
keep writing, Don't stop!

Rich

ROAD SCHOLAR PUBLISHING GROUP

Blueprints
Copyright ©2011 by Richard Heller

This is a work of autobiographical fiction. Characters and names are the imagination of the author. Any resemblance to an actual event, person or animal, living or dead is purely coincidental.

Published by:
Road Scholar Publishing Group LLC
P.O. Box 25243
Scottsdale AZ 85255
Reboh@cox.net

Publisher's Cataloging-in-Publication Data

Heller, Richard, 1952-
    Blueprints / by Richard Heller.
    p. cm.
    LCCN 2010940553
    ISBN-13: 978-0-615-41872-8
    ISBN-10: 0-615-41872-4

    1. Blacksmiths--Fiction. 2. Human-animal relationships--Fiction. 3. Adult child abuse victims--Fiction. 4. Bildungsromans, American. I. Title.

PS3608.E455B58 2011   813'.6
                      QBI10-600241

Edited by: Barbara Crane
Cover Design & Interior Layout: Fusion Creative Works, www.fusioncw.com

Front Cover: photograph of Richard Heller and his dog Billy taken by author, in 1970, somewhere on the coast of Northern California.

Printed in the United States of America

For more information please visit: www.RichardAHeller.com

For my wife Lyra,

our son Daniel

and

Alan Sheppard

(1930-1980)

ACKNOWLEDGMENTS

I acknowledge my debt to Holly Prado Northup, poet and mentor. It's a debt that can only be paid back by giving it my "all" on the page.

With deep gratitude to the writers who were in my writer's workshop; Joan Isaacson, Bill Banks, Vicki Mizel, Marie Brown' Pal, Kathleen Bevacqua, Gina Battaglia, Garrett Brown, Jason Greenwald, Linda Ruggeri, Fernando Castro, Doko Sharrin, Sharon Melina Rosner. Their constant encouragement and caring criticisms kept me going.

I am grateful for the friendships of Fred Chernoff, Loretta, Mike and Mark Sheppard, Lerae Leaver, Doko Sharrin, Frosty Horton, Gloria Storer, Tom and Ann Gallon, Fred and Beth Rosen-Prinz, Marla Rivera, Gregg and Cathy Pittman, Rebecca Barkin, Jim and Julie Visner, Chris Allport, Jay Storer, Betty Mott, Kristen and Eric Yang, Lawrence Casperson, Michael Covert, Lisa Casperson, Sarah Oberpriller, Carol Walker, Mark Thomas, Fred, Johnny Gonzales, Sherry Stevens, Adrienne Fayne, Brent McEwan, Tim Cooper, Lee Serrie, Lynette Treffinger, Sara Greenspan, Peter Benjamin, Cynthia Maloney, Larry Rosen, Michael Norman, Charlotte Bornstein, Savannah Finch, Judy Miller, Aura Kuperberg, Zoreh Gottfurcht and Reggie Shelton.

Special thanks to my editor Barbara Crane for her patience, skill and contagious laugh, Fred Chernoff, my intellectual conscience, Frankie Farrell for the title and Linda Jacqueline Reboh at Road Scholar Publishing Group, for her tireless support and willingness to make this book available.

CHAPTERS

*Sometimes, hidden within the hollowed,
bottom staircase newel of old homes are its important papers:
blueprints, notes on construction, photos and other things.*

*This book is about the other things: the private reasons why I
built my home. When finished with these pages, I'll roll them up
and place them within the house's banister, which I made.*

1

AS A CHILD

On April 6, 1952, I was born; a sad day for my mother, father and me. Sixteen years later my parents told me to leave. With no goodbye, my feisty Shetland Sheepdog Curry and I drove away in my Jeep, ending my childhood. It was a relief for all four of us.

Tujunga, in Los Angeles County, was a small mountainous foothill community in the 1950s, and fifty years later it still is. This was where my parents' first home was, situated between two other new, small tract homes. On one side lived a Nazi, looking sharp, wearing his little brown uniform on weekly occasions. On the other side of us lived members of the Hell's Angels, less than shy about showing their colors daily. We lived there only a short time but what happened in our home, if the outside world had known, would have brought the police to us before they'd ever thought about investigating our neighbors.

I first saw the world through my mother's fears. My life was filled with her ritualistic pursuit of perfection to ward off sickness. A drowning woman, she pushed me under to keep herself from sinking. From the very first, I was never held. I ached for touch and then learned to fear it. The cold hands of my mother only came to keep me clean. In those moments set aside for motherly love, there was none. I was cradled in precognitive disgust, left like a beast to beat my head in frustration. I pounded my head against the crib's wood pickets until they were stained with my blood. Then my mother and father padded the crib's interior.

When I was five we moved closer to the city of Los Angeles, a few blocks east of Griffith Park, where my sister Mary was born. For some reason my mother lavished love on my sister. But it was of no matter to me; an older boy named Hugh was paid 25 cents to teach me how to ride a bike; I felt free. We moved again, this time to an area called the Oaks. My sister was three and I was seven.

I was punished with my father's belt most nights. When his strap wasn't handy, he'd improvise. One night he slammed my head on the edge of our carpeted steps. The worst part of my father's storm was his verbal rage. I was the lightning rod for my father's anger. Lightning only struck my sister when I left home for good.

Growing up in this household, I learned that I could be blamed for every pain or struggle my mother or father had. Over a half a century has passed, but I still fall asleep with the concern that I didn't document my day's activities to have a concrete account of my whereabouts, just in case I'm accused of something. With each new day, these childhood feelings are subdued by the previous night's sleep and find their way to the status of crazy thoughts.

Memory is a ghost, and I'm a ghostly reminder that the past stays unchanged for my mother. At first, she yielded to my request to stop reinventing the past and just let it rest if she wanted a relationship with me as an adult. But haunted by her brutality towards me and the need to have things perfect, she tried to recreate our past. I began to feel crazy with my mother's fabricated reminiscing. In a contorted form of good manners I don't speak of the past with my parents. I'm possessed by a feeling of being deeply flawed, so I've never raged at them.

EDUCATION

Forty-three years later and four canyons to the east, my wife Gillian and I have raised our now twenty year old son, Berrigan. But in 1959, when I was seven, the Bronson Caves were more of a home for me than my parents' two story house in the Hollywood Hills.

With my dog Curry, I would hike all day. It was only a short run up the neighbor's steep driveway and through their yard in this hilly community to the park.

Within the borders of Los Angeles's Griffith Park in 1903, there was a rock quarry, but it was abandoned within a short time. Later, in the 1930s and now, the quarry's caves, known as the Bronson Caves, are used in "A" and "B" movies, like "The Giant One-Eyed Cyclops" and "Attack of the Fifty-Foot Woman." God, I wish I could have slept with her. "Lost Horizon" was also filmed up there. From the age of seven into my teens, I spent all my waking hours hiking in these hills of the park with Curry. Rainy days were the best with the smell of sage and the melancholy gray light making silhouettes of the trees. I thanked God it was Curry and me alone.

Miss Downum was my second grade teacher, may she rot in hell. When I didn't come out with the rest of the kids after school one day, my mother came into the classroom as Miss Downum was yelling at me. "Your arithmetic is all wrong. You don't know anything. You're a stupid little child."

Then she turned on my mother, "What kind of home are you providing for him? He is totally unprepared for the second grade. He is not able to do anything."

Once again Downum turned on me; "Write in crayon over your wrong answer with this right answer. Go back to your desk now!"

I saw my mother holding her face as if she could catch her tears, and briskly going out the way she came in, leaving me alone with this teacher's insults.

With blue, green, red, orange and other crayons, I made multiple layers of colors over the wrong answer, then covered it with black crayon. I etched in the right answer with a sharp pencil, bringing forth a brilliant rainbow of colors. Mrs. Downum looked at what I'd done, and with my mother gone, Mrs. Downum said, "What kind of child are you?" At the same time she slapped me across the face. Instead of killing her, I sank my fingers deep into my face tearing at my own skin. Blood dripped down, and I hoped I would die.

"You did that to yourself. You are excused," she said.

The classroom was never the same. The dreary walls, teachers' voices and those obedient other seven- and eight-year-olds – it was a death shroud, and I wanted to live.

The next day, I took my chance at lunch. Heading toward the lavatory, I faked right and went left through the side gate, past Mr. Aims, the janitor. I made it. I hiked for hours in the park till night fell. Then, after dark, I entered my parents' perfect, empty house and their constant demands that I wash my hands and not touch anything.

Soon after it was discovered that I was ditching school, I was enrolled in a school that was over an hour away. For a while this meant I wasn't able to hike during the week. On the weekends though, smiling at Curry, I'd unchain his real chain and my emotional one from my phobic mother and my passive-aggressive, silhouette of a father. Running past hillside homes, deep into the park, we'd hike; then, tired, we'd sleep in one of the Bronson cave's alcoves or recesses. I dreamed this cave went deep into a large mountain with winding passages. The cave did go into a mountain, and a couple of tunnels did spring from it, but the length was only five or six hundred feet. The cave went all the way through and emptied into a large rock quarry, where the walls rose three hundred feet. I climbed easily from the backside of this little mountainous area and found myself on top of the cliff. From this ledge I could look down onto the quarry and cave. Always enjoying a hike on the edges of cliffs, I felt pride when my father hiked with me one Saturday and said, "You're not scared being so close to the edge? You really are surefooted." He never hiked there again with me or, for that matter, any other place.

Sometimes a person would venture through the main cave or one of its small tributaries, then decide to climb up and out over the bowl's rock wall. Reaching the area directly under the top, they'd see what they should have seen before they started the endeavor: a rocky cornice. Whether they didn't notice it at the bottom while looking up or thought by the time they reached that point they'd be experienced climbers, I don't know. But they were always able to get rescued by yelling for help.

I loved how the firemen dealt with these intrepid Hollywood mountaineers. Hiking around to the back of this maquette-sized mountain they'd look over the side at the forlorn wanderer. Then one of the fireman, hand over hand, lowered himself on a rope the few feet under the cornice's lip to the victim. The firemen at the top held on to the rope while tossing a rescue harness down to the rescuer. The lowered fireman would then put the safety harness around the Sir Edmund Hillary wannabe's legs and rear-end and attach the harness to the rope. Next, our city's finest, on top of the ledge, aided by the fireman under the ledge, guided and pulled the fleshy cargo to the top. You'd think they would then drop the rope and harness once more for the rescuer. Instead, one of the firemen on top would grab the back of the belt worn by the fireman who was closest to the overhang. Then he'd lean over and reach down with one hand to meet the waiting fireman's hand. With one simple move, the fireman was back on top of the cliff aided only by the other fireman's hand. Mind you, it's about a three hundred foot drop.

The park was my constant refuge. Never one to use trails, I hiked through the brush. At least a few times a year I would become acquainted with poison oak. At first, my histamine responses were less than noticeable, but with constant tromping through this poisonous plant, my reaction each time got worse. The outbreak raged through my skin and sucked the happiness out of my carefree youth, the way mistletoe sucks the life out of a tree.

It was within this park that I grew up.

My final departure from home at sixteen was made easier because of the time I spent in the park and the relationships I made there, before I inevitably left my childhood forever. The park and its visitors showed me things that were beyond a school education.

Pete and Alger were one of those park relationships I will never forget.

Pete was a big man. This in and of itself did not make him a big man. It was the type of man he was: kind, patient and brave. The same could be said of his German shepherd, Alger.

Pete was a truck driver when I met him. He had studied for the Jesuit priesthood, but his superior at the seminary said Pete liked women too much and would be better off finding another path. Pete had been on stage in New York as an actor and had worked as a stevedore. He was also one hell of an oil painter.

We walked many hours in the hills of Griffith Park with our dogs. Pete taught me how to be truly observant when looking at things, whether it was other human beings in the park or animals and landscape. It was during this time with him that I gained the eye of a sculptor. The message in my family was that art wasn't real work. Even though I fought hard against the undertow of art, I knew it was beyond my control.

As Pete mentored me, Alger, Pete's shepherd, mentored my dog Curry. Although Curry was big for a Shetland sheepdog he was still a small dog, but it never stopped Curry from picking fights with dogs four times his size. Alger, unlike so many other big dogs, didn't take offense to my little Napoleon but instead loved his feistiness. Alger was always there to back Curry up.

In the later part of my twelfth year, I was as big as I would get. My father was about six feet tall; it was thought that I would certainly pass him. At five foot eight and a hundred-fifty pounds of hyperactive muscle, people always thought I was much older. By the age of fifteen, no one ever asked me for my I.D. when buying beer, but Pete knew that under my wiry build was a child.

There were others in the park that I walked with. When I was about eleven, Pete warned me to be careful, to keep an eye out for one new individual that visited the park with his dog. His name escapes me now, but this guy jumped me on the trail above the area where I normally let Curry run. He got on top of me, and a fight ensued. I won in the sense that I was not sexually violated. It would be great to say that I kicked his ass, but it was more that I put up too much of a fuss to make it worth his while. I told Pete what had happened. What followed the next day was to be my first time watching two men fight.

"I heard you tried to jump Alan," Pete said to the attacker.

"Lay off, Pete, nothing happened anyway," was this monster's response.

"It's time for you to find another place to walk."

"I didn't do anything."

It wasn't much of a fight. Pete hit him once in the face and the man fell onto the parking lot's gravel, bloodier from the fragment of rock than the punch, although it was harder than anything I had seen on the school playground. He escaped quickly to his car and drove away before Pete took another swipe at him. After Pete finished muttering a few words under his breath, he turned to me, "You have to pay attention and not trust everyone. But I don't think we'll ever see him again."

While writing about this man who jumped me in the park, I recall that he had a Siberian husky. After my son Berrigan got over the death of his one-hundred-pound "vicious" Doberman he had for eleven years, he wanted a Siberian husky. I had an uncomfortable feeling about getting a husky, and I didn't understand why. They are typically a gentle, non-aggressive dog and seemed like a perfect match to my son's new college life. Berrigan had been sleeping with Hamish, his sharp-toothed, hundred-pound, temperamental Doberman, since he was young and had the scars to prove it. Why was I uneasy? It always amazes me how smells, sounds and the sight of things stimulate unresolved feelings.

Pete, Alger, Curry and I always walked past the park's groomed area, where Griffith Park becomes semi-mountainous. Oak trees, pines, coastal redwoods, European sycamores, American sycamores, sage and yerba santa dress these foothills. Their woven canopies of branches, blankets of grasses, pillows of white sage and manzanita gave a world of cover for the inhabitants.

For me, it was a lesson in looking at the undulating vibration of color with each of the subtle changes in seasons. Sun merged and cascaded onto this land year after year. Rain catalyzed the fragrance of the medicinal brush. I learned through Pete to see the seasonal pastels and primary colors interplay between the sun's rays with the deer, coyotes and songbirds. Red-Tailed hawks and Peregrine falcons changed their behavior along with the earth's movement. As we walked, Pete pointed to where the does migrated with their fawns.

The city of Los Angeles finds winter in name only and gets stuck in acting out the fall and spring with nothing to thaw. Even people who spend time in the park find themselves playing out the act of an on-coming winter with heavy sweaters, a Thermos of coffee and shortened stays. Forgetting that these trails are not obscured by early snows or any snows at all, they hurry home in spite of the truth. This was when I stayed late. Movement has always made me warm, whether in my studio late at night or in my preteens on a hike. I've always felt my schedule should be to wake up at two or three in the afternoon and go to bed at eight in the morning. I have always moved better in the moonlight.

Pete and his dog Alger taught me that life did not have to be about having material things. Fulfillment could come through appreciating life itself. Alger understood the level of wealth that lived inside Pete. This German shepherd never left Pete's side. No dog, ball or steak took his attention away from his human friend.

2

ON MY OWN

I started to drift away from home at fifteen years old, when at least a few nights each week I didn't show up for dinner or anything else. I faded into a shadow.

When I left for good, I still found myself living in a part of the Hollywood Hills not far from where I was raised, my mother was raised, and where my mother's mother lived. My great-grandmother gave birth to my grandmother in a barn in Watts, or so my grandmother said.

The first real home after leaving my parents' house was my full head of long, brown hair that turned blond in the summer. It kept my body warm on the coldest nights.

At seventeen, I lived in a CJ6, which is a long wheelbase Jeep. It was a larger civilian version of the MB military jeep I owned when I was fourteen. I leased this first jeep to Paramount Pictures for the making of the movie "Catch 22." My friend Eric Gordon, who rented vintage World War II vehicles to the movies, called me one day.

"Alan, Paramount Pictures needs another jeep for the making of Catch 22. Are you interested?" I wanted to say no, but $1,700 sounded too good to pass up. This was the early 60s. It was a lot of money.

I had met Eric a couple of years before. While driving around the neighborhood, a man stopped me and gave me Eric's card, telling me that Eric Gordon was an expert on military vehicles. At fourteen,

I had put together models, fixed family and friends' TV remote controls and made a dog run for Curry to get him off that terrible chain. Picking someone's brain about working on my vehicle sounded great. I called him as soon as I got home.

"Hello," a deep voice with a British accent came over the phone.

"May I speak to Eric Gordon?" I asked.

"I'm Eric Gordon."

"Hi, my name is Alan and I have an MB jeep, I was given your card by a man who said you could tell me about my jeep."

"Sure, Alan, bring it over."

Eric lived at the other end of the Hollywood Hills, which meant I'd have to take major streets and risk being caught driving underage and without a license. Not too long after that, I overcame those fears, but this time I made arrangements to have my father drive me to Eric's the next weekend.

As I walked into the backyard of his 1920s small version of a Hollywood Hills mansion, I called out to him. A handful of military vehicles were parked in the large, shaded yard. A voice replied from under a 1940 Dodge Power Wagon weapons carrier.

Two old, combat-booted feet stuck out from under the side of the Dodge.

"Mr. Gordon?"

"Alan, is that you?"

"Yes, and my father also."

"Good, let me finish tightening up this U-joint, and I'll be with you."

The yard was neat but was a Hollywood jungle, with pine trees, redwood trees, palm trees and ivy. At the very back of this foliage-dense compound was an old wood shingled two room house, which was Eric's office and library. This GI Eden smelled of sweet rhododendrons, ancient canvas and 90-weight motor oil. The mechanics' creeper rolled Eric out from under the truck, creaking loudly as it traveled along the hard dirt. I watched as the rest of his boots and legs emerged from under the Power Wagon. His legs didn't seem to end. Then came his torso, and that didn't seem to end either. Finally his whole body was out from under. I always considered my father to be tall, but when Eric stood up, he towered over my father like the trees in this yard.

"How tall are you?" was the first thing that came out of my mouth.

"Six feet, 9 inches, and it's nice to meet you and your father," he said in a rustic British accent as he lit his pipe with his huge, work-beaten, sinewy hands. I felt comfortable and at ease.

I have always felt safe with people that are bigger than me, a sense they won't break in my presence.

Through conversations with Eric, I became more familiar with my jeep. After that day, I started to tinker with it, never doing anything to compromise its reliability or its military persona. With this new skill of turning wrenches – getting my hands greasy – I abandoned repair shops and roads, replacing them with a tool box and desert mining trails.

I've abused everyone that I care about with my shortcuts through the mountains, deserts and on urban roads, rural roads, foot trails and no trails at all.

I don't actually get lost, but I'm attracted to things, not destinations. I hold each moment of this life sacred, never wanting to miss anything. The concentrated effort it takes to find out where I am going short-circuits this deeper process of exploration.

It has been a pilgrimage without a deity to drape around my idiosyncrasies. I let the sound of my breath, footsteps and old smells guide me.

With friends, all of us in our mid-teens, in my military jeep with its flathead four- banger engine moving us up the highway at a break-neck speed of 45 miles per hour, we found peace. The desert winds sandblasted our faces. After hours of driving, we'd arrive at the end of the road. We then locked the front hubs, pulled one lever on the floor back and pushed the other forward into four-wheel drive low range. We drove late into the night, over dunes and rocks. Finally, sleep would catch up with us. The quiet, desert night sounds would subdue our teenage hearts and we would find deep silent sleep.

At night, the desert's Milky Way is a woman; her silhouette shows through a black gown. You can look, but you can't touch. She whispers promises. The smells of a desert storm upon the sage and the warm touch of wind: by morning all that's left is the harsh sight of daylight.

Men are the real romantics, especially the ones who never lie to women, the ones who go to the wilderness, whether it is the sea, mountains, or the desert. We go not to be alone but to be chased and caught, knowing that She will never come, but we hope.

Fair women, I make a plea for all of us men who don't wear a fancy yoke by fate or choice. Once caught we will stand with you till our last breath and think it nothing to give our life for yours. In return, on behalf of my kind, be gentle with us. I caution you to be careful for what you ask us to defend.

Mothers: You say you want to change the world? Change it by loving your sons. Tell them they are beautiful and tell them to spend time only with women who respect kindness.

It was three years after meeting Eric that I agreed to lease my jeep to Paramount Pictures. It turned out to be too big of an emotional price though. The jeep liberated me physically and mentally from the city each weekend; with it gone, I was stranded in Los Angeles.

The pain of being in L.A. would get to me sometimes, to the point I thought I'd explode, and it was at these times that I would run all night. I never planned to run as far as I did, but my pace was fueled by the sadness of an unhappy childhood.

It was early in the morning and raining when we got off of my neighborhood friend's 305 Honda Scrambler motorcycle. "So Alan, I guess you won't need a ride home from school today?" Andrew Burns always seemed to know when I wasn't going to make it to the inside of a classroom.

"Yah, I hate this place I'll see ya' tomorrow." Normally I'd walk home and get Curry. We'd walk in the park or drive out to the desert. But with my jeep now in Mexico, there was no way to get Curry and me out to the quiet of the desert. The hills beyond Los Angeles looked reachable so I walked without Curry. In a short while, I found myself on San Fernando Road. I started to jog. In a short time, I was in the town of San Fernando, then later jogged on to the Sierra Highway. The Sierra Highway was the only way to the Mojave Desert at the time, a small, winding, rural road which rolled past ranches, open space and small communities. Somewhere on this road I decided not to go home, but just to jog forever. I bought a small but well-made green canvas knap sack, canteen, fruit, nuts and bread at a little general store somewhere on this road.

I jogged late into the night. Around two or three in the morning, the rain coming down hard, almost out of food and all my money spent, the thought of finishing this frenzied trek another day occurred to me. I stopped jogging at a train stop. I knew one of the parked trains went back to Los Angeles.

An engineer must have taken pity on me in the pounding rain. I yelled to him, "Which one goes to L.A.?"

He replied, "Find an empty car. I'm not looking."

I shared a freight car with an old man who looked too drunk and frail to have lifted himself into the freight car. I didn't worry about my riding companion and fell fast asleep. At my parents' house that morning, I changed clothes and pretended to go to school. Instead, I slept the day away in the park.

After the months of filming in Mexico were finished, my beloved jeep, which took me more places than I could have imagined, came back to me ruined in a vehicle stretcher. It arrived home from Guaymas, looking like a fatigued, steel prisoner of war.

I sold my mechanical friend back to the studio for its appraised value, with a strong sense that this jeep wasn't even my own, and someone from Paramount Pictures was driving mine. The thought of not having that friend to take me places makes my blood boil even now, although I never put up signs on power poles: "Lost, 1945 military jeep, last seen in Guaymas, Mexico, khaki green in color, with matching canvas top and center-to-center mud and snow tires, also known as gravediggers."

During that summer my father told me to leave, and a newer, this time civilian Jeep became my home. If I wasn't sleeping in it, I'd stay late at parties or sleep in Griffith Park.

At sixteen I discovered that a cardboard box or the Hearst Castle can be a home. For the next six months, I lived in this second Jeep. It was my home. Dean and Roxanne were the previous owners of this yellow, longer version of my military one. They were professional photographers who traveled throughout Mexico and Guatemala. Dean had constructed an elaborate plywood storage cabinet that occupied the rear area's interior. The height of this cabinetry came up flush with the back side of the front seats, and Dean had hinged onto the top lid another sheet of plywood, which folded over the front seats to make a comfortable bed. The Jeep's top was canvas. The sides and back could be rolled up or kept down, depending on the weather. This was my first real residence. I used the engine exhaust manifold to heat cans of soup and warmed Van de Camp chocolate chip cookies on the steel floor cover over the transmission.

I drove and slept everywhere. I got a speeding ticket, pled my guilt and was sentenced to traffic school. This was the Sixties and not only did Fairfax High School offer traffic school at night, it also offered an encounter group in the night's curriculum. Yes, another warm place to spend the early night. While in this group, I received praise for my free spirit for living in a Jeep. One older member of this encounter group transcended social correctness of the time. "You do your thing and I'll do mine." And how can anyone forget that ever popular phrase, "There Are No Shoulds," which I interpreted to mean, you don't have to do anything.

This older man told me that he "didn't buy I was a free sprit" and wanted me to get a warm room or an apartment to live in, which I heard as loving, fatherly advice and took him up on his suggestion.

I don't remember this older gentleman's name. But I will never forget his courage for going up against the thinking of the time. He showed paternal care towards me, a young man whom he didn't know but who desperately needed advice. My father's passive hatred of males would have never allowed him to give me this much-needed advice.

In November, two weeks after the gentleman confronted me in the group encounter, I rented a quaint, white wooden cottage with a shaker roof in the Hollywood Hills. A Dutch door entry, exposed wood beams, hardwood floor and tiled bathroom made up the studio's interior. It was the upper half of a two-story cottage. The lower half was brick and had been converted from a garage into a studio apartment and was occupied then and maybe even now by my friend Telford. He was a rock bass guitar player from Australia. Slight in build, Tel quietly showed his passion for life, growing enough weed to keep him content. Fair-skinned with long straw-like hair, he played his guitar softly and tended our landlady's garden with a delicate hand. He had no need for a driver's license.

CURRY

In a way, my behavior has been more like a dog's than my canine Jeep roommate, Curry. Since I was seven, Curry, has endured so much rustic behavior from me that he could not restrain himself and finally did bite me once in protest.

Actually, I was bitten by Curry more than once. I was eighteen; it was at the end of a hiking trip in the Sierras with my friend Dane Burns, Andrew Burns' brother. Lying on the grass in front of the ranger's station, I thought Curry would make a comfortable place to rest my weary head. Normally, he didn't mind my using his shoulder as a pillow when he was on his side.

He caught my nose where it merges with my brow. Blood ran down over my lip into my mouth. "You bit me! I can't believe it, my own dog." Dane was on this same slope also resting. Dane looked over, saw the blood dripping down my face and started to laugh. They had both had enough of my short cuts. I'm at times more persuaded by impulse and comfort than the needs of those I say I care for.

A second bite happened a few years later, at the end of a three-month walk through the Sierras with Curry. A three-week hike fortuitously turned into a three-month trek. At the time, I had long blondish, auburn hair and a fairly long reddish-blond and black beard, but I never quite looked like a hippie. I appeared more like the offspring of a wiry, male, calico-colored black bear and a 95-pound, sharp-featured, blue-eyed woman. Curry, being a Shetland sheepdog, was the epitome of adorable. These small Collie types can conjure affection from a stone, even though Curry was pretty surly and had no qualms about biting anybody. Together we appeared to be an approachable pair to anyone who might need directions. We looked like a meager substitute for a nature television show, but when a hiker craves some sort of entertainment, almost anything will do. I am a wanderer and exist mostly on instinct, so during encounters with other hikers, I tried never to give directions. In a moment of carefree abandon, Curry and I could have gotten a fellow traveler bitten and then lost.

Food was never a priority for me. I lived both in Alaska and the Sierras, for the most part on peanut butter and honey sandwiches, water and tea. During conversations in the High Sierras with other hikers, a theme arose from them: "Boy, I wish I didn't have to carry out all this food." Concerned that I might not be getting a balanced diet, I'd offer to buy some of the food and stove fuel they didn't want to carry home. Their reply was, "Here just take it; this means I'll have less to carry out." I did have enough peanut butter and honey for me, and Ken-L-Rations for Curry to last the initially-planned three-week hike. With this new source of food, Curry and I could now lengthen our stay. We began to wander. For three months, we walked over ridges, from trail to trail, into dense forests and above alpine land-scapes. As the summer flickered out, so did other hikers. Hiking for a week in cool weather and not seeing another person let me know winter was coming with no need of a long autumn. Realizing this would be my last week in the mountains till the next summer, I was sad. Here in the Sierras with Curry I never felt judged as a success or failure; I was just an observer of beauty – the sounds of rushing streams from melting snow packs, wind blowing through trees and canyons, ravens mocking every sound.

The Sierras send all the summer hikers back to their warm homes with the first loud notes of winter. Sitting on a large rock on top of the razor-jagged ridge at 13,000 feet where the trails of Mount

Whitney and John Muir meet, I struggled with a decision. Should I go to the top of Mount Whitney, a two-or-so mile hike, climbing up to 14,494 feet? Or should we hike down, not risking getting caught in the snows of early fall without insulated boots, crampons or ice axe? The choice had to be made quickly. Just as I made the decision to race to the top, Curry bit deep into my calf and growled without losing his grip. I got up and finally shook him off. He ended up having the last word; we walked down.

Hiking with a wound that's not life-threatening always seems to lessen the throbbing pain. Twelve miles above the trail head, we started down the steep winding switchbacks and creek crossings. Finally the trail drops down into dense forests, then to Whitney Portal campground.

While hiking down, I thought about leaving these mountains and felt unprepared to go back to cars, job and city lights. But I was not equipped for the snow, wind or ice of a Sierra winter and, if caught hunting by the Fish and Game department, I'd be in big trouble. Two hours into the seven-hour descent towards Whitney Portal, I was glad Curry had bitten me. The wind started to blow cold and hard. The temperature dropped from a nice forty-degree day to somewhere in the twenties with wind driven snow. Fourteen-thousand foot peaks were entangled with clouds that acted like fish nets holding a fighting load of tuna. Then the net of clouds burst, releasing hail and snow. The storm shimmered in the dim sunlight above the mountains' horizon.

Putting on my long, waterproof poncho, which covered me and my pack, the loud sound of the storm became a symphony as I watched Curry prance down the mountain at my side. The very last mile down to Whitney Portal was made under a dark casket of clouds that let in only the last beams of autumn's ghostly lights.

Whitney Portal's campground was empty, abandoned and peaceful. It was a decompression chamber; I wasn't ready to reenter the twentieth century. At the camp's water tap, I washed my bitten calf for five minutes with soap. I knew soap could take care of the problem, remembering that Curry had bitten me on the hand years before when he and I were very young. That first time, I'd been instructed over the phone by a pediatrician to wash the wound with soap for five minutes.

Curry was right about Mount Whitney; his tactics were rough, but I'm stubborn.

I thrive in coolness; Curry thrives in cold. He would have been fine making his way to the very top, and I wouldn't have.

After cleaning this third bite, I figured it was too late to hike down to Lone Pine. Dusk's faint light stretched into the campground long enough for me to string the tube tent and hammock between two trees, and Curry took his place for the last time that summer on my chest. Sleep was deep, peaceful, with the snow lightly tapping against the tube tent while the wind rocked us.

In the morning, the ugly, now unfamiliar sound of a combustion engine approached. It was the forest ranger. We talked, and he gave Curry and me a ride down to the ranger station. I took a sink shower and put on a clean, creek washed tee shirt. Hitching home on highway 395 took all day and into the night. The last ride dropped me off right at my corner. I walked up the short hill, steps past the front gate and through the front door, finding my still unmade bed from three months before. I fell asleep before I could tear my tee shirt from my body. It smelled of the mountain lakes it was washed in.

It was strange taking out all the things which were in my backpack all summer. There on the wood floor was the tube tent, down sleeping bag, two pairs of socks, one pair of shorts, two long sleeved tee shirts, canteen, mess-kit, backpacking stove, freeze dried food, poncho, and down jacket. I understood then that my real home will always be the stars, moon, sun, earth and clouds.

It's not just me; Curry had his share of putting us in harm's way.

He liked to fight, and while hiking and hitchhiking in Alaska a year before the Sierra trip, we came upon a crossbreed Great Pyrenees wolf. Normally, Curry would start the fights and I would break them up. Not this one. I could feel the ground shake – or was it my knees – when this mass of fur that outweighed Curry and me together started to growl.

"Curry, you're on your own," I said, as he walked up to the mountain of hound, or should I say strutted, hair bristled, tail curled up, all twenty-five pounds of him.

Disbelief differentiates those who have been domesticated from those who are still wild. The dog part of this wolf dog could not believe that my little tri-color, small Collie type was intent on intimidation. Curry could've easily walked under this dog. I've never hesitated in pulling Great Danes, Shepherds, or Akitas off Curry. This time I got weak, as the wolf part of Rover unearthed a low growl and bristled. The huge dog turned his head, body soon to follow, showing teeth suitable for ripping apart a moose. In the space allotted to canine angels, Curry veered away, back to my side without unbristling his hair, still in one piece. With his eyes, Curry said; "OK, Alan, I checked him out," as the blood rushed back into my limbs.

Curry fought for dominance; I fight to escape. A week after leaving the Sierras, I hired on part time at my uncle's material combining plant in downtown L.A.'s grimy old industrial area. I was the only white guy except for Paulie, the shop foreman; everyone else was ether Hispanic or Black. About a month into working there, I got into a fight in the truck-docking area between the plant's two buildings. The union steward was a wiry black man in his forties, a little taller than me and a bully. He lied, accusing me of breaking a large roll-up door in the loading area.

"I saw ya' break that door yesterday, you're gonna pay big time. I'm gonna get ya' fired. You're disturbing what I got goin' here. You understand what I'm sayin', motherfucka?"

I got silent and punched him. We swung back and forth. It wasn't too long before all the other workmen abandoned their combining machinery for the entertainment outside. They broke us up. As we all walked back to our jobs once more, my foe opened his big mouth, and I went for him again. In the first go-round he connected all right, but his blows were so feeble in the second fight I started to feel sorry for him. Now I was just deflecting his blows, not really striking back. I didn't care, because I was on my way out of this job. The others broke us up once more. A big guy held me the second time. His grip was strong but his voice was kind, and I was calmed.

My uncle and the plant foreman helped to stop both rounds. This time, though, my uncle said, "We'd better get you out of here before we have a riot." I knew there wouldn't be a riot. These were good men. They had pride in their work and were treated fairly.

After the fight that night, back at my little cottage in the Hollywood Hills, I heard a knock on my door. I opened it to see four black guys in leather jackets. I never got strangers at my door; I thought to myself, "I'm going to die." One man started talking, but he had to repeat himself twice, "We're looking for Nathan, the jazz drummer. Do you know where he lives?" I was overly happy to show them to Nathan's place.

When I went back for my pay check a week later, just about everyone I worked with shook my hand and told me how happy they were to see me. What my uncle didn't understand was that the shop steward bullied everyone; I was told he was a little quieter from that day forward. The other men weren't scared to fight him; they simply needed their jobs. I'd been set free. After that, I didn't work inside if I could help it, even avoiding shoeing horses in barns. I feel imprisoned indoors.

I don't seem to be able to just quit a job, move away from a bad relationship or living situation. I have to push, punch or be punched, slapped into change. I see this as a pattern created in infancy, when I was placed in a crib, untouched and alone. I pull this template out and use it, creating drama when too scared to see another option.

Within the second year of living above Tel, I needed to find a trade. I love horses, and my family has a legacy of horse ownership, so I enrolled in horseshoeing school.

Each morning from the Hollywood Hills, I drove to school while cooking my breakfast. It was hard to give up cooking in my Jeep. This time I made a wire cage under the hood to hold canned soups or beans against the exhaust manifold. On the Jeep's floorboard by the stick shift, I'd set my usual two boxes of Van De Camp's chocolate chip cookies to warm. Thirty-five miles away at sixty-five miles per hour, my food heated as I rolled down highway 60. Halfway to school, I ate my breakfast in a pasture. Thirty-five years later I still like to eat and sleep in my vehicles. I've written part of this book sitting in my truck.

Telford was a good friend and put up with my habits: meat-eating, listening to folk music, shaping of horseshoes on the anvil after heating them on the hot plate, and whatever other noises and smells emanated from my place in the middle of the night.

Our landlady and friend was Elizabeth Huntington, but everyone called her "Aunt Lizzie." She was a tall woman in her sixties, a nurse, poet and free thinker who sweetened the pages of my late teens and early twenties with the honey of the thinkers of her time.

I lived in this cottage from the age of sixteen-and-a-half till twenty-four. During this time, I left the cottage unoccupied for those three months while I hiked in the Sierras with Curry. At one point, a popular trail I was on merged with a ranger's station and a general store with a telephone. I called Aunt Lizzie and told her where she could find money hidden in my cottage, which would cover the next three months of eighty-five dollars per month rent. She never touched the money. The year before, I sub-leased my place to a friend, while Curry and I lived for seven months in Alaska in a tent.

Living in the cottage was the height of wonderment and the beginning of new friendships. Here, I experienced my first real heart and soul relationship. It was never consummated with flesh or verbal commitment, but every healthy part of my being knew it was right.

I had my first date with Heather at a rustic, Italian restaurant in Laurel Canyon. In the 1950's, this little cafe was the hangout for movie stars.

Heather was my first love, but she never knew it. I remember that night as well as the days spent with her. It wasn't the words that passed our lips, or for that matter anything else that couples usually do to anchor attraction. I was at ease; there was quiet, deep warmth with time passing between us. During this time even water rushing from the tap was full of life. Everything stopped. I was there and only there. She was as close as I will get to a woman in this life.

I think women and men only let their hearts be seen once at best, and if that person they choose is not ready to accept that power, they retreat and never quite open up again.

Heather's slender athletic torso and arms could have found their way around me if I had let her. With age she would patina well, and her long legs could have moved stride for stride with mine. The memory of her is as much a part of me as my blood.

Was there a moment or a scene which could describe what brought me to such intense feelings of attraction? No, but years later I might have found the answer while looking for a companion dog for my eleven-year-old Great Pyrenees, Rosalind. When she met another Pyrenees there was a knowing, a familiarity, constrained exuberance and copious amounts of drool.

Many years have gone by, but in my filing cabinet in a folder entitled "Important Papers" is the short letter Heather wrote to me. A long time ago she left a five-pound can of my favorite honey at the door of my cottage: and a note *"Honey for the sweet of the earth, you."*

I had wanted to save this young woman from the pain I thought I'd caused my mother, not knowing that it was my mother who was the source of her own pain.

Like so many children, we are the center of our world and we think the reason for everything good and bad that happens is in our hands. I was lost in the maze of my mother's fears. Her childhood was fraught with life threatening illness which would have killed a lesser woman. At some point in the face of her sickly youth, superstition took over, and she became fearful of dogs, dirt, and untamed, dirty little boys. How would any of us gain a sense of control over the possibility of death due to asthma, if not for some sort of belief? She was helpless against her thoughts of being susceptible to anything that wasn't washed many times, and this became my burden. I felt as if I were a leper and anything near me would be destroyed. As a young adult and even now as an older man there is still a part of me that sees myself this way. That was why I stayed away from beautiful Heather.

Having been on my own for two years I did start to heal. But then, just a couple of years away from being twenty, I could see the curtains closing on this scene of my redeemed childhood, only forever now replayed in memories, wishing I'd had more time to know love. It was also the end of the 1960s.

I pulled out the poem and letter Heather wrote me that I hadn't looked at in many years. The words brought me back to the old door step of my cottage over thirty years ago.

To have let her in to be part of my life would have been a statement that I no longer saw myself through the pernicious eyes of my
mother. But I ran from Heather's love. In this letter, she showed me
who I was. It has only been in the last few years that I have come to
understand what she wrote.

> *Alan,*
> *Howdy!*
> *It's about 11:30 am, sat morning.*
> *It's such a beautiful day that*
> *I've decided to go for a bike ride.*
> *I'm not sure where I'm going to go,*
> *but because I think that some un-*
> *known force is going to lead me to*
> *your house: I thought I'd write this.*
> *I've had this unusual storm of happiness*
> *and warmth toward people lately. But*
> *nobody seems to understand my actions.*
> *So piss on them.*
> *OH Alan, if you only knew how*
> *nice it was to see you for those few*
> *moments that night.*
> *This action, I mean writing this,*
> *Getting on my bike and riding somewhere*
> *and <u>maybe</u> delivering this letter is so*
> *impulsive. Something I'd never have done*
> *before. Being impulsive was a trait of*
> *yours I always admired.*
>
>   *Must be off now*
>
>   *Love,*
>   *Heather,*
>
>   *give my love to Curry.*

Heather was the first to tell me I was a free spirit, which only now makes real sense to me. In the past I thought my uncontrollable need to be outside running and laughing was a bad thing.

The awareness that there might not be a tomorrow is the fire which has always ignited my nature. Avoiding instructions that come with things is how I live. Why waste time making my bed? Hopefully I'll be there tonight, and if I die before bedtime, I would like to think I didn't spend my last moments of life making a bed. The thought of spending my life in one area is a death sentence to my psyche.

I've paid an unwarranted, self-imposed price for being myself. The feeling of never measuring up or being too different has weighed heavily on me. Maybe God should have socially and psychologically categorized me and then stamped a bar code on my newborn butt, telling my parents who their child was and what innate gifts and liabilities lay within. It could have saved precious time for all concerned, but then there would be less mystery to it all.

This first love, Heather, was my bar code, imbued in my heart. In her eyes, I saw that I was more than Okay. I hope someday to return the favor, but I'm sure she doesn't remember me. Some people say they have no regrets. I do.

3

TWO LIES

In my mid-teens, I stopped going to Griffith Park. I felt as though I had outgrown a lover and left without saying good-bye. Before this time I had ventured out into remote places in my 1942 military jeep, driving at fifteen without a license.

A hundred miles away from my parents' house, the Mojave Desert became my soul's playground, with its endless old mining trails, rock formations, mines and mine shafts. Desert storms with their flash floods, sunrises and sunsets punctuated my time there.

In my late teens, I did return for a short time to the park of my youth where I met Carina. She had great legs and a wonderful dog named Ragland, which she brought to the park. I was eight years younger than Carina. It was with her that I lost my virginity, or maybe it was more of a getting rid of than losing.

Carina asked me after I let go, "Are you a virgin?"

"No."

I now assumed that she knew I was. I can only imagine that I must have been quite awkward; probably my only saving grace was that I had watched dogs and horses.

In this clash of feelings, touching a woman's nude body and letting go of my life- giving fluids, could I be expected to let myself be so vulnerable as to tell the truth that I was a virgin? No way. That would be like asking for directions. After this first sexual encounter, as we lay in bed, she said, "Alan, someday I would love to teach a young virgin everything about a woman's body."

"Oh," I said.

My pride has always gotten in the way of learning things or being mentored. Carina's little trolling adventure for nubile love brought her to me, a virgin anonymous. I wish I could do this first time over. If I could be that young man all over again, sex would be filled with joy and laughter, as Carina showed me what she desired, followed with conversation about everything and then more lessons. There is freedom in honesty.

In the late Sixties and early Seventies, a lot of us took self-inventories. The focus shifted from politics and free love to pop psychology and experimental therapies without the aid of wise reflection. Primal therapy emerged during this time from the work of Dr. Art Janov, who authored a book called "The Primal Scream."

During this time, Carina was struggling with psychological pains from childhood, as it seems many of us were, and was trying to work them through with the aid of Dr. Janov's theories. The intimacy of our momentary relationship when I was in my late teens brought me into my own murky waters. With the same Primal Therapy tools Carina used to find the deep pain that lived within her, she attempted to help me on my journey. The essence of the Primal Scream process was simply psychological awareness through isolation: spend time alone with no books, TV, radio or any other distractions in a stark room with windows covered, and you'll become aware. This adventure brought me to my early childhood discomforts long enough for me to understand that Janov had found a powerfully insightful therapy. But it was a journey that might not lead back to a healthy emotional state, if not under the guidance of a professional, like Janov.

Through this process I experienced early childhood abuse, which I normally buffered with a maze of distractions. Books, movies, friends and the joy of the outdoors kept these old pains at bay.

At this point, I realized how important it was to live within a society. The intensity of being closer to Carina than I had been to any person before, followed by my self-imposed week's isolation, brought me back to the raw pain of not being touched as a child. While in this isolation, I sought the same relief by pounding my head against the walls as I did as a child against the wooden bars of my crib. But, unlike a toddler, this time I could walk out my front door, reattach my phone, put books back on the shelf and play the stereo, once again making it my home. I understood the antidote for my unsupervised primal therapy was also going out with friends. Bringing a friend home and sharing a good time under the covers made my recovery sweet. It's amazing how resilient we all are if we give time a chance to heal us.

I was not in love with Carina. Feeling that things were a little crazy I dropped the sexual part of the relationship. Not wanting to say that to her, I lied, telling her that the relationship was too intense for me.

Thanks to Carina, I welcomed new encounters. Gwen was pretty and softly voluptuous with creamy white skin. She bruised easily. Gwen was my age but was not really my type. I have always been attracted to athletic women with freckled faces; they never need makeup. Maybe I figured this type of woman would have an easier time traveling and handling me. I was wrong about Gwen; she could and did handle me. I believed somehow that there was harshness or roughness to me, Gwen showed me it wasn't true and also what healthy female desires were. She wanted every part of me; it was more than I was willing to give. She wanted a relationship made of more than sex, but one with walking, conversation and food or lingering in bed a little longer. I knew intimacy only through pain and neglect, so I didn't stay long with her either.

4

UNDER THE GREENWOOD TREE

A few months after breaking up with Carina, I met Carina's ex-husband, Glendon, while walking Curry in the park. We became friends. I let him mentor me in building things out of wood, and I mentored him in the art of driving Jeeps off road, hiking and camping. He was even more involved with "primaling" than Carina. And this would be his undoing.

I later found out that friendship with Glendon meant you were supposed to do anything for a friend, even stupid or criminal things. During this time, I worked at a playhouse on the Sunset Strip. I thought it would be a great job. They were going to do Shakespeare's, "As You Like It." I love Shakespeare and had spent time in the park with actors helping them with their lines, but I was not familiar with this play; I was looking forward to the theater job. I was hired as an usher and backup person for the lighting, so I had to be at the dress rehearsal.

Somehow, things did not seem quite authentic in this production of "As You Like It." I was impressed with the ominous height of the man playing Oliver de Boys, and except for one cast member, they were all male, which is almost in accord with traditional Shakespeare to have only men in the cast. As the lights dimmed for the dress rehearsal, Orlando sang what was later to become a favorite Shakespearian song for me.

Under the greenwood tree

Who loves to lie with me,

And turn his merry note

Unto the sweet bird's throat,

Come hither, come hither, come hither!

Here shall he see

No enemy

But winter and rough weather.

Then, with the sound of crashing thunder from the orchestra, Oliver de Boys entered.

Ooh he picks his nose

Beats his uncle meat

Smell his hair you can't see his dirty feet

He's mister bad, he's bad ass.

He strutted across the stage in black leather with chains adorning his tall physique. His feet in black platform boots, he walked two muscular men on leashes of chain and leather collars, while they snarled, growled and walked on their hands and feet. Yes, it was an almost all male production of "As You Like It," but after that adherence to Shakespearian protocol, it took a quick turn to a committed gay production with a smattering of S & M.

In terms of an English literature course, how could it get any better than this?

The play was an insightful journey into my own family dynamics. Orlando was forced out of his family home and found refuge in the forests of England, and I found bliss amongst the oaks and chaparral of Griffith Park. This production of the play was actually very good. It followed the original story word for word and then some. When I saw what I was in for, I bought the Washington Square's paperback edition of "As You Like It" in its original form and read it along with the actors on the nights that I ushered, in between seating such notables as Divine, the three-hundred-pound transvestite, famous for his roles in the John Waters' films. At one point, I could regurgitate the whole play and then some. Did this new version improve the play? Well, I'll quote Will: "The little foolery that wise men have makes a great show."

It seems all good things come to an end, and so did this play. A week after closing I went to the playhouse to get my last paycheck. At the box office I asked the manager, as usual, for my money, and he told me, "I don't have a check for you. The play has closed. And you won't get a last check." In the play, Oliver de Boys did not feel the obligation to give his younger brother Orlando his rightly deserved inheritance, and this production company felt no need to pay me my last wages. I got pissed at the manager of the theater, but it only made him plead that he knew nothing. Later that day, recounting my misfortune to Glendon, he said, "I'll get your money."

Glendon at thirty-two was fourteen years my senior. It only made sense that he would have a deeper understanding of financial matters than I did. I felt assured that through his business acumen the money would be in my hands momentarily. For the record, Glendon was about 6'1" or 6'2", white, a New Yorker, Jewish, with an Afro hairstyle. He was taking a break from a high-paying job in New York's financial district. He drove a new Porsche and was generous with his spending. I was now going to see how a businessman handled things.

"Alan, let's go down there and talk to the guy," he said.

Glendon initiated the conversation with the man, who was less than interested; then Glendon pulled out from under his shirt a forty-five automatic. "My friend wants his money as soon as possible, do you understand?" The bureaucratic looking man in the box office, changed immediately from rude to terrified as he stuttered out a, "Yes, I understand." We both got back into the Porsche and sped off.

"Glendon, I don't want the money. Forget it," I said,

"Why?"

"I'm not going to have blood on my hands over a week's salary."

I wonder to this day if Glendon felt I let him down, or he was relieved that he didn't have to kill someone.

Bad things sometimes come in threes. Glendon liked my CJ6 Jeep, and bought a new Jeep, which was a fancy version of mine.

After following me out into the desert a few times, we realized he had been sold a lemon; every time we went out we had to tow it back to L. A. with my Jeep. Trying the normal route of warranty protocol, Glendon lost patience and decided to take a different course of action.

The phone rang; it was one a.m.

"Alan, it's Glendon. I need a favor."

"OK," I hummed from my sleep state.

"I want to get rid of this Jeep. I've tried handling it with the dealership, but they won't take any responsibility for it. I need you to come over with your Jeep and help me tow it out to one of those remote places in the desert that you've taken me to."

"Now?"

"Yes."

"Why?"

"I want to roll it off of a cliff and collect the insurance money."

"No way, Glendon, I'm not going to get arrested for insurance fraud."

"Alan, what kind of friend are you? I'd do anything for you! All you have to do is tow it out there and take me back after I dump it. You won't be involved."

"Let me think about it. I'll call you tomorrow."

"No, it needs to be done tonight. Either do it now, or just forget it."

"Then forget it."

I wasn't able to sleep. I thought about how most people buy cars on time. Having to come up with a monthly payment, they drive their cars to work. If the car breaks down, how do they then earn the money to pay off the car?

Coincidently, a few years later I bought a Dodge Power Wagon for my new horseshoeing business. The damn truck's power train was not bolted in straight at the factory; clutches and U-joints had to be replaced almost as often as filling up the gas tank. I once replaced the truck's clutch half on and half off a curb on a windy night. With tin snips and hack saw, I cut the floorboard, so I could do the exchange within the truck's cab. After I put in a racing clutch assembly and had the fly wheel resurfaced, the weak link became the U-joints. I bought a mechanics' vise, bolted it to the rear bumper and was able to change out the U-joints in about ten minutes, no matter where I was. Once I did it wearing a tux, in the church's parking lot, before being one of the ushers in a friend's wedding.

I called Glendon back. "I'll be over in ten minutes."

"Thanks, Alan. I'll give you half the insurance money."

"I don't want anything."

I arrived at Glendon's around two in the morning; we took the tow bar off my Jeep's front bumper and attached it to the front bumper of his, then hooked it to my tow hitch and drove off into the night. In those days, I considered a radio a luxury, so we talked. I defended my position, and Glendon defended his.

"Glendon, it's the ethics of doing this, or the lack of ethics, that bothers me. I feel it does not serve either one of us to put ourselves in a legally compromising situation. Furthermore, it gives the carmakers and dealerships the upper hand."

"How does it give them the upper hand?" Glendon asked.

"They win because we have reduced ourselves to their tactics. Then they can think they're justified in selling us an inferior product;

they'll think we're just like them." Glendon's New York accent, which at the time was unfamiliar to my ears, made whatever he said sound less caustic and more vulnerable.

"Alan, unfortunately that kind of thinking will only lead you to the bottom of the garbage heap."

"Well, I'm here only out of friendship."

"And that is why I love you, Alan."

Now, writing this, I reflect on the obvious, that true friendship is accepting people for who they are, not what type of favors they do for you. We volleyed – my ethical idealism and his New Yorker "this is how it is," forestalling the inevitable. At some point we would go our separate ways, but it would not be that night.

"Alan, where are we going to go?"

"We'll go as far as we can go before sunrise, where the cliffs are high."

Deep into abandoned mining country we drove. Like the litter of the desert mines, the soil's salt, wind, rain and sun would draft the civilian Jeep to be its own, as it did with the rotted out old miners' vehicles. When the trail got rough and steep, I stopped. We unhooked Glendon's Jeep, he got into it and followed me. His Jeep coughed and wheezed asthmatically as it made its way farther into the desert night. I normally traveled into the desert on moonlit nights. But this one was dark, pitch black.

"Glendon, I think I know where we are, but let's wait for a little bit of the sunrise." Finally, we could make out the silhouette of the mountains around us. The trail now faintly came into sight and so did the red cliffs to the west of us. Glendon pulled his Jeep off the trail to the left, onto the slope that thirty feet ahead met up with the edge. He parked the Jeep sideways on the hill, got out and tried to tip it over. I told him he would have to drive it farther out, where the slope became steeper. I watched Glendon freeze with fear. Then he asked me to do it.

I got into his Jeep, backed it up to the top of the hill and took a more measured approach. Almost to the edge, just above the steepest point I pointed the vehicle toward the south, across the slope. This positioned me on the uphill side, in case I'd miscalculated the steepness, giving me time to escape, I hoped. I thought I might be the ballast keeping it from going over. As the morning light flickered onto the mountains across the canyon, I jumped out. Glendon now easily lifted the hundred odd pounds of the Jeep's weight and pushed it over.

Compared to the noisy crashes on TV, this one was almost silent. No explosion. Down five hundred feet to its resting place, it would quietly bake, freeze and rust like the tools of a miner's dream.

There is so much joy in destroying some things. We drove home intoxicated on destruction, grinning till it hurt. Our smirks glowed like neon signs. It couldn't be any more obvious that we had just eaten the canary. I think that if men don't go to war they find other ways to bond, so for a short time the ravenously indulgent appetite to keep this friendship alive was satiated. I never cared to find out if he got the insurance money.

After this Jeeping display of friendship, the distance began to grow between Glendon and me. He seemed to grow nervous over the months that followed. Around this time, Glendon met a wonderful young woman named Audrey, and within one year they were married; her first marriage and his second. The change in his behavior became more noticeable. He bought two Komondor flock guardian dogs, which unless socialized, can become very aggressive and are useless in the city. Their thick, corded white coats can deflect some of the sting and penetration of buck shot, a wolf's fangs or a bear's claws; it's almost like having an armored dog. Komondors grow quite a bit larger than the 100-pound standard, and these two dogs had done just that. There was no way for anyone to enter the yard while the gleaming, huge teeth peeked through the white dreadlocks of these three-and-a-half foot tall dogs. They ran the fence growling and barking, in a cumulus blur. Glendon and Audrey's phone was also disconnected during this time. Next, they moved to a remote, rural farming community in Washington State. I don't think Glendon had ever seen a chicken with feathers still attached before this move. In Washington, his dogs went wild and killed a neighboring farmer's bull. As a result, the dogs had to be destroyed.

I would get phone calls from Glendon that were just, "Hi, how are you?" or telling me about some purchase he had made. He still had money and seemed to be able to buy things at will. Knowing we shared an interest in guns, he told me about a good deal he had made on a Colt .45, commemorative World War II, semi-automatic pistol.

A few months later, one night he called me, "Alan, I want you to have my .45"

"Why?"

"I think you would like to have it."

"That's a great offer, but I'm not much of a semi-automatic fan, and it's just too expensive of a gun to give away."

"I want you to have it, Alan."

I had learned how to say no to Glendon, and I did. Two weeks later, I got a call from his wife Audrey, telling me that he was impossible to live with and she had moved out. Two weeks after that call, Glendon phoned me; my girl friend Gillian answered the phone.

"Gillian, I know we've never met but if you think Alan is a sensitive man, well, you should meet me."

"Ah, let me see if I can get Alan for you." Gillian answered.

"Trust me, Gillian; I'm one of the most creative people you'll ever meet."

"Glendon, here's Alan."

Glendon made very little sense over the phone, and I was not sure why he was calling. The conversation was not attached to anything we had in common or what was going on with him, how he was feeling about his second wife leaving or that he had to kill both of his dogs. Instead of telling me that he was in pain, he was telling me about what a great person he was. Confused by the tone of his monologue I kept thinking that what he really needed was a safe place with someone, but I didn't go there with him. Instead, we talked till all the air was out of his bellows, ending the conversation in a cold bed of coals.

It was about a month after my last conversation with Glendon that Audrey called: "Glendon is dead. He shot himself with his .45."

If only I'd seen what was going on: It was right in front of me, though he was a thousand miles away. I should have taken the gun when he offered it.

When I talked to him that last time, I wondered: Was Glendon's gun used in a shooting? Or was he crazy enough that he might use it on Gillian or me and then kill himself? So I held back from what I really wanted to say to him. If I was a good friend I would have said, "Glendon you're in terrible pain, you've shot your dogs, your fears have chased off Audrey, and now you are all alone in an unfamiliar environment. Get yourself a plane ticket. I'll pick you up at the airport tomorrow. Stay with us."

In this world of guilt by association, I felt unable to protect myself from all the things which could befall me if I helped Glendon. I didn't trust the court system. If I tried rescuing him, I could end up sharing a cell with him. I wanted Gillian to be safe. I had hoped for a green light from above, telling me it was all right to rescue Glendon, but green lights rarely show; you just have to risk. I didn't, and he died. Thirty years later, I wish I had done something.

5

PAW ON THE
GAS AND MERCY

I have lived without the company of people: some might say too long, others would say not long enough. Used to getting lost and wandering, the natural world communicates to me: trees, animals, the things that are intuited instead of heard, seen or touched. In that world, I discover myself.

Early in my relationship with Gillian, which began over thirty years ago, we alternated sleeping at each other's houses. Curry and I had spent the night at Gillian's. In the morning Gillian took Curry out to pee and to retrieve something from her VW, two blocks away.

I heard a sound inside of me, undetectable by my ears but felt by the same senses that respond to what's heard.

Throwing my jeans on and nothing else, I ran the two blocks to find Curry struggling to free his right rear paw wedged between the parked VW's accelerator pedal and floorboard. Gillian attempted to free Curry from the parked car, but each time she tried, he lunged to bite, yowling at the end of his cuffed paw, snarling, and snapping into the air. Because he was unwilling to bite me, I was able to untangle him without a row.

It's both a curse and a blessing that the world works better for me when I listen to my inner voice. The blessing is seeing the world with its beauty, the interrelatedness of everything. The curse is I feel alone and separate from society at times. I follow the lead of animals and love, and this is what saves me. At times I veer away from plants and animals but they seem to patiently wait for me to come back to their world.

I've witnessed souls, mine and others, interplay within a dust devil of life and death.

A few weeks ago, after shoeing some horses at a stable, a group of women who board their horses there came to me, "Alan, the Mexicans won't kill their chicken. The chicken has been attacked by something, and one of her eyes has been ripped out, along with her beak."

The women could see the "God, why me?" expression on my face.

"Alan, we're begging you."

"Can't you find someone else to do it?"

"We asked them to kill their chicken, but they just laughed at us. Alan, we're begging you."

"Oh, God, why? This is something I really don't want to do," I said half under my breath, as a woman handed me a big, dull knife. Refusing the knife idea, I picked up the hen and put her under my arm. I wished for a gentle exit to her life, a death without consciousness.

Unfortunately, a shovel and my boot heel were my tools. There would be no way to get her home to cook, in the hopes of making some sort of sense of it all. She escaped my hold. I chased her and caught her again. Death was fast but not fast enough. As my boot heel crushed her skull, and the shovel's blade severed her head from her body, we made eye contact. I could feel a merging of souls, hers with mine before she left.

If chickens are considered unwilling to fight, then nobody deserves to be called brave. People can call me crazy, and at this point I really don't care. By staying conscious to the need to kill her quickly, but at the same moment, feeling the pain of taking this beautiful animal's life, I recognized a being with which I share this world. I cannot make peace within me nor should I, but I can mourn.

I kiss horses when no one is looking and talk to flowers: this is the path I seek to understand how I belong.

6

ORPHANS

At twenty-one, after shoeing full time for a couple of years, I ran a horseback riding program for Mountain Glen's Home for Children. They had seventeen horses. It was a residential situation for emotionally troubled children, nestled in the Angeles National Forest. Originally, years before it became a home for children, it was Cecil B. DeMille's Paradise Ranch, where the director entertained his famous guests. I inherited the riding program from a young woman who was going back to college. She seemed to be afraid of the seventeen individually donated horses, except for a very old, sweet, gelding named Buddy. I must admit they were an unruly bunch. With horse donations, occasionally there is an underlying reason why their "loving pet" is being given up; the horse loves to kick, bite, or rear.

Horses, like people, need to abide by a code of ethics and laws, but none of my newfound, equine compatriots were conforming to any such thing.

Lily was a Western Chunker. She was a big paint mare that could be ridden all day or hooked up to a plow. As the unruly dictator of the corral, she ruled with an iron hoof. Lily had everyone under her spell, including people. The person who passed the baton of the horse corral to me showed me how she caught Lily. Holding a coffee can full of grain, she cajoled the mare to turn around, but not before the horse gave it both barrels with her hind legs. Lily's feet flew into the air filling up the large space between her and the woman: You could almost hear the rustling of a martial arts uniform.

"This is a horse you put children on?" was my question.

Her answer was, "When I can catch her."

Each of the horses had their own aberrant ways. To address Lily's issues, I bought ten feet of soft rubber hose about one inch in diameter. When Lily turned her rear end to me and kicked out with both legs, I let her have it with this folded in-half rubber hose. I matched her kicks with blows from the hose. Lily never made contact with me, that would have been my death, but I made contact each and every time on her rump.

With each slap of the hose I gave her a warning, "Stop that!" When the old girl turned towards me I would praise her. After a short time, she came up to me and wanted to be petted. I told Lily what a great girl she was, and then cleaned the mucus around her eyes. Horses enjoy having the mucus removed by human hands.

Five years later I was still running the horse corral and living in Tujunga Canyon when the canyon flooded. On February 10, 1978 it rained violently. From fifteen minutes after midnight till 3:30 am, nine-and-a-quarter inches of rain fell in the vicinity of Mendenhall Peak. Mountain Glen was at the foot of the peak. Gillian and I lived about a mile down from Mountain Glen. That night the sound of five freight trains driven by Thor rattled our old cabin's windows. In the morning, Gillian and I woke up expecting to look at the river a hundred and fifty feet down the path from our bedroom window as usual. Instead we saw a wall of white rapids worn like a shawl on the body of muddy water above eye level twenty feet away.

It poured on and off for three weeks, and with one more torrential downpour during this time. After the rains had finally stopped, and the canyon was no longer a raging river, the faint remembrances of the violent torrents a month before now funneled its way down to Hansen Dam. The waters were still strong, but no longer was it a deafening roar of boulders being tossed like marbles. Alongside the river were very deep pools of mud.

Eight kids on horseback followed me down the riverbed. I told them to follow directly behind the horse in front of them. One boy, riding a sorrel mare named Jill, got out of line and found his way into a deep bog. In no time the mare was sucked up to her belly in the mud, and the boy only had to step off into the mud to dismount. Jill was a weak horse; a product of bad breeding. She had a hard time keeping her balance on hard flat ground. (Try riding a horse who doesn't have good balance. It will make you wake up and develop a good seat.) Jill always looked a little drunk as she walked down the road. Lily, being the matriarch of the corral, not only kicked when she felt it necessary but also kept the other horses in line.

When Jill went into the mud, I yelled to the boy, "Get off her now." Then I had the child who was riding Lily get off. I took the saddle off my horse, Loki, unbuckled the cotton cinch from Loki's saddle and made a breast collar of it, along with another horse's cinch for Lily's chest. Lily's western saddle became a makeshift pulling harness. When riding, halters were always left on all the horses over their bridles, with lead ropes attached, coiled and secured in cavalry style to the saddles, just in case a horse needed to be tied or led. A horse's mouth is sensitive and can be injured if tied by the reins. While wrestling to keep Jill from thrashing around in her feeble attempt to get free of the mud, I removed the bridle and put on another halter over Jill's to give added strength and support. I tied several lead ropes together end to end, and then tied one of those ends to Jill's halters and another cotton rope to the horn of her saddle.

Putting Lily in position to pull Jill out of the quick sand, I dallied the loose end of the ropes around the horn of Lily's saddle. I thought it would be a little bit of an ordeal to get Lily to pull Jill out of the mud, given that I had never worked on having Lily pull anything before, but I didn't even have to cue her. Lily knew exactly what to do. With one hard try she was able to pull Jill free from the suction of the deep mud. With a few more pulls she dragged the frightened and exhausted Jill onto dry land. I fell in love with Lily then and there.

Gary Ives and his wife, Meg, lived in one of the log cottages that were part of Cecil B. DeMille's Paradise Ranch. Their home was warm and rustically beautiful. A large veranda forestalled an immediate encounter with the front door. They made frequent trips to Old Mexico, and their front porch had the evidence of furniture shopping there. Leather and wood basket chairs and a table were on the porch, where in the warm months after work, I was always invited up to sit outside and drink wine. It is here that I developed a fine appreciation of inexpensive wine. I have been forever spoiled. Friendship and thoughtful conversation made the wine far "richer in body," as they say; better than anything you would find at the finest wine shop. So, no thank you to the expensive stuff. Give me a bottle of cheap wine, and we will look for truth.

During the winter months we enjoyed wine in the living room of their log cottage, with the large Gold Creek rock fireplace doing its job.

Thanksgiving is a time when families think about history and eating or at least the history of eating. In preparation for that day, my parents always closed their doors to outsiders, which I was. They did it in the most fashionable way, reminiscent of our British past, by the lifting of a kind of metaphorical drawbridge. I had no place to go for Thanksgiving, as usual. Gary and Meg heard that and immediately invited me to their Thanksgiving dinner. I was at home with them; I will never forget their kindness. Gary saw my discomfort with eating at the Thanksgiving table and said "It's OK to eat the turkey with your hands."

The feeling of my parents' coldness still bothers me on November's day of thanks. At sixteen I spent Thanksgiving alone. On that first of many solo Thanksgivings I stayed in the midst of restaurant goers and ordered hot tea, waiting for them to abandon their half filled plates of food. Then I feasted on their rejected fare.

Today I am not an outcast. I have friends, son and wife. The sting of early family rejection has been subdued somewhat. With the insecurity of my parents entering the last days of their lives, the thought of having no son at their deathbeds has made them want a relationship with me.

Never having a home built of love when I was a child, it seems like I'll forever be building and fixing and then moving on. I dream of dying alone in silence.

7

FIRST DATE WITH GILLIAN

In the early days of my relationship with Gillian, while I was running the horseback riding program at Mountain Glen, she asked me out for all our dates. It wasn't as if I didn't ask her out also, but she said no each time.

Gillian worked in one of the new child care cottages, which was within the vast acreage of the DeMille ranch. Many years ago, the old DeMille lodge, north of the new buildings, was the central meeting place for the visiting celebrities who came to DeMille's Ranch. Years later, after it was donated to Mountain Glen, the old lodge was used for the publicity work for Mountain Glen. Unlike the old DeMille's Paradise Ranch structures, the new Mountain Glen's Home for Children consisted of plain one-story cinder block buildings, but they did have fireplaces. As you came up the steep road, the first five of these buildings were set in a circle around a grassy area. Each building was sectioned off into two groups of children by age and sex and called "cottages," making a total of ten cottages. Up a short flight of stairs from the cottages was the large swimming pool and gym. Above the pool area, a large structure housed the psychologists, psychiatrists, administrators, cafeteria and what was called Intensive Educational Unit. "The Unit," was one rung below a psych hospital. These modern buildings were situated a mile down the steep and narrow road from the old DeMille ranch and horse corral.

Gillian, like the other houseparents, would make the long steep trek to the top of the hill to the horses. I soon realized Gillian was coming up all of the time with the kids from her cottages instead of taking turns with the other staff members. If I had changed the riding schedule and it no longer fell on Gillian's shift, would we have ever met? There are people I run into over and over again; I don't think Gillian would have been one of them. I wonder at times if we were supposed to be together. It seems that I force almost everything, like making horses go through deep water and insisting that Gillian loves me.

On the days Gillian's cottage rode, it was usually the same children each week: Jake, Felix, Jewel, Manny, and Penny and houseparent but not always; in this case, it was always Gillian.

At twenty-two, a long-term relationship for me was breakfast the next morning. I was seeing someone else, but only for a short time, and she was not local.

On Thursdays when cottage A and B rode, the conversations with Gillian grew more and more interesting, or maybe it was just the sound of her voice that enticed me.

Gillian rode Lily or another mare named Willow. Willow was tall, 16½ hands, a chestnut dun thoroughbred, seven years old and big boned. Like the children, most of these horses had been somebody else's problem and then dropped off at Mountain Glen. For the record, the horses were beautiful; so were most of the children.

Once, I put Gillian on a mare named Tiara, but it was only once. Tiara loved to rear. Staff members Garrett, Ron and a child named Jewel who, became my right hand person, were the only ones that I would let ride her. As Tiara's name implied, she was graceful and beautiful. But her demeanor was that of a Beverly Hills *femme fatale*. If possible, she would have been the first horse to shop for jewelry. Just as a flamboyant consumer's posture straightens in response to an unfulfilled expectation from a sales person, so did Tiara's. When she opposed something, she'd rear to the point of almost going over backwards.

Gillian, like so many people, used the reins for balance. The higher the horse reared, the harder the beginner pulled. When Gillian mounted Tiara for the first and only time, Tiara reared higher than I'd ever seen a horse rear without going over. Gillian glanced at me with a terrified look. There are those who respond with action to danger and those who go into denial. Gillian pulled harder. The mare struggled, fighting hard not to go over backwards, and won. Tiara saved possibly her own life and very likely Gillian's.

I wasn't going to allow a needless death to occur. I couldn't bear the guilt of yet another person's death laid at my front door by the irresponsible acts of others; this time it was Gillian, telling me she'd been trained in horsemanship in Europe and also by a retired United States Calvary instructor in Malibu.

Getting on Tiara's bareback in very soft dirt, I pulled on the reins, and of course she went up. I pulled hard and used my body, grabbing her forelock. As she went over I swung from her mane off to the side then quickly sat on Tiara's neck right below her jaw. I started talking to her.

"Guess what, girl? I'm just not ready to let you up. You can't keep rearing like that; you're going to get yourself and somebody else killed. I'm going to keep talking and petting you, and when you're totally relaxed with me holding you down, I'll let you up, and again I'll get on your back, pull on your reins and this time you'll back up. If you rear we'll do it all over again, okay, girl?"

Sitting there on the soft ground with my legs straddling her neck, we were on a behavior modification ride toward safe, less theatrical responses. Before letting her up, I repeated to Tiara: "I will just sit here, pet you and talk to you as long as I feel the need to." After that half hour of discipline, every time she'd normally rear up, Tiara would instead lower her head, go to the side a couple of inches then collect herself. Then I'd say, "Good girl." With the others that rode her, she would now rear six inches and jump forward a foot; things were safer for all concerned.

The way I understand it, my family has always been involved with horses. Starting in Scotland, breeding horses and then in the 1740s when the clans were destroyed, they fought for the English in Austria on horseback. In Austria, my great granduncle owned a very large horse farm. My great grandfather, who owned a livery stable, was a hack driver. My grandfather broke horses in America, and my dad has always been a good rider. So when my people say they know how to ride, it means they know how to ride. Yes, Gillian had ridden with a retired cavalry sergeant and rode in Europe, but she didn't mention that she rode with the Sergeant while enlisted in a Girl Scout troop, and in Europe it was just a couple of riding lessons in a ring with someone giving voice commands to the horse.

I didn't see it then that Gillian had no sense of danger. I was twenty-two when I began running the horse program and teaching a vocational program with the horses for the Los Angeles County School on Mountain Glen's property. But a few years before at the age of eighteen in Northern California, I was about to start college; I'd gotten a job driving the college's bus.

While pulling away from the curb after picking up students and teachers, my bus's right rear tire went softly and slowly over a small bump. It was my first day on the job. I was slow and cautious. There is no way to be slow enough to fend off fate. Do I believe in fate? Yes. Do I try to superimpose my will over fate? Yes, with each breath I take. The two-year old girl's flesh and bones were hardly enough to be felt as anything other than a bump in the road.

When a mother leaves the responsibility of watching her two year old daughter to the girl's four-year-old brother at a busy, street curb's edge, it isn't just fate. I do believe that at times, irresponsibility waltzes with tragedy. What emotional fate now surrounds this brother? We are always what we are when it's about family. If he had this one and only sibling, though it was only for two years that her heart beat, he would still always be her brother. Though his young thoughts could not comprehend what his hands were unable to control that day, it will live on within him.

A part of me died that day. I work hard at feigning joy but deep sadness is under my skin.

No passenger at that stop entering or exiting the van saw or thought anything about the lack of an adult in this wake of death. I can only think that dreams, intuition, or other unearthly signs failed me that day, or I failed to hear them.

Running to the baby in the hopes of saving her, I could only scream, "She's dead." My boss wanted me to come back to work, but I was so grief stricken I could barely speak. I've tried not to visit this area since.

I conducted my little training session with Tiara after Gillian and the children left for the day. Getting crushed in the saddle is a bad way to die and brought on flashbacks of the bus accident. Normally, I was a better judge of who could ride which horse and who couldn't. Cupid had disarmed my common sense.

After a few weeks of riding with Gillian only on the mare named Lily, I got comfortable with Gillian. She then asked me out for an afternoon cup of coffee. As I reminisce about those days, I get turned on.

Sitting across from Gillian in front of her coffee and my tea, the chess game was afoot; I felt uncomfortable. There are times when interior walls and ceilings move in on me, like the schoolroom of my childhood and my mother and father's sterile home.

In the coffee shop with Gillian on this first date, I became verbally stilted and physically apprehensive. I thought Gillian sensed this. Whatever was said over coffee did not hinder the flow of attraction for me; it must have been mutual. While still locked in the pretense of interesting conversation she asked me out for another date, this time couched as a common interest in seeing Baba Ram Dass, a guru and writer who had been a professor at Harvard, where he was known as Richard Alpert. I had never heard of him, but Gillian thought that I would find him interesting. I found Gillian interesting.

SECOND DATE

My friend Robin, whom I had a crush on many years ago, has teased me about being oblivious to hints from the opposite sex. I never thought Gillian was attracted to me; some of the things she would say were confusing. "I don't give compliments, but my coworker, Sherry, thinks you are wonderful with the kids."

Gillian said she would meet me at the Baba Ram Dass lecture. I interpreted her plan to go separately as a signal she was going with someone else. I invited my good friend and next-door neighbor Somerset, who had heard of Ram Dass; Gillian came alone. Flanked by Gillian on my left in the seat next to the aisle and with Somerset on my right, I listened intently to Baba as if there were going to be a test afterward. At some point the spiritual insight got to a fever pitch, and the real reason we were gathered here became evident to Gillian. This was a date within a date. She now asked me midway through the lecture to walk down to the Pantry, an old, wonderfully funky restaurant two blocks away. I told Somerset we'd be back soon. Things were progressing. This time we talked over food and then walked back to the verbal concert, just in time to hear more of the same thing.

Baba Ram Dass also wrote a book, "Be Here Now." Which I have to confess, I later read and enjoyed. But was it only I who felt that being here now was not where I wanted to be? There was no desire on my part to be enlightened into accepting an altered state without passion. To *be here now*, would have been to be in the back of the auditorium making love to Gillian, instead of listening to a lecture.

Why is it if you lecture to one person, it is considered being at best insensitive? But if you're lecturing to a crowd of people, they will sit for hours and actually pay you for it? My attention was on Gillian's athletic 5'6" body, strong, light, well-sprung ribs, breasts that showed beauty and function can be one and the same and straight, white teeth. She had a beautifully broad smile and still does. Heart shaped, well defined calves and powerful haunches filled my eyes. There are times when old style descriptions of farm animals work better than anything new I can come up with.

Her thick French braid looked as if it could stand the test of harsh weather. She had an enduring rustic beauty.

In Gillian I saw my heart through her lean, strong form. When buying a truck, I get on the ground under it and look at how it's made. Will it stand the test of time? In helping a person find the right horse, conformation and disposition are factors; I look at things from the ground up. Gillian's feet arched high. Her slender ankles and muscular calves reminded me that she was once a ballerina. Her thighs conformed to athletic standards and tapered to the knee. Her hips were in balance with birth. Thirty years later, the blush from a hard climb up the trail above Juneau is all that is needed to color Gillian's face. She is beautiful when she sweats. I love watching her dance.

My lips had not yet touched hers that night at the Ram Dass Lecture, but she gave me a kiss on the cheek as she got up to leave. Turning to Somerset after Gillian left, I told him, "She kissed me."

"All right, Alan," he said enthusiastically.

This first date ended with Gillian leaving before Ram Dass was done talking; I stayed.

These days I take my wedding ring off when I shoe horses and sculpt. While shoeing a horse, my ring could possibly catch on the end of a tool or a not-yet-clinched nail coming out the hoof wall. My excuse for not wearing my ring when sculpting is that when welding, my finger might be burnt off, but I take the ring off even when my hands are in clay or punching the keys on my laptop. The weight of the ring burdens my thoughts to the point that words don't make it to the page nor will my hands do justice in moving the muddy Dover white or terracotta soil into images of form. It is the weight this earth gives to the ring that makes me take it off. Gillian keeps me in this world, with son, house, family, friends and life. She reminds me that I belong.

THIRD DATE

Our next date was camouflaged as a request from Gillian. "Alan, could we go on an early morning ride?"

I did take the staff on rides without the children every once in a while. It was good for the horses to have adults on their backs; plus, it heightened the confidence of the staff who might be apprehensive riding with the children. The best part of the whole experience for me was that I got to share time with some wonderful people. House parents were not paid much, so this riding time was a nice way to give back to them.

Gillian suggested that we get an early start for our third un-date by sleeping up at the horse corral the night before. We met that night after work, and I suggested we sleep on the porch of the old Cecil B.

DeMille lodge. It was actually Gary Ives who made the suggestion to sleep up there, when I mentioned to Gary that Gillian and I were going to sleep at the horse corral. Gary probably thought Gillian and I were going to sleep in one of the horse stalls.

Gary was a mentor for me and many others. He smoked a pipe without pompousness while working in his vocational shop with the kids. Gary was of average height and build, with a head of hair that matched his Airedale's coat. Gary's rugged demeanor was softened by his ability to listen to people's problems with a keen ear and to give advice when he thought he could be of help. He had been a sheriff and then a detective before coming to Mountain Glen in the 1960s. I don't know when it was, but Gary developed an interest in Carl Jung and introduced me to Jung's thinking.

Some of the professional therapists at Mountain Glen with their overly interpreted psychological evaluations of children accomplished little or nothing. Gary's straightforward insights, however, were strikingly true and straight to the point. His one-liners were legendary; one was retold to me not too long ago at a party. As Jay and I were reminiscing about our Mountain Glen experiences, he recounted a time he was having a problem with one of the adolescent boys who was usually not too difficult; Jay, a conscientious young house parent almost forty years ago, went to Gary for a deeper understanding of the new obstinate behavior in the young lad. Gary at this time was one of the head staff at Mountain Glen in its non-bureaucratic days, before the modern facility had been built. He listened to Jay's dilemma.

"Bobby won't listen and he's getting into fights with the other boys. What do you think is going on with him?"

Gary's reply was, "His balls are probably dropping."

Gary and Meg lived in one of the ranch's log buildings. This old ranch, with its rough cut log cabins, lodge and barns, sat within a beautiful grove of oak trees on a gradual slope, with a stream running through it. The movieland imagination of the builders of Paradise Ranch had enhanced the natural water setting in this shaded, sloping canyon with a swimming pool fashioned into the stream at its widest point. Then, these set-building men cemented in the part of the stream that meanders through this little hamlet, keeping the stream's natural look. It became a water slide as the stream curved around the log structures, finally dropping into the stream's pool. Gary and Meg's log cottage was just a short walk from the other rustic structures.

The lodge's beautiful veranda surrounded the building and looked out over the oak covered canyon. We picked this part of the beautiful, unpeeled log porch to sleep on.

It was late and dark, and forgetful Gillian had forgotten her sleeping bag. She suggested we share mine.

Gillian got into the sleeping bag wearing flannel and denim and so did I.

I don't like silk or satin; they forecast sex. I like sex in a flurry of unpredictability. We were bound to closeness by the sleeping bag and bridled from immediate impulse by the fabric around our skin. Shoulder to shoulder on our backs denying our skin was in contact, my muscles trembled and flexed. We started to talk as hundreds of bats flew overhead, the fluttering of their wings swooshing off the thermals of our faces.

I love bats and enjoyed the vaporous show as Gillian's head went turtle-like into the sleeping bag. "Bats are our friends," I said. It was hard to convince Gillian of this, when bats were constantly crashing onto the old wooden deck of the veranda all around us.

After the bats left, we continued talking as if we were still on our second date at the Ram Dass lecture. But this time, we both took turns being Ram Dass.

Gillian went first, "It's so true that life is a circular process, with circles linking together the hope of spiritual motion."

Then I chimed in, "Do you believe this circular form of growth continues after death?"

I could not take it anymore. I grabbed her and started to kiss her; anything to shut us up. She returned the favor.

Gillian's body was burning hot, but as hard as she had pursued me, the feeling of strong wanting was left at her starting gate. She wanted me but there was no quake, just sadness encased in beautiful flesh. As I kissed and touched her body with mine, I felt for just a second a nymph inside of her trying to get permission to come out and play. That sweet whisper has kept my desire for Gillian alive. Tender warmth did not fill the moment with innocence and love, which in my short sexual life I had grown to enjoy and wish for more than the physical act itself.

Years later, while listening to one of those late night radio talk shows as the host interviewed a popular psychologist I began to understand what Gillian was going through emotionally. The doctor's description of the symptoms of molestation rang true in how Gillian dealt with the intimacy or lack of it between us. The schism between Gillian wanting a relationship with me and at the same time avoiding me caused me many sleepless nights. She was alive but stayed motionless till intimacy had paraded by each night. I needed my aloneness violated, and Gillian needed to be left alone.

I was born to a mother who showed only fear and venom. In my infant months, I was raised in a padded cage that was once a crib. In the dark of day and the glaring light of night I sought love, or at least to be held. Relentless sobs of frustration never brought forth the touch of another person. I thank God my mother and father padded my crib, because I banged my head till blood dripped down my face. I only stopped when lulled by exhaustion.

I banged my head to escape like a raccoon gnawing off his leg that's in a steel trap. Not being held the first years of life would have killed a lesser soul, but I was born to live, and I will till all the hair is gone from my head and my muscle and skin dry on my bones. There is something of my past that still moves within me. And when I bring up the past, I can't avoid saying these things to myself. "I will fill my lungs in no one's prison, I can live alone with or without you, whoever you might be. I will eat off the ground when that is the only food. I will strain water through my dirty socks to take out cow shit so I can drink, because providence is in my blood. I am thankful to be alive."

Without thinking of the connection, I have often sculpted Daphne and at times thought of Apollo: the story of these two immortals in a mortal way was mine and Gillian's story. To have never received my mother's love when first born, I must have pissed off Cupid, as did Apollo. With one gold-tipped arrow, Cupid pierced Apollo's heart, condemning him to forever pursue Daphne. Daphne was then wounded with a blunt, lead-tipped arrow from Cupid's quiver to forever run from Apollo. To escape the advances of Apollo, Daphne's father Peneus turned his daughter into a Laurel tree.

I had sympathy for my wife after the late night radio interview. I was able at some point to convince Gillian to get help, to seek out the truth of her unwarranted shame. As for me, I have seen love twice in my life. Both times I hid. Love is freedom; caged animals fear the thought of freedom as much as they loathe imprisonment.

After we'd caught our breaths from this first intimate encounter, Gillian said to me, "You remind me of my last boy friend."

The morning of this third "let's not notice we're on a date," we saddled up Lily and Loki.

Loki, the horse I always rode, became one of my dearest friends. He was a small Arabian gelding, sorrel chestnut in color. Born and broke on the Hearst Ranch in San Simeon California, Loki was a true runaway type who loved to terrorize those who were unable to rein him in from running full speed. Once it was understood you couldn't stop him, he'd make an abrupt right turn. There was an almost undetectable moment between full-out running and a fraction slower when he'd make his move. The rider would maintain forward motion while the saddle and Loki would complete the turn. The sign that you had ridden Loki was some healthy abrasions. When I first rode Loki, he attempted his runaway routine with me; he walked away with the abrasions. Running full speed and then within a breath of movement, he started to turn to his right. I pulled his head all the way over to my right leg using the right rein, driving my right knee into his right scapula. Afraid of falling, Loki tried to abort the turn. With my knee pushing on his shoulder, he fell and slid like all those who had ridden him. As he made his dirt landing, I stepped off and brushed him off.

After Loki recovered from this episode, later on he tried a half-hearted turn to the left. This time it was a less dramatic version of the turn to the right. Years later when I left Mountain Glen, Loki was given to me. He was my retirement gift. I am no fool; Mountain Glen didn't need the liability of such a horse in their program and was relieved to see him go. When Loki was in retirement at my house, I would bring him into the house when we were alone. We would watch the nightly news together and eat snacks.

After saddling Lily and Loki, Gillian and I rode past the Intensive Educational Unit cottages and Jim Hite's ranch, toward the college lands. The dirt road climbs, then levels off into a small valley of oaks and crosses Gold Creek. Gillian and I were now past the dancing of words, having found a time to become sexually close. Mares and stallions talk of intent; we talked about Baba Ram Dass's lecture, then finally we put that to rest. No longer was the conversation quivering with anticipation. I enjoyed Gillian's company, and Lily always took care of anyone who was on her back. Gillian looked good, wearing her white overalls and gray tee shirt tucked in, sitting on top of Lily's brown and white body. The sight of them soothed my eyes. After a few hours of riding, we headed back down the trail to the corral passing through a shaded expanse of the land owned by the University of California. Gillian told me she was studying herbs with King Vidor's daughter. Gillian started to identify plants for me. Pointing out Indian Tobacco Leaf, I asked her, "Can we chew it?"

"Yes."

I broke off a piece for both of us, and we started to chew. The taste became instantly bitter, dry. The old expression, "bitter means bad" instantly came to my mind. I knew then that this herb was poisonous.

"Gillian, spit it out now!"

We made it back to the corral without a symptom, but that night we both had to go to the hospital. The doctor told us if it had stayed in our mouths any longer, the Indian Tobacco Leaf would have killed us. I was almost in love and dead within the same day.

It seemed the only time that Gillian would go out with me was when she was doing the asking: she has always needed control. Early on, I asked her out several times and the only time she said yes she stood me up. Gillian had agreed to go on a hike in Idyllwild with me; she was going to sleep over at my place so we could get an early start. Seven a.m. came and went without Gillian showing. I left her a note on my door and drove to Idyllwild with my dog Curry. I was hurt when I started to drive, but hiking all day made me almost forget her. By the time I had gotten in my truck to make the drive back home, I felt liberated and ready to start dating other women. Unfortunately, when I got home Gillian showed up at my door and apologized for missing me, and I was reeled back in like a bewildered salmon.

8

CHOICES

A month before I met Gillian, I wrote a love letter to the girl I was dating, but she never got it. At that time, I incorrectly addressed most letters I mailed. When there was no reply to my note, I thought that was the end of the relationship, but it probably wasn't. She was Gary's daughter from his first marriage. Meeting Suzan for the first time was one of those things that an old man takes to his grave.

At least a couple of nights a week I had dinner at Gary and Meg's log cottage and drank wine late into the night. Gary's thirty-foot sailboat sometimes made it to Catalina Island and sometimes never left its Long Beach mooring, but almost every weekend it became another place to enjoy meaningful conversation and red wine. During the work week a handful of us ate lunch together in the cafeteria at Mountain Glen. During lunch one day Gary said, "Alan, my daughter Suzan is coming into town in a couple of weeks. Would you mind showing her around?"

"Sure, Gary, no problem."

Two weeks later, Gary called me at the horse corral.

"Is it OK to send Suzan down to go for a horseback ride?"

"Sure," I replied.

It was a warm, late summer afternoon. The children had all gone back to their cottages, so this was a good time to take her for a ride. Gary is a good-looking man; I pictured his daughter would look like a female version of him. Rust colored hair, like his Airedale dog; a rugged but kind demeanor; and good wit to match. Gary did tell me she could ride. So I looked forward to a nice chat and a ride with the daughter of one of my favorite people. I pulled two horses from their stalls that needed to be ridden and saddled them. While I was getting the horses ready, I occasionally glanced up the road. A young, beautiful blond woman came into sight carrying a bota bag. She was tall and slender and wore a tube-top, jeans and cowboy boots.

"Hi, I'm Suzan; you must be Alan. My dad said this was for us," she said, handing me the bota bag full of Gary's wine. I noticed her tan, strong, slender arms. Before I could get tongue-tied, she put me at ease.

"Alan, this is great, thank you for taking me riding. I used to come up here to be with my dad and ride when I was a kid during summer vacation." She was a good rider and sat deep in the saddle. Her voice had a sweet sound that resonated to a song in her heart even the horses heard; she made it hard for me to catch my breath.

On my journey toward love I've unknowingly stepped on the hearts of others. What I have always believed is that I am of no consequence to Suzan or anybody. Regardless, I needed to clear the air. She deserved an explanation for why I didn't call her when she came back into town, and for that I feel bad.

I had fallen in love with Gillian. I felt someone sweet and kind like Suzan would be too easy to hurt. My wandering and harsh ways at times even get dogs mad at me. I needed someone who liked to fight and was willing to go toe-to-toe with me.

Before having the job with the horses, I was trained at Mountain Glen to be a "floater." All who had this position cut their teeth at IEU, where the children stayed who needed the most help.

The first day on the job, I was sent down to Hansen Dam in a van with five of the most troubled children in the unit. We rented two canoes, which were, of course, instantly turned over once everyone was onboard. I loved all the outside activities we did together. These young victims of bad parenting guided me to an understanding of what they needed and by this listening I created my own niche with them. I worked four days a week. Two of those days were long shifts over the weekend. On Saturday and Sunday, I would take five or six children on all-day hikes out the front door of IEU, into the Angeles National Forest. It was fortunate for the children that the institution was nestled within these mountains. Mountain Glen was ten or more winding miles up into the canyon with two small but dangerous stream crossings in the road. When it rained, the stream swelled to the point where it could send a car down the creek. During one very hard rain, the girlfriend of Jim Hite, who owned the ranch past the road to Mountain Glen, died attempting to drive across one of the creeks to see him. I think the roads, hills, and streams were the real guardians for these children.

With no hope of a Mountain Glen van to pick us up, the children had to finish each weekend hike with internal fortitude. New members to our hikes would feel at times they couldn't go on. The fact that it would get dark, and we only had sack lunches always brought them to their senses. Plus, group pressure helped to pry them off their butts. I dearly miss my hyperactive friends. Even when they were exhausted, they could still hike.

RUNNING NAKED

I have made a lot of bad decisions on the cusp of a woman's ass. The soft curves of the female form have led me to envision that love-making is something other than what it is: a moment to thaw from icy solitude. At best, I have managed to be friends with lovers.

"We are all existentially alone." Thank you, Jan Winston, Gillian's therapist from years ago for this insight.

Gillian was similar in many ways to my first love, but Gillian's love for me was clouded with abuse from her past, so she protected herself from my maleness. I often felt Gillian was really not attracted to me, but at times when I'm in love my perception has been off. I thought the way Gillian was built that we'd be a perfect match. She was strong, a fast runner, smart, happy and extremely argumentative, but she was no match for her fear of men. Almost every night physical intimacy tiptoed past our bed, and she didn't stir.

On one of our first camping trips together, after Gillian, the dogs and I had a good night's sleep, just fooling around in the early morning drizzle, I climbed out from the truck's wooden camper shell. In the Northwest Washington mist, I ran nude up the logging road where we were parked with a Bowie knife in my mouth, while the still-waking Gillian watched. Years later, she told me she thought I was crazed and was going to kill her that day. I have always had more energy than most people can handle. I don't know why she finds me attractive, but I'm happy she does.

We lived together about seven years before buying the house we call home. Early in the relationship, we shared each other's living spaces. Gillian's place was on Fourth Street in Santa Monica, the silent film star Fatty Arbuckle's old estate. Through time and Fatty's financial circumstances, it was sold and made into beautiful little apartments where young adults lived.

My place was shared with six other dwellings on the property, each with a separate patio. These hillside grounds in the Hollywood Hills were terraced with flagstone walkways and flowered areas well shaded by trees. Aunt Lizzie, the landlord and owner, lived in the small house at the top of this lush garden and sloped yard.

Telford lived below me and took care of the garden in exchange for a reduction in rent. Somerset Brown and Gaveston Wicklow shared the cottage next to Tel. I and my dog Curry loved this hillside courtyard with its small patios and winding brick and mortar steps. Nathan was a jazz drummer, and Mandy was a student; they lived together in the little bachelor apartment under Aunt Lizzie's house. In the courtyard, across from my cottage lived Sandra Weaver; she cut hair for big name rock and roll stars. We used to call them "hair stylists" and she trimmed my hair for free. I remember her as pretty and kind. When "Playboy" magazine started "Playgirl," Sandra came to see if I was interested in the distinction of being the first centerfold for their new publication. She was a hair consultant for "Playboy," but I don't remember which areas of hair.

Normally, I would have said yes. Nudity has never been an issue for me. But while working at Mountain Glen, I thought it would have been inappropriate if somehow "Playgirl" magazine was circulated up there; I declined. A year before, when I didn't know I'd be working at Mountain Glen, a friend named Tug Ryan, who was an ex-football player and had done a stint in prison for armed robbery, was sitting with me at Ship's Restaurant on Wilshire Boulevard in Westwood. This was during the time of a harmless, inexpensive, social exercise called streaking, which would never truly find popular acceptance, because promoters wouldn't be able to make a dime on it. I don't remember how it came up, but Tug looked at me with a big grin on his face.

He said, "Alan, I'll give you thirty-five bucks if you streak in here. When you go into the restroom and take off all your clothes, I'll bring the car around with the engine running. You can just jump in, and we'll take off, after you've run through the restaurant. I dare you, Alan."

I thought about it for a short time. "Thirty-five dollars?" I said.

I walked to the restroom took off all my clothes, stuffed them into my cowboy boots and stared at my nude image in the mirror as another patron came into use the urinal. "Far-out, you're really going to do it," he said, "Wait till I get back to my seat, OK?"

"Sure, no problem;" It's really amazing how much of one's clothing can be stuffed into cowboy boots.

Running fast to the other end of the restaurant, I heard the vocal ruckus I had stirred up in my wake, indistinguishable as either cheers, jeers or both. I made it to the door, where, Tug was supposed to be waiting in the car for me. Instead, he wanted to see the action from inside, but as I attempted to fly past him at the door, he blocked my exit. As I mentioned, Tug had been a football player, but what I didn't mention is that he outweighed me by almost a hundred pounds and was almost a foot taller. I did not make it through the tiny crack between him and the door.

"Let me through, you fucking asshole."

"Alan, I'm going to give you five more bucks, just run up and back one more time."

It must have been quite a sight, my butt facing all the Ships' patrons while Tug and I were making financial arrangements. The sounds from the eating public were now accompanied with applause. Was it for me or my captor? At the second to the last table I grabbed a butter knife. At that point Tug scrambled, jumped into the car and opened the other side for me. I jumped in, put my hand out, and forty bucks instantly touched my palm.

All of us tenants and our friends congregated in this mystical courtyard at Aunt Lizzie's. At the front of my door was a stone and cement two step walk-up to my patio. During one summer, it was taken over by four or five young beautiful, nude females, who were friends of my neighbor Sandra. They enjoyed the summer sun on my patio. This respite made of mortar and brick was eye level and five feet away from my cottage door. Their long, bronzed bodies moved while lying still. Perfume and shampooed hair turned me on. They were more than just a thing to lust after; they were art. But for all their beauty, nothing could make up for my romantic needs. Mixing romance and love with lust brings meaning to me, more than a sexual moment. The inward journey of getting to know someone kills the emptiness.

I have received no real long-term satisfaction from genital orgasms. I need all of life's orgasms: body, mind and soul to be satisfied. I knew that then and I know that today. Yes, I was shy in the sense of initial offerings to women and still am. The desire of connection for me only comes with the foreplay of closeness. It has never been within me to approach women, although I hunger for their touch. There was no sympathy from these glistening, tan, lean, hungry women for me. Each time I entered or exited my place, there always came a request to spread tanning lotion on their forlorn, naked bodies. "Hi, guys," flew past my lips as I escaped out the door during the day.

"Hey, Alan, why don't you join us? You can lie next to me."

"Um, I'm busy right now, maybe later."

"There's even room for your dog. We don't bite, at least not hard," one of the women said.

"Alan, it really is OK," said another.

"Curry, if your owner won't join us, why don't you? Curry, Curry, come on boy, you can lie right here. See, Alan, Curry likes it up here and he smells so sweet, just like his owner," a third one said. Great. The dog, who I just bathed, was on their side. I was pissed that they did not ask me if it was OK to use my area, and now they were inviting me onto my own patio. I declined their offers. I was attracted to these women. If one of them had asked to use my bathroom, and in the privacy of my cottage we had made a connection, yes, I would've wanted to have sex.

Now that I am older, romance has faded to a little bit of cynicism, but that could be extinguished by the right woman. I have learned to be generous through the years; too many lonely nights have taught me this. And sometimes romance takes second place to sex. But I still hope to find love that embraces my body, mind and soul. If there could be a way to make it up to these women who sun bathed, beckoning to me on my patio, it would unburden the guilt and remorse I feel for acting like a stupid idiot by not risking to love.

Tug eventually found his way up to either my place or Somerset's, whose cottage was below Sandra's. Tug was like a shark, and within a short time, all the women left the predatory waters.

My landlady Aunt Lizzie, though not a relative, saw me in a way I wished my mother had—as a good, gentle, strong man. I will never forget how I felt when I moved out six years later to live with Gillian, and I had cleaned my little place for the last time. Aunt Lizzie's words were so warm.

"Alan, you left your place so clean; I've never had anybody leave things so nice. I'm going to miss you. It's just not going to be the same when you're gone."

Thinking about sweeping that hardwood floor for that last time brings me back to Aunt Lizzie's stories of travel with her husband, who died when they were both young. In her cottage up the flagstone steps from mine, we talked over red wine about her past, my future and this crossroad of life we met on. She gave me books that helped to mold my thinking. Leo Szilard's little book, "The Migration of Intelligentsia," guided me to understand that thinking politically is paramount whether your fingers hold a test tube or your hands grip a sledge hammer. Within the walls of her house, between the covers of her books, or drinking beer with her at Barney's Beanery, I had a home at Aunt Lizzie's. When I left my parents' place at sixteen there were no tears, not even a goodbye, nor did I expect one. Five years after moving from Aunt Lizzie's, I was happy that she could come to my wedding. She and my unwashed dog Curry were two of my most honored guests. It made this marital thing legitimate, her being there.

Aunt Lizzie has been dead many years now. All that I can say is, "Thank you, Aunt Lizzie, for showing me your care and love." It is said that by mentioning the dead by name they come back to you. "Aunt Lizzie, I miss you."

Why did I not bathe Curry for the wedding, even though he was my best man? I put less important things ahead of my dirty dog on my wedding day. We should have taken a shower together. I probably wanted to save room in the shower for Gillian. Percentages were in favor of Curry saying "yes" to me for a shower. Today, I am haunted by the picture of my old friend at my wedding for better or worse. There he is in the wedding album, spread-eagled on his back with his dirty coat, belly skin and old testicles exposed to the other guests. What a good thing it would have been to enter into this adult time by cleaning my loving friend and me.

A twinge of sadness comes over me; the old vibration of my heartstrings echo. I neglected myself the way I neglected my dog, falsely thinking that a woman is a carnal version of a Collie. I was clean, but it was only a temporary thing.

From the first days I was cognizant of thought, influences foreign to me have trespassed onto my psyche. They attack me with ideas alien to my better judgment.

Could it be we live within a twisted universe, which winds and flexes with an insatiable appetite for movement, filling up every void in the same way we lust for sex? I feel this energy enters into the quaking seconds of attempted thought, taking this moment of space in me before I can think an unconventional thought.

No one should write when they're tired.

9

LIVING TOGETHER

1974

A woman's breasts, ass, legs and SAT scores are minor assets in the amalgamation of love, but I didn't know that at twenty-two. So I moved in with all the above and more.

Three years before marriage, Gillian and I were on the way to our newly rented house—our first place together—with all our respective belongings in tow, and I had second thoughts.

It wasn't about Gillian and me, but about the people we were renting from. As we drove from Gillian's place down Washington Boulevard toward the on-ramp to the 405 Freeway north to the Calabasas foothills, I expressed my reluctance. Gillian interpreted my misgivings as my having cold feet about moving in with her. She had a bout of upset and tears, jumped out of the truck at a traffic light and started to walk around the block. I drove around the block, Gillian jumped back in, and we continued to drive to the place we would call home.

I was in love with Gillian, but had I bitten off more than I could chew? If we didn't move in together, where would I go? I wondered what had I just done. Giving up my first real home, where I lived for over six years, and my dear friend and landlady, Aunt Lizzie, was like leaving family.

Gillian and I had rented a large, open, one bedroom home that had a nice fireplace in the living room. The house sat on an acre of land in the Santa Monica Mountains near Calabasas.

Our new landlady epitomized corpulent female dominance. Her husband, the landlord, was very proud of his muscles and frustrated with his wife's size. All of their discontent was focused on the outside world, such as the plumber, hay deliveryman, tenants and other neighbors. This landlady lorded over her little spread like a sow hearing the farmer call her children "bacon."

They were a tag team. She would incite people and then "Dwight" would step in and make short order of the situation by exhibiting muscle. A year into living there, in a brief phone call, she started to lay into me with paranoid accusations: "Your horses are ruining the fence, and you're staring at me when I drive by."

My retort was, "You're nuts."

Her response was to call "Dwight" to the phone.

"You're talking to 'Dwight' now," came over the phone lines.

My reply to him was "I don't care if you're Jesus Christ on a pogo stick." "Dwight" hung up, and from that day forward they left us alone. Afterwards, surrounding neighbors thanked me for standing up to Dwight and his wife.

I came to the realization that I was just as frustrated as my landlord was; I had had it with Gillian's lack of affection and with the long drive each day home from Mountain Glen. I felt it was time for me to move closer to work and to leave the relationship with Gillian. Even though she rejected all my sexual overtures, I still felt obligated to invite Gillian to move with me.

With this new awareness of my dilemma, I made a proposal to Gillian that I knew she would refuse. "I am moving into a borrowed tent that I will set up over a covered septic hole in Little Tujunga Canyon. We'll have an array of neighbors that will fill the pages of a book someday. There is a woman lion tamer, another woman who owns a tiger, and the property next to ours houses an obese seventy-year-old-male nymphomaniac living in squalor. Next to him is a Zen

Buddhist worm and goat farmer, who cannot get anything right and is a sadist. There are always those visiting cast of characters draped in bandoliers enjoying a Sunday drive seeing how many rounds of bullets they can get off on a ten mile ride in the canyon." I did not really phrase it this way to Gillian; I just said "I'm moving into a tent." (I must confess that I didn't consciously set the tent up over a septic hole, nor did I count on such a rich crop of neighbors, but there is always the unconscious.)

Gillian, bless her heart, took me up joyfully on my generous offer.

I've lived in tents in Alaska and hammocks in Mexico. I slept in a tree in Mexico for seven months. While there I used the liner of an abandoned eight man military tent as toilet paper, until there wouldn't have been enough tent-cloth for an infant's diaper. There have been many other remote and maybe even perverse locations where I have laid my tired head. I have even been known to fall asleep riding my horse Loki.

In 1976, Gillian and I had all the comforts of home in Little Tujunga Canyon or, at least we imagined we did. I could read my books at night by the light of my Dodge Power Wagon's headlights, while seated on our port-a-potty with my back resting against the bumper in the great outdoors, while Gillian drove from one end of Southern California to the other for teaching work, wearing her Guatemalan *huipil* blouse. The *huipil* seems to define anthropology teachers from the rest of the college's faculty, with its red, blue, and yellow design on a field of white cotton.

Before this time, I did love Gillian, but I fell deeply in love with her while living in the tent. Gillian took wooden crates, two saw horses, two planks, and with a Coleman stove, she made a kitchen that not only functioned well, but was beautiful. She had situated this kitchen area under a huge oak tree that you could feel loved the joyous activity. I loved that tree, and even now while writing this, the hair on my arms stands up, for the life of this wonderful tree still surrounds me.

Women have a heightened sense of smell, damn them. Gillian's finely honed nose detected that I had set up our borrowed tent on an old septic hole. Gillian and I love to fight and always will. Just when I think I am right about everything, she is right about something. Sure enough, it really stank in the tent. After a few hours of ancient fermenting fecal matter inebriation, Gillian demanded the tent be moved. I moved it the next morning. I could feel the feminine touch at work.

During the period of time we lived in this tent, Gillian proposed to me, and I to her. We were hiking in the western Sierras, along the shores of Kanaka Creek in the Mother Lode country, when Gillian got on her knees. With the sounds of rushing water behind her she looked me in the eyes. I heard, "Will you marry me?"

She seemed to be half-kidding, but there was a truth under the words, like stones blurred in the creek's fast moving waters.

I replied "Yes." My eyes have seen death, abandonment and hate, and I didn't want to waste a second of this life not in love.

We lived in the tent in Little Tujunga Canyon for seven months. There is something about seven month stays in tents; they never seem to be any longer than that.

Credit, ownership and permanence were now calling me. Iowa Farm Boys was the name of the travel trailer sales lot where we bought our 1962, mint condition, 24-foot Silver Streak Trailer. It would be our next home.

REMEMBERING THEM, 1967

All night long, howls close and far made music around my tent. I knew it was night, for even in the land of the midnight sun, fur and fangs stay constant. The vigil for breeding and eating binds all shape shifters at night. In the seven months I lived here in Alaska, I never once went eye to eye with one of those fellow travelers, but they were always around.

Curry, my enduring friend, was big for a Sheltie, but not for a dog. I kept him near. At five-foot-eight, 175-pounds and eighteen years old, I spent most of my time in a rage. It was better for me to keep away from others of my kind. The sound of wolves reminded me to avoid things that could get me shot. It's easy to listen to the truth of ancient hounds. Curry was fair game, but I was not, so they hid from us. But one day I accidentally scared a wolf away from his meal. All that I saw was his big tail disappearing into the brush. His paw prints and teeth marks were the only things he left behind. The feast he abandoned was big and old, well-furred, but with ribs showing. It was a wolf like him. He had started to gnaw on him. The dead wolf was still warm. I wanted to skin him, but he looked too familiar.

I have spent time with wolves kept by people. Part wolf or pure, their stories are as tame as their surroundings. But the wild ones, coyotes or wolves, fill my mind with thoughts of what we've become and our loss of wildness.

I hate them and love them.

1977

I have always been able to sense coyotes and wolves. What happened some thirty years ago in the middle of the night will haunt me the rest of my life, and if I don't make it to heaven, it will be for a decision made on the first of those two nights.

It was raining hard in Little Tujunga Canyon. My wife and I had just upgraded from living in the 8'x 8' tent, into the Silver Streak travel trailer. Our five dogs, Arden, Calypso, Curry, Amber, and Torrey; our cats, Goldie, Delilah; and our goat, Pepsi, had good shelter. We all went to bed.

"Alan."

"What, Gillian?"

"Arden wants in." Half Lab, the other half Australian shepherd, he was strong. He did carouse all night long, when he had a mind to. Weather never seemed to bother him. Two years before, he trotted from Gillian's parents' house in Santa Monica, to my place in the Hollywood Hills, all in one night just to enjoy the company of Gillian's other dog, Calypso, who was in heat.

"Alan, Arden wants in."

"He'll be fine, Gillian."

In the morning, all our other animals were fine, but there was no Arden. We looked everywhere. I searched the hills for days on my horse Talisker, looking for him. Arden loved riding on Talisker with me. On trail rides he would run; for every mile Talisker trotted, Arden would do almost two. In the last minutes of a ride, he would run full blast, jump the fifteen and a half hands onto the part of the saddle that rested on Talisker's withers, and there is where he would finish the ride. Talisker loved just about everyone. But Arden and Talisker had a very special love for each other that I did not understand at the time.

Arden's demise had come from the call of a coyote in heat. She lured him into her pack, and there and then the pack killed him. Gillian and I could feel that Arden's energy was gone from the property that first morning he was missing, but we could not stop hoping that we would see him. Even now, we see him in other dogs. We just look at each other, and no words are uttered between us. We both know what the other is thinking.

A few weeks after Arden's death, the movie called "Star Wars" came out. Gillian wanted to see it. Closing the ranch gate after feeding and cleaning, we drove our sad hearts down the canyon road, into the city. I don't like violent movies, car crashes, gunfire, and battles; they are not what I go to movies for. Gillian and I will never agree on violent movies, although I do enjoy sitting next to her.

At twelve midnight, Gillian opened the gate to our ranch, got back in the truck, and we drove the short distance down to the creek, where the Silver Streak was parked. My hands feel thirty years older, as I punch these computer keys. I found my goat first. She had been ripped apart. Her intestines hung out and her other vital organs were exposed. She was still breathing and looking at me with her warm brown eyes, the same eyes that looked at me as I milked her and shared the milk with the dogs and cats and drank it myself, morning and night. We loved her and her joy. Curry was seventeen and was now blind, but he loved her most of all. They played for hours. He chased her, and when she would lose him, Pepsi would "baa" to him and she would stay motionless until Curry bumped into her. Then the game of chasing would start again. I took my rifle out and shot her and cried. In the dark of that night, I buried her.

Before I had finished making her earthen bed, Gillian yelled, "Where's Curry?" We looked all around, called out to him for hours, but we saw and heard nothing. Now, with Arden not here protecting the property, coyotes could have their way with the least defensible members of our family. I didn't realize how well he guarded us. Three years before, I had seen how vicious Arden could be. Late one night, I was pulled over by two sheriffs in Malibu Canyon, in Gillian's 1964 white VW Bug, with Arden riding shotgun. Apparently, there was a guy an inch taller than me, with different color eyes but the same name. The real difference between us was that I pay my parking tickets, and this guy lets them go to warrant. When the sheriffs handcuffed me, Arden went crazy; I thought he was going to break through the VW's window. I've seen vicious dogs, but nothing like this.

As he started to pull out his revolver, I told the sheriff that it would not be necessary to shoot him. I could get him to calm down, and my one phone call would be to my girlfriend Gillian. The sheriff chimed in, "That's one angry dog you've got."

"It's my girlfriend's dog.

"God."

We never found Curry, and I haven't had goat's milk since. It pains me to miss them. Curry's little brass bell, which he wore in grizzly bear country in Alaska hangs from the outside doorway of our bedroom now some thirty years later. If I decide to be buried, it will be in the coffin with me.

I could have bought a flock guardian dog, such as a Great Pyrenees or an Anatolian shepherd. Instead, I built a big fence around the little cabin that was on the property, and moved the trailer next to it. Our horses were big, strong and healthy. I never killed a coyote, but I did shoot in their direction a few times to scare them off. Things were safe once again. At night, the dogs would follow me down to the horse corral to feed in the cool of the night. The dogs, cats and I sat still on the ground and listened to the sound of Talisker and Coffee eating alfalfa. The sounds of the fifty-gallon drums made into feeders have a distinctive drummer's clamor when slightly moved by the horses' noses as they fed along with nature's evening music. Sometimes, Gillian would join me.

One full moon night as we walked with our entourage of animals down to the horse's corral, we heard Talisker squeal out a neigh at the same time we heard the thud of a hoof hitting something alive. Coffee, a 16-hand Appy mare, ran around the big open field of the corral far from her feed. In the light of the moon, Gillian and I watched three coyotes surround Talisker and take turns getting trampled and kicked. There was no need to help Talisker, as I saw my gray gelding kick a coyote high into the air. Two days later, Talisker and I picked up the trail of the coyotes at the corral, followed it to the same clearing where Arden was killed. Up on a knoll past the clearing, I saw a coyote almost slither down deep into cover. Going back down into the wash, I circled around in back of the dense creosote and chaparral. I motioned Talisker into it, and the chase was on. We chased the coyote down the short draw to the wash, then up a small canyon with high walls and no way out. There at the end, with nothing but steep walls on three sides of him, he stood sideways to me, tongue out and panting.

I got off Talisker, picked up a large, heavy rock, and with less then seven feet between us, I raised my arm to let the rock fly. The coyote knew he was dead. As he turned his head away from me, I saw the whole side of his jaw had been bashed in with the bottom teeth on that side drooping over like dead flowers with the bent stems of his gums still holding his now useless teeth. Close enough now to see the dried blood of the fight two nights ago splattered from his kicked-in nose and lower jaw down to his shoulder. I lowered my arm and dropped the rock. He looked at me, and I spoke to him almost in a whisper. "You'll be hunting only lizards the rest of your life."

We had other problems in the months that followed, but never again did a coyote set foot on our land.

The next winter, while driving through the Panamint Range of Death Valley in the quiet stillness of the snow, I felt them. Turning to Gillian, I said, "Over the next rise I think we'll see some coyotes." There – playing, running and inhaling the crisp winter air were two of them. It was there that I let go and forgave.

10

NUPTIALS

After living together for three years, Gillian and I were married. Her parents didn't like me and weren't paying for the wedding. So I made all the decisions for the marriage ceremony: where it would be, the kind of dress, décor, food and anything else that had to do with a wedding.

If only I had continued this controlling attitude in the rest of our marriage, life would have been so much more pleasant for me.

I wanted the wedding to be outside, since I have never been comfortable indoors. Anna and Randy Shawcross's ranch fit the bill. They started out as my horseshoeing customers; I made a set of hinged corrective shoes for one of their horses that had severely contracted hooves. Soon after meeting the Shawcross family we became friends for life; when I say for life, it is the feeling of beyond and before this life. The ability to go for long periods of time and not see them but then to pick up where we left off, or to sit quietly without words, is what feels different from this culture's social expectations of how friends should relate. Sharing silence reveals what each endures, like streams that dry seasonally but each year are found again by the rains; this is what I have with Anna and Randy.

They owned a twenty-two acre ranch in the Santa Monica Mountains in 1977. The only dwelling on the property was a large, one-room, hundred-year-old log lodge with a river rock foundation. When I told Anna and Randy we were getting married, and that I was looking for a place to have the ceremony, they suggested their place. It was perfect: beautiful big oak trees, and a large clear running stream shaded by big oak trees, which ran deep all summer. Everyone had to ford the stream in their cars to find the wedding.

I organized the event right down to the wedding registry at Humes Sporting Goods store and Mort's Army Surplus. I let Gillian choose the wedding dress, and both of us were to decide on who would marry us. I would have been happy having a parrot doing the officiating.

Gillian's friend Stacy Johnson offered to make the wedding dress as a gift. I could see the way Gillian was designing the dress: It was going to look like a nun's festive summer outfit. How prophetic. I felt it should have been an off-the-shoulder, off-white cotton dress with an earthy texture and feel. The bottom of the dress should have stopped at mid-point on her calf. But I promised I'd keep my mouth shut, and I did. The dress turned out to be very plain and unflattering. Years later, Gillian told me she regretted not letting me take charge of designing her dress.

In times of need for spiritual guidance, I have found myself in a sweat lodge, alone in a Presbyterian church, or in the company of other men of Scottish origin.

Gillian is a non-practicing Jew, but she didn't like my idea of having a parrot officiate the wedding. Gillian wanted a rabbi to conduct the ceremony. I thought a non-practicing rabbi would be appropriate. I could not find one, although a couple times I thought I had come close. Shouldn't we be defined religiously by what we practice? Gillian practiced Zen Buddhism.

"Fine, we'll interview some rabbis," I said. The first one we interviewed was called the Dancing Rabbi. He flirted with Gillian and had issues about marriage in general.

We decided on Rabbi John Nottingham, a man of modest height but ample girth. He was the perfect person for the job. He was Puck-like in nature, with abounding energy and a deep warm voice that sang with emotion. "I'm happy to marry you both, but I always have a counseling session with the couples first," he said. It occurs to me now how bold his inquiries were, but his smooth melodious delivery made the probing easier to hear. In comfortable leather chairs, Gillian and I sat side by side, answering Nottingham's inquiries. I felt safe within the walls of his San Fernando Valley suburban rendition of Freud's Vienna study.

During this time, I was also attending Gillian's group therapy sessions; it was almost a prerequisite if I wanted to be involved with Gillian. If any poor, unsuspecting person was interested in a member of "The Group," they faced the same dilemma. Everything that went on in our relationship was brought into "The Group" for discussion, and then judgment was passed on the relationship.

Each Sunday night when Gillian came home from "The Group," I would find out whether or not I was right or wrong in something I said or did. How could my position be defended if I was not there to argue my case or plead my innocence? By joining "The Group," the therapist was unconsciously obligated to see me as right, at least some of the time, and she did, now that I was a cash-paying participant.

It seemed I was being lulled deeper and deeper into blandness and celibacy with each session. These conclaves were all about making nice with no deep psychological problems ever being confronted. Pervasive acceptance was the order of each Sunday night. The therapist's final goal was to have the whole world in her group, the way Catholics have audience with the Pope, or Muslims bow to Mecca. In my nightmares, she was the reincarnation of the ancient queen of Great Britain, Boudicca. We had core issues that were never ad-

dressed, and the axiom for almost everything was, "Be kind to yourself." Couldn't the therapist have come up with something better,
like, "Life is short so go for it, but don't get incarcerated?" The fear
of intimacy still hangs over Gillian and me twenty-five years later.

In our one session with Rabbi John Nottingham, Gillian and I
were asked hard questions with no punches pulled. "First off, let me
tell you both what I see with most couples. They usually have problems in at least one of four areas: money, sex, religion, or extended
family members. So, guys, who wants to go first?" Gillian went first
and kept things clean. I think she was trying to set an example for
me on how to run this ecclesiastical couple's therapy session. Gillian
had been trained well to make nice. Never one to be clean, it was my
turn, and I went for it. Money, family and religion were not issues
for me, for I had none. My pain and frustration centered on the one
thing that I did have: a healthy sexual appetite.

"Can you tell me more, Alan?"

"Well, we don't have any intimate contact."

"Literally, you don't have any sex?"

"I would say once every few months, and that's only when I'm
fed up and ready to leave the relationship. She avoids me by falling
asleep and is affectionate only when we are in public." Opossums
play dead to save their lives and ostriches put their heads in the
sand. Gillian looked that day for refuge in some sort of combination of mammal and fowl survival tactic. With every question that
Nottingham asked Gillian, her emotional pain grew. First, the inquiries were all directed toward me. This was heavy stuff that the rabbi
had unburied, although it lay just beneath the surface.

"Gillian, how do you feel about what Alan is feeling?"

"Well, I don't think it's totally true."

"Is there a part of what Alan is feeling that you can appreciate?"

"He just doesn't remember all the times we do have sex; he likes to exaggerate."

"Do you hear that Alan is unhappy?" Sadness overcame her beautiful face with no words to defuse her awareness of my frustration. For the first time, I felt heard. The session should have been a marathon. Unfortunately, we were only getting married, and the new awareness, Gillian thought, could be explored further in Gillian's group. As if her therapist had any clue of how to get to the place that John Nottingham guided us to in one visit. A thick path of bread crumbs couldn't have led Gillian's therapist to the awareness we had now; for this one moment my feelings felt legitimate.

When we left Nottingham's office, I was laughing and Gillian was crying. I felt hopeful, and Gillian had nowhere to hide, raw with vulnerability. Sex, money, religion and expectations for the relationship were all fair game in his home office. Gillian's secrets were in view. I felt free to set a new direction for a healthier marriage.

Although Judaism is not my belief, John Nottingham appeared to me as a true divinity coach. John's way of love – love for himself, people and life itself was inspiring. The issues uncovered for me that day taught me that we needed a different counseling approach if we were to heal our past perceptions about relationships, so we wouldn't take them into this one.

Of course, we didn't do that. Instead, we went back to what we were doing before this pre-marriage interview. The memory of that day faded, as work and other things got in the way. A self-imposed caste system was my adopted way of life in our relationship; I was the one who was the untouchable. Never being able to read women like some men can, or able to catch the hints that women drop when they're interested, I went blindly forward.

11

WATERS PARTING

About 120 people shared the day with Gillian and me. Friends Terry and Alison made a stag party and cake at their house the night before this marriage butchered me up like venison. I'm not cynical, well, maybe a little, but I can't blame Gillian. I was the one accepting a marriage without sex. Whether the biological phenomenon of procreation takes place or not, the practice gives me confidence that there will be a tomorrow. It ties me to the earth. I made it through the stag party without compromising my celibacy. All of us men were very tame that night. Stag parties are mournful and lonely affairs where we grieve our spent youth and acknowledge the clipping of our wings.

I remember living next to one of my horseshoeing customers. She came to me one day: "Alan, would you mind it if I use your patio for a little party on Saturday morning. You're invited."

"Sure, no problem."

On Saturday, I walked out to find my neighbor, nine other women, my neighbor's vet and her stallion, all around the hitching post next to my patio. Yes, it was a party all right. The vet left directly after cleaning the blood off his tools. The gelding was looking at me through groggy eyes, almost asking me, "Where the hell were you, Alan, when this was going on? What kind of male comrade are you?"

Turning away I saw a large ice chest in the corner of the patio. One of the women started putting finger foods out on the table and opening up chilled Champagne. Laughter, crystal clinking, and smiles: a collage of white teeth, big red lips and wide-eyed, ecstatic glares coming from these women was too much. I excused myself. Later I told my neighbor to find someone else to shoe her horses. I get that day and my stag party confused. A drooping head under a patio overhang is all I see.

The day after my stag party was our wedding, Terry asked, "Is there anything I can do for you today?"

"There's one thing that would be great if you could do it." I raised my left hand, and the words flew out my mouth. "You see this left hand? It would be great if it always had the company of a beer; I think I'm not going to make it through this day."

To hold the drinks for the day's event, Randy and I hauled up from the pasture two of the three old bathtubs that were used to water their horses, Gray Girl and Poco. We took sawhorses with two-by-tens and made tables for serving. Randy even took a swipe with his old tractor around the oak-shaded, wildflower-covered valley floor. The property's hills encircled this little meadow like hands cupping water. The land's grasp held a horse corral, ancient oaks and the hundred-year-old log lodge that was home for the Shawcross's: Randy, Anna, their daughters Sirena, Cinnie, and son, Blaine. On this day it would hold Gillian, friends, family and me to celebrate and bear witness to the promises we made to each other.

I felt nervous until I saw Laird Macgregor, who was like a father to me, and Laird's sons, Paul and Tom, who were like younger brothers to me. The first time Laird and Gillian met we drove from Mountain Glen to Laird's muffler shop in the town of San Fernando. When it became apparent Gillian was the one, out of all the people in my life I wanted to introduce Gillian to, it was Laird. So three years before we wed, they met.

Gillian had an abrasive or combative nature and sometimes still does. Laird had a temper, and always said what was on his mind. I was looking forward to their meeting. I love fireworks. In truth, I am so proud to know them, to have them both in my life, although it is only in memory with Laird now.

Gillian and I drove into the parking lot. We entered the reception area of Laird's muffler shop, where I did the introduction. They were nice to each other for about four minutes. Then Gillian picked up from the windowsill a Monroe load leveler shock absorber, which was on display behind one of the waiting room chairs and said condescendingly, "Where does this thing go?"

Laird's response was predictable, "I can put it anywhere you want it." Unsettling looks were exchanged. Gillian quietly put the apparatus that was designed to absorb shock and smooth things out back on the window sill. Men with academic demeanors enjoy bantering with pretty and smart young women, giving this kind of chatter full berth. For Laird, it left the door wide open for a fight, and Gillian knew it. She backed up into politeness and meekness like a dog hesitates when its bluff has been challenged. All Laird saw was a stupid question. He didn't have an indirect bone in his body or room for small talk.

I wish Gillian could have said, "Laird, I've heard so much about you. It is great to finally meet you. I consider this like meeting Alan's family." But that was not to be. I wanted her to show her heart, the one thing good men respect and love. I know now that for Gillian to show her heart at this time would have made her feel vulnerable. She saw her heart as dried out and faded, hardly beating with hope.

After Gillian and I were married, and as time went on, Gillian and Laird became very close. Laird seemed more excited about my wedding day than I did. His smile told me that whatever I got into, I could make it work, and that I would.

Things were taking shape in preparation for the wedding. Big Red had been hired to cater the wedding. My mom and dad were happy to see me get married and paid twelve hundred dollars for her to do the catering. Randy leaned over to me when we first met her and whispered "Big Red" for obvious reasons: She was big and had red hair. Red was a member of my father's therapy group. I think she was working out her catering issues! Big Red, I guess referring to her great ability to create, commented, "The cheapest part of the catering will be the food and drink; I'm what you're really paying for!"

As Randy and I filled the bath tubs with beer, ice, and wine an hour before the guests were to arrive, we realized we needed more alcohol and less Big Red, so we made a run down to the nearest store in Randy's truck. I borrowed sixty bucks from him for the extra drinks and ice.

Friends brought blankets to lie on and musical instruments. Gillian and I hired one of the members of an Irish band we liked at the time, Hot Lips and Fingertips, to play his fiddle. I told the musician to play anything he felt like and just have a good time. Friends with guitars at times accompanied him. More people showed up than were invited, which I liked; it made things seem a little out of control.

Everyone forded the stream with no problem. Even my father's old friend drove his Model T across it.

Gillian's parents were there showing their protest by wearing formal attire: Gillian's mother in a chiffon evening dress and heels, and Gillian's father in a suit, while everyone else was, if not in jeans, at least in something comfortable. As the day proceeded, Gillian's parents slipped into obscurity.

The drama actually started a few days before the wedding with Gillian's maid of honor. She started to make demands on us. I began to set limits, such as, "Now is not a good time for you and your new boyfriend to stay with us at our one bedroom ranch, with our four dogs, two horses, two cats and one goat." The real reason why I refused to have them stay with us was that she liked to hurt friends and had slept with Gillian's former boyfriend while they were still together. For quite a while she had her eyes on me, while I was dating Gillian and earlier. This one-of-a-kind friend was not too subtle in the way she let me know I was to be the next notch on her belt. She batted her eyelashes, gave me broad smiling looks and occasionally flashed something that is normally kept within the confines of clothes—clues that even I could pick up on. I was having enough trouble with Gillian's fear of trusting men; I didn't need to have my soon-to-be wife any more insecure about being close than she already was. The love I felt for Gillian gave me insight into the deep, wonderful person she truly was. It feels in some way that I knew her before her birth through a vision formed by the clarity of caring; maybe it could be called the access to the divine in all of us. Is this what romantic love is?

I was truly blind to all other women. Gillian's so-called friend also worked at Mountain Glen and had ridden with me a few times before I met Gillian. But while I was visiting at Gillian's apartment within the converted walls of Fatty Arbuckle's old estate in Santa Monica one afternoon, she unexpectedly dropped in to show us her new T-shirt. It had a picture of two sunny-side-up eggs on the front, over her breasts, and she insisted on showing me her breast, under them. Gillian, who didn't feel deserving of an exclusive relationship, accepted trespassing behavior from her female friends. She found humor in this and other displays at the compromise of her heart. My comment to this interaction was, "Gee, isn't that nice."

The thought of Gillian's maid of honor making eyes at me at our small house the night before our wedding left me uneasy. I put Gillian up to the task of telling her to spend the night somewhere else. Of course, before venturing off on this mission Gillian got it sanctioned by her therapist by phone.

"Alan refuses to let my maid of honor spend the night," she said.

The therapist replied, "Well, it's Alan's house, too, and it is his right." I loved being part of Gillian's group.

After that, Gillian called her maid of honor. "Alan doesn't want you and your boyfriend staying with us, and it's Alan's house also, so I have to respect his feelings."

"Fuck you Gillian, you call me your best friend, and then you turn me away. You've lost your identity in this relationship," Then she hung up the phone.

The next day after the dust had settled she called Gillian back to apologize and to invite Gillian's old boyfriend—the one she'd slept with whom Gillian hated—to the wedding. During the conversation Gillian gave her an ultimatum. "Either be at the wedding without him and wish me well, or don't be there at all."

I knew she wouldn't come for Gillian, but only to ruin the day. She did come with this uninvited old boyfriend, who had been fired from Mountain Glen a year before we got married. At Mountain Glen he'd tried to get one of the older kids to fight me as I rode by on one of the horses. My reply was; "I'm ready anytime for you and your friend hiding behind the wall." At the age of twenty-seven I wasn't disagreeable about mixing gravel and dirt with flesh. He never bothered me again.

Sex and friendship to this dishonorable maid was all about control. It wasn't some great psychological insight on my part: her hands were cold across the reins of each horse she rode at the horse corral.

She sat a horse pretty well, but unless your heart is with a horse you might as well be on a bicycle. If only all the important decisions in my life could be made on top of a horse, my life would be much simpler. Gillian confronted the anti-happiness couple on the other side of the creek crossing. Gillian told them they were not wanted, and with that they left. I wonder if the purpose of wedding parties, beyond being a group celebration of intimacy, is also to protect the day's fragile moment.

I could just picture it: a few of my guests liked to drink and fight; having these two wedding crashers come across the stream to get the shit knocked out of them by my guests would be like bringing in extra entertainment.

Uncle Jeremy was the only relative of Gillian's I liked. He was a strong man, with a solid six-foot frame. His shaved head was like everything else about Jeremy; he predated the dictates of fads but was always in fashion. A haberdasher for forty years, originally from New York, he never learned to drive a car but he always got to where he was going in style. For thirty years, he lived in Santa Monica, California, a few blocks away from the high-end men's store where he worked. You picked him up, whether it was to go to dinner or a baseball game, and he would pay for everything. When I shook his hand, warmth streaked though his palm into mine.

Cancer never knocks but only seeps in like water from a leaky pipe. Jeremy's leak was in the form of a brain tumor. Shortly before the wedding, he had gone from a verbally engaging man to a man with no words. He would not have missed Gillian's wedding for the world. He didn't. By the way, he dressed casually that day. Jeremy rested on Randy and Anna's bed in the old hunting lodge while the wedding preparations whirled on around him. From the bed he could hear and feel everything beneath the pulse of his excruciating pain. Gillian's dear friend Miriam Swift, who was an acupuncturist, dimmed the lights, applied a warm towel wet with brewed herbs to Jeremy's head and put needles deep in his skin. The rage of symptoms were subdued for at least a while.

VOWS

An hour went by, and there was no John Nottingham. Where was he? Did our pre-marriage therapy session, which in so many ways was unfinished, scare him off? Maybe in good conscience, he could not show up for our wedding? Did he bite his tongue when something should have been said about getting to the bottom of our intimacy problems? Like: "Fire your therapist and get somebody good, or I won't be the one to marry you." Should he have taken me aside and said, "This is the biggest mistake of your life?" Nottingham was the one with the cold feet. Forty-five minutes after my anti-marriage thoughts started, he showed up. He had gotten lost thinking Triunfo Canyon Road went all the way through, and it didn't. I did not heed what might have been divine guidance that day, and I stayed instead of leaving before Nottingham arrived.

Nottingham said his apologies and went to work, weaving his magic. Are religious people allowed to do magic? He had all one hundred and twenty-some-odd people make a circle around us as he began the ceremony. He kept it Jewish-lite, so as not to lose me and the majority of agnostics and atheists in the group.

I do believe in God. While lost in the San Jacinto Mountains at the age of eleven, I prayed to God to get me off the mountain, and He did. From that day forward, I promised to believe. But I soon broke my promise and did whatever a young boy does if he doesn't drink, smoke or swear. I believe God has infinite patience with me, and I am thankful for that. I do attend church every eight weeks when I shoe horses for a customer who lives near an old, small church made of rock and timber. In the afternoon, the woman in the church's office hands me the key, and I let myself into its modest beautiful chapel. I sit alone in the dim light of midday, and sometimes pray, sometimes sleep and sometimes cry.

Wasn't "I do" good enough? Hebrew is not, genetically, my tongue, and for a brief moment I had to speak this ancient language. I was transported far past five thousand years to Neanderthal times, or maybe earlier. My tongue could not wrap around the words that I was supposed to repeat. It lasted a few seconds, but it sounded like my tongue had a foreskin.

I don't like to wear a hat. Laird wore a Smoky the Bear hat and his sons Paul and Tom wore World War II bomber hats as part of the wedding procession. My grandfather wore his cowboy hat, which I still keep some twenty-seven years later, since he is now under the ground and doesn't need any more. I like having something of his close.

In line, as if waiting for a table at the last supper, Pat Lewis (childhood friend), Somerset Buchanan, Tom, Paul, Laird Macgregor and my dirty dog, Curry, in my arms, all stood postured like those who have made the solemn march to life's end. This was my male wedding procession.

As I looked around at the huge circle of people, I couldn't help thinking about an event that happened around the same time as our wedding in cities around the country. It was called "Hands across America." The objective was that at the same time we would all hold hands, and things would be a little better in the world. I wonder if anyone fought for a parking place to get to that event. For me these two affairs had a similar connotation: promises based on hope. We don't know what the future holds. What I saw that day in the eyes of everyone in the wedding circle was hope: hope that Gillian's Uncle Jeremy would live through the day; my aunt would find peace with her husband; my father would have better relationships with his older brother and his dad; Laird would not have another bout with cancer; my friend Somerset, who was at my first date, with Gillian, would find someone to love. Most of all, I hoped that my life would not change even as my life began to change.

With a kiss and the smashing of a wine glass with my boot, which I think is a Jewish tradition to get the groom to wear shoes, Gillian and I turned the next page in our lives.

Outside in the hills there is no curfew. We all drank, laughed, sang and had a good time. Some had a better time than others. My old friend Pat Lewis and his wife reenacted what Gillian and I were supposed to do later that night. They looked happy at the far end of the small lake.

My aunt, who was a few years my senior, was blessed with a pretty face and an hour glass figure with most of the sand still at the top. She had found another one of my old high school friends in the water. Errol was young, handsome, tall and evidently available. What I never understood was, why did they have to do it so close to shore? Like two innocent marionettes sharing strings and guided by drunken passion they pleasured each other, while trying to look as if nothing was going on; just having fun in the water. I take it back. They weren't marionettes, they were hand puppeteers.

But the censor police were out in force. While I was busy having fun, my mother and father motioned to me from the far end of the glen. I hoped they were going to say something about how wonderful the day was, or how happy they were for me, some sort of feeble attempt at redeeming themselves in this last half of their lives. As I got close to the water's edge where my parents were standing, I thought, "What a wonderful place to have a reflective conversation with my parents, under these old oak trees by this enchanting little lake." Instead, they were pointing to something in the lake. How nice; my aunt and friend were getting to know one another in the water, about ten yards out. Evidently, my aunt and Errol had made a lot of trips to the proverbial punch bowl and were now enjoying the consequences. My father said, "Alan, go out and get your aunt."

"Why?" I said. Why would I want to do that? They were having a better time at my wedding than I will probably have for the rest of my life.

Then my mother chimed in, "Alan, get your aunt now; she's married!" Ten yards in above waist-deep water, I moved slowly towards them in preparation for landing my aunt, hopefully giving them enough time to put back whatever they had pulled out. I trudged ever closer to Aunt Karla's deliverance back to monogamy and was glad her husband wasn't at the wedding. My aunt's newfound playmate traded his desire for convention, and so did my aunt, while my mom and dad stood quietly on shore.

Like water-logged, lifeless puppets that had lost their amorous puppeteers, they went limp. I picked my aunt up from her watery, adulteress bed and carried her back to the banks of marriage. I sat her down on the ground by my parents' feet, and in some sort of way they pretended to help her regain her composure. My parents were dressed in casual white and intended to stay that way. So, they stood over my aunt's drunk, floundering form, waiting for her to once again become part of the more formal, less intimate drinking and singing. I am sure my aunt had a totally different perspective on her participation in the wedding festivities than those who watched her. My aunt was aglow in her wet, muddy stupor. Meanwhile, Errol recovered in the water, enjoying a half-hearted, inebriated breaststroke.

I was having a good time. Terry had stopped handing me beers at my request, and I was now nursing just one.

People seemed to be having fun. A year before, I made a deal with Gillian's therapist to board her daughter's horse on our small ranch in exchange for therapy. We invited her daughter to the wedding, and she proceeded to get drunk. I cleaned up the throw up. I've always hated sloppy drunks. Big Red had realized there was nothing for her to do, and she disappeared, along with the expectations of Gillian's parents that this was to be a wedding of pomp and circumstance. Gillian's maid of honor was never heard from again. My dear friend Jean stood in as maid of honor for Gillian with the love and caring only Jean could give. My hands participated in every aspect of the day, and still there was no peace for me.

Gray Girl was one of two horses that were boarded at Randy and Anna's. She was a big, lovely white mare whom I would do anything for. With all the wonderful people and love that truly abounded that day, it was her carrying off Gillian and me into the hills on her bare back that blessed the day for me. Gray Girl's sweet caress of movement forward stilled my thoughts long enough for me to feel my heart, I understood for the first time that sex was only one part of love between a man and a women. More than that, as Gray Girl's hooves touched the ground, I began the process of building roots on this earth; I was no longer scared. We rode away like a newly married couple drives away from their wedding guests, Gillian holding onto me as I let Gray Girl take us into the hills. I knew I did not need to take care of anyone; Gray Girl was taking care of me and my wife. Her animated steps echoed so much loving pride and honor that I understood from Gray Girl's knowing reaction, that this was an important day for me. As far as people go, we were on the side of good. In these relatively short moments, I did calm Gillian's incessant need to control.

"Where are we going, Alan? When will we be back?"

"It's OK, Gillian, we're just going for a ride." An hour and a half later we returned. It was very late in the afternoon; most everyone was gone, except for my friends Doko, Adam and Randy, Anna, Cinnie, Sirena and Blaine. I think Randy or Cinnie put Gray Girl back in the pasture with Poco. I found my way to an empty wheelbarrow next to the lodge. Anna took a photo of Adam and Doko looking like they were consoling me after being taken off a cross. I had long hair and have always been on the lean side.

I hadn't spent any time with Gillian until that ride. A friend of Gillian's was a Zen photographer; he volunteered to take the wedding pictures as a gift. I have an answer to the Zen koan, "What is the sound of one hand clapping?" Answer: no film in camera. It was a real Zen Buddhist photo shoot. Lucky for us, Jean's boyfriend, a professional boxer, took great pictures and made an album for us. The day came to an end and we drove back to our small shack on fifty acres. I fell asleep alone while in the company of Gillian.

12

YOKES AND WINGS

A switch turned on somewhere inside of me right before we got married.

My life was perfect before this time with the responsibility of only seventeen horses and my dog Curry. I always made enough money to live on, and there was a steady flow of friends willing to roll around between the sheets with me before I met Gillian. Things were good. Then my life changed from youthful night into the flickering, constant light of day in the name of patriarchal burdens.

It was my own impulses that led me to this adult male hell, not Gillian. That first night of our marriage coming back to our home in Little Tujunga Canyon, it seemed no longer a step up from the seven months in the tent or the months we spent living in the Silver Streak trailer.

In 1978, the winter after our wedding, the floods came and cut us off from the outside world. I reverted to my former hermit ways. Gillian had a job in the valley. With the road washed out, the only way in or out was by horse. For three months we rode down to a truck I had borrowed from Laird Macgregor and parked on the other side of the river where the bridge had been. From here Gillian drove to work. During this time she saw my underside.

I was in my element: no cars, no people and alone with trees, birds, bobcats, horses and dogs. I had never been happier. Then men from the county started rebuilding the road, and they were making their way like rigor mortis up my canyon.

The three-month period of Shangri-la when there was no road, I diverted the natural spring, which ran above the ground for the first time in a hundred years, to our ranch. We watered the horses, dogs and ourselves with this pure water. In a month the dirt road had progressed to a few hundred yards from our shack. The spring we were using ran on the other side where the road had been and where it would once again be after the county work was done.

With the road still closed to all vehicles, I rode down to where the men were working and asked to talk to the foreman. Short on words I told him my situation. "After the floods we lost our well and now our water source is this spring that crosses where the road used to be. Can we put in a temporary pipe under the road till I can figure out where to put a new well?" He had sympathy for us and said, "Yes, but in a month or so we'll have to start work on the permanent asphalt road; the county won't go for it."

My days passed in bliss. I'd get up in the morning, saddle Coffee and Talisker and ride with Gillian to the road, a mile down the canyon. Then ride back up to the shack, unsaddle Coffee and ride up the canyon to Mountain Glen on Talisker. There I taught animal husbandry and took the children for trail rides in the foothills into the early evening. As night fell, I'd ride home silently. At home, while Gillian was working late teaching at a sundry of colleges, I'd read and listen to music. Life was great in our little shack. A month later the road was still dirt and would be that way for a year, but the road was now not only open to the inhabitants of Little Tujunga canyon but also to the sightseeing public, who had nothing better to do than look at the remnants of nature's will.

It was a Saturday, and Gillian had gone back to driving to work and to the Laundromat and matinee on Saturdays. When she came home, she said, "Alan, you look like a reclusive, unshaven miner. Look at you, in red Long Johns with a twelve-gage shotgun, peering out your window from behind closed drapes. Alan, what the hell is going on?"

Gillian tells it this way:

"I approached the house with the laundry on my back. It was very quiet. Nothing stirred. This was very strange to me because you are always busy fixing something, talking with neighbors, playing with the dogs, mending the horse fence. Suddenly I noticed the curtain that covered the window facing the road pull back slightly – only enough to reveal a sliver of your face peering out at me. I acknowledged you and said, "Hey, Alan, come open the door."

"You disappeared immediately as if you didn't want to be noticed. The door didn't open. Concerned and confused by your behavior, I approached the front door and knocked. No answer.

"I went to open the door cautiously but it was locked. Not a good sign. You had been talking lately about the serenity that accompanied the disaster and your ambivalence about the return of the road. Also, knowing there is a part of you that fashions yourself as 'a bit of a hermit,' I began to feel that you had gone off the deep end.

"Well, I opened the door with my key, to find you standing in the middle of the living room, double barrel shot gun in hand and dressed to the nines in the latest flaming red flannel Long Johns – you even forgot to button the butt flap so your ass was half hanging out. Your eyes were wild. You would not make eye contact. You demanded that I close the door immediately and step away from the window because someone might see me. You informed me the gun was loaded and you didn't want to hurt someone unnecessarily.

"So there I stood. My thoughts were racing through the several years I spent working with genuine lunatics in the Neuropsychiatric Institute at UCLA. The moment of truth had arrived. Was I going to run out of the house and save myself from the possibility of having my head blown off? Given my history of violence with men this was within the realm of possibility. Or was I going to trust in what I believed was just a temporary bout of insanity? After all, we are all entitled to lose it once in a while. I chose to stay.

"I approached you very slowly and said, 'Alan, I love you. Please put the gun down.' You stared at me. You stared at the shot gun. You were frozen. Then I put my arms around you. I told you I loved you, and that everything would be 'just fine.' I promised. You looked at me sheepishly and said, 'Do you really think so?'

I said, 'Absolutely.'

"You began sobbing – deep wrenching sobs – and quite quickly came back to reality." (This will be the last time I let Gillian put her fingers on the keys of my computer.)

We lived with the new road about six months, then moved from Little Tujunga to another community. Thinking a husband was supposed to provide a less rustic situation, I led us to an old stone one-bedroom house in the flat lands of the Shadow Hills. I need the mountains, but hills will pacify me somewhat. But it was with this move of house belongings, dogs, cats and horses that I lost me. Riding or hiking out my back door is how I find myself, and that was now gone.

In 1979 we moved again, this time into the Laurel Canyon area of the Hollywood Hills. Here, back in the hills of my youth, we rented a small, one bedroom house with a fireplace on Wonderland Avenue. Of course, the house would be too small for Gillian but perfect for me.

FATHERHOOD

Although we were married for almost three years and lived together three years before that, I continued to avoid being a parent like one avoids the plague and was still under the assumption that, unlike Peter Pan onstage, I was not tethered to a cable.

Gillian had her way with me one night, and a bigger house was needed before the nine-month human gestation period was over. In my normal way of driving around for hours, the way a dog circles many times before lying down, I finally found the right house. Then it was Gillian's turn to explore the inside.

This time the house we found was almost at the top of Lookout Mountain Road, still in Laurel Canyon and less than a mile from the place we had lived before on Wonderland Avenue. A movie set designer owned this new place. As she showed me around, she started flirting with me; I took this as a compliment.

This new house and garden were at the end of a long, steep driveway. Nothing of the dwelling could be seen from the road. At the end of the driveway, an abrupt left turn brought me to the property's entrance far above the road. A tall fence and dense foliage kept the rest of the world out.

I opened the massive, rustic wooden garden door, and walked over the threshold. I was instantly transported into an enchanted garden. If Maxfield Parrish's pool scenes and Tolkien's hobbit landscapes could breed, this garden would have been the offspring. Walking the narrow stone path in the shaded grass, I passed a small, multi-windowed, old wooden studio that looked like it was strictly for serious art. To the left a few yards ahead, was an old wine vat, fifteen feet in diameter that had been cut down to five, making it a five foot deep, above ground swimming pool. Surrounding the pool was a deck. After we moved in, the pool and deck with its bougainvillea-covered trellis backdrop, made a stage for my audience of trees, flowers and grasses. All of the flora applauded and smiled at my skill in enjoying thoughts of love. In my imagination I shared this pool with the maidens of Parrish's paintings. With each plunge, through all the seasons even in winter I felt loved.

The unheated pool felt heated even though it was as cold as ice in the winter. During the cold months, I ran a mile the last half-mile uphill and from my heated frenzy I'd jump into the cold water and stay.

Past the pool, off in the distance among alders, pines and redwoods, was a 1920s Cape Cod-style cottage in perpetual shade, hidden from the rest of the world. The interior consisted of a living room with a fireplace that had a poor draw. If we weren't careful, it smoked everyone out of the room. The small, warm kitchen looked out over the garden through wavy glass panes. We used a large alcove in the living room as a small dining room. Sunlight uttered fragrances of color onto the table's flower arrangement from seventeenth century stained glass windows, most pungently at dawn's light. At the other end of the living room down a short hallway, the house's one bathroom had a red cylindrical tub that was over three feet deep and three feet across. Elongated highly polished chrome fixtures controlled the water. The wall's covering was nailed up, redwood planks.

There were two bedrooms side by side. The first one was right off the bathroom and living room through a small hallway. This room was large and somewhat Craftsman in architectural style. Crossing the width of this first bedroom brought me to the door of the second bedroom, with no hallway separating the two. A seventeenth century small but ornate carved wood church door with stained glass inlays secured the privacy to this second bedroom. Passing over the threshold, taking a step down, I found myself in a huge, round thirty-foot high wine vat, which smelled of Cabernet Sauvignon. The wine vat's wood was stained dark from years of holding the grape's blood. The windows were large. They did not transport enough light for reading but enough to see the lines and knuckles of my hands when I prayed. The windows were imported Italian stained glass. A multitude of amber, sienna and burgundy prisms migrated through the stained glass that was long ago inserted into the walls of this old wooden tank. Some of the windows could be cranked open to see the garden.

Though these panes were probably bought, I feel at some point in their long existence these stained glass windows were ill-gotten, for their beauty was far greater than I had ever seen. Paul Newman and Joann Woodward made this place their home when first wed.

Proving the truth of Laird Macgregor's saying, "Look by your feet for fire wood before you venture all over the forest looking for it." I found a midwife who lived only half a block away from us.

I believe in going to the hospital if you are sick, unable to help yourself, but not if you are just being born. There are things Gillian and I agree on: this was one of them. Beth was the name of our midwife; notice the word "our," denoting ownership and endearment; I hate when people do that. Beth was a woman of average height and build. She wore a simple Rolex watch that further gave the impression of no frills but said that time and competence were important. Yes, Rolex does make watches that are plain in design and intended only for keeping time when counting seconds can mean life or death.

I planned that Gillian would give birth in bed. So I made a bed that was seven feet by seven feet and hung this Frankenstein configured birthing box from the twenty-five- foot-high rafters above us in the wine vat bedroom. From one-inch diameter hemp rope on four, twenty-two-foot leads swung our new bed. A good push would rock us for an hour. I wonder if this could have been the predecessor to the vibrating bed. Other than moving to this better place and building the bed, I was on automatic pilot. The nine months went by without a conscious thought about the deeper meaning of being a father.

When Gillian went into labor, she could not figure out where she wanted to drop her celestial load. She had me and Beth and Beth's young assistant walk from the bed where we started, to the bathroom and into the bathtub. I filled the tub with warm water on Gillian's request. Then Gillian wandered out of the tub into the other bedroom, then onto the floor where she pushed for I can't remember how many hours. We coached. We realized due to a horseback riding accident (not my fault, mind you), Gillian's coccyx bone was broken in such a way that it obstructed the vaginal canal. The four of us decided that since I was a "hands on kind of a guy," I could stick my finger into the orifice of life and re-break the coccyx bone. (Just what I wanted to do with my day off.)

I had a good grip on this root of a past primate's tail. When I started to pull I could feel the tenderness of the vascular tissue, and I got scared. What was I doing? Women die giving birth and infants meet their demise before entering this life. Is there no limit to my hubris? In this tunnel of childhood to parenthood, intrinsically longer in the males of our species, I was now confronted even before my son entered this world with accountability, and I had to acknowledge my ignorance in so many areas. In the past, I would never have asked for help. I still sometimes do not ask for directions. Exiting the adult side of this tunnel, I asked for directions.

"Let's call the doctor," I said, Beth concurred, conferred with the doctor we had for backup, and then I talked to him. We all concluded that the human head at this point is soft and Gillian would try to push out the greased monkey. This other-worldly creature did fall into this earth.

In the newfound traditional birthing process, I was asked to cut the umbilical cord. I did reluctantly, knowing that in Berrigan's life this was going to be only the first of many letting-go experiences. Next thing you know he'd be off the tit and looking for it the rest of his life, along with his umbilical cord. So be it! I got stuck with that dilemma, why shouldn't he?

I was there for the whole eleven hours, lifting a one-hundred-eighty-pound Gillian all over the place; but I was not really there, even when I had my index finger up Gillian's vaginal canal. Yes, I had escaped being touched emotionally.

Then Berrigan grabbed my finger with his hand while still wet; I was lost, forever. Tied eternally to this earth whether I lived or died, I was now immortal in legacy.

An elephant of love had swallowed my heart. It grabbed my hand and walked me to the heavens and then left me back on earth, with the feel of a bare ass landing on hard gravel.

I checked to see that the entire placenta had come out, as I know to do with horses and dogs. "It looks good to me."

I asked Beth what she thought. We agreed that it was all there, as if I really knew. I put it into a bag to throw it away when Gillian from her vaginal expectorating stupor, moaned, "Put it in the refrigerator." In my weak state I had fallen prey to another one of these new ancient traditional requests. Bless her heart, she wanted to cook it for the two of us. Mind you, I can probably count on one hand the times Gillian has cooked for me. Women of this ilk think that Atlantians had freezers.

I am a sculptor and love art in general, but the contrast between the vanilla ice cream, ice cube tray with its frozen diamonds of water and the clear plastic bag holding the blood-engorged afterbirth was just too much of a contrast for my aesthetic sensibilities. I have watched dogs roll in the carcasses of deer and cows. I have seen dogs

eat their own shit, horseshit and the ignorant horse owner who feeds
the hoof trimmings that are left behind after I shoe their horses. If
the dog is lucky, he will vomit the hoof trimmings up, but if he is
unlucky the trimmings can get caught in the canine's esophagus.

The placenta was good protein. Not wanting anything to go to
waste, which is my nature, I would feed it to the dogs, I thought.
They took one look at it and quickly ran in the opposite direction.
Did Gillian give birth to the anti-Christ? Walking over the threshold
into adult male doubt I began questioning the ethers and the mun-
dane. Feelings and thoughts started to collide. Now summoned to be
even more accountable than even the I.R.S. would ask, this accountability came from a deep love and feverish parental passion.

The exhaustion of Gillian's birthing Berrigan left me unready to
go back to work the next day, but I had to. That weekend Berrigan
slept on my chest, his little wonderful heart beating next to mine.
I did not realize then what a pleasure it was that he did not talk or
understand the needs of human beings, who had their desires finely
honed and developed by television ad men and women.

13

MOTHERHOOD

Berrigan, six months old, was on Gillian's hip wherever Gillian went. Gillian and I did not come from loving homes. But we had the luck of having loving animals and mimicked the familial intimacy of our healthy animals' ways, especially our dogs.

Yesterday I heard a story that will stay with me for the rest of my life. At Stanford University in Palo Alto, California, in the 1970s, forty-two human observers – some were primatologists, a few news people and the curious – watched as two chimpanzees on separate forty-foot chain leads were supposed to mate, or at least this was the scientists' plan. The male chimp pursued, while the female chimp refused and tried to get away. As the story was told to all of us radio listeners, the male was intent on breeding without the prelude of trust. He grabbed the female's chain, and, hand-over-hand, reeled her to him. She jerked the chain from his hands as she was being pulled closer to his primeval universe. Was this woman chimp dealing with becoming the missing link through some natural struggle of abstinence and selection? Was it her innate goodness that gave her the strength to defend herself against this possible rape?

"The female chimp pulled her chain leash out of the grasp of the big male chimp. From a distance she made eye contact with me, and then walked into the crowd of us Homo sapiens," the reporter said. "She and I never lost eye contact. When she got to where I was, the female chimp gently grasped my hand through the crowd and then led me to the only other set of female hands in the crowd. Not letting go of my hand, she took the other woman's hand with her free hand and made a circle of us. She then looked over her shoulder at the male chimp and screeched at him. He did not enter the crowd."

I hope she is my ancient grandmother. How many times have women circled? If I had a daughter, I would tell her to hold hands with other good women.

As a child I loved to write, but the controls were so infinite within my parents' sterile house, there was hardly enough room to breathe and to still have a roof over my head. I put off writing until it was safe, not knowing then that there is no such thing as complete safety. Forty years later, I began to write again, focusing only on my creative side and refusing to participate in Gillian's decision to remodel our house. It was almost totally destroyed. Then and there I learned I am part of a family, that I matter and I can live in both the artistic and everyday world, just not in the same moment.

Whether it is the womb, home or the spiritual umbrella of creativity, the need for protecting yourself comes from that place in the chimp's knowing she belongs to something bigger than her. This chimp's wisdom echoes in me, whether I write or build. My body and soul needs shelter and family.

BEAR AND DOG MOTHERING

Six years before Berrigan was born, Gillian's dog, Calypso, gave birth to eight puppies; one died, which is not uncommon. She was a forty-five pound Australian shepherd and a wonderful mother. Calypso taught Gillian and me how to be good parents of our newborn boy by her example.

She was uncompromising with her puppies. We had made a comfortable place in the bedroom closet with freshly washed cotton blankets for Calypso and her litter. She had a doggy door in the bedroom and used it to take breaks from them, later teaching the pups how to use it to housebreak them. She housebroke them without the help of Gillian or me.

After giving birth, a higher instinct within her took over. Calypso licked all the pups clean, and when we left the room, she placed them on our bed. Three times, we placed her litter back in the closet, and each time she put them back on the bed. Calypso won, and Gillian and I learned to give in to nature when dealing with something as earthbound as birth and good mothering.

Ten years ago, in 1992, Berrigan, Gillian and I were in Glacier Bay, Alaska, walking from our campsite along the water's edge near Bartlett Cove. We stopped about twenty-five yards from where three black bear cubs had just jumped off a wooden dock into the water. The sow watched from the dock as her cubs swam away. From out of the thicket, flanking the water's banks, another, I could only guess, female bear, larger than the mother, came onto the dock and nudged the mother bear into the water toward the swimming cubs. It was at that moment the mother bear engaged with her cubs. I was reminded of my own mother, who never took the plunge to embrace me or my sister. I know others were appalled by my mother's coldness. I can't say why this mother bear didn't go into the water without being pushed or what my mother's true feelings were about me, but I felt she saw me as dirty, untouchable, untamable and imperfect. Later in life, other women with a steady, heart-pounding tenderness embraced me. They saved me.

In the 1950s, being a Boy Scout was popular, and my mother once participated in my Cub Scout activities. The other Scout mothers engaged with us cubs by helping us build things or with athletic endeavors to get merit badges. But my mother lectured to our band of uniformed human cubs. All the scouts that day left the meeting in what seemed like a fear induced stupor. I watched them enter the playground wide-eyed and with unsure slow steps. The emotional wind had been knocked out of them. It was not as bad as you might think for me. Because of this encounter with my mother, I gained a higher level of respect from the other boys. They feared her more than I did, which made me braver than them. I don't ever remember seeing my mother smile while I was growing up.

The cold, stern tones of her instructions on the procedures for gaining merit badges left little doubt in any of the boy's minds that my mother was scary and unapproachable. Young boys in general like mothers who are sweet, and so did I. Years later I've come to understand my mom suffers silently with crippling fears. It's the kind of silence that breeds angry impatience, especially towards healthy boys who warp the scales of hygiene.

The gloomy eyes and somber quiet of the other Cub Scouts who exited the school's scout meeting room that day gave me an inkling that something was not quite right at my house.

14

OUR OWN HOME

After living in the wine vat for a year and experiencing Berrigan's birth there, I felt we needed to own our own home. Permanence, stability and all of that now beckoned to me.

When I marshalled Gillian into the plan, she found our new house. It was a 1923 California Spanish, Hollywood Hills home next to a 1911 hunting lodge. In the early 1920s the lodge became a brothel and now was redone into a multimillion dollar home. It sits to the west, or on the uphill side. On the other side is a house that was built, like ours, in 1923. Both homes were built by the same man.

Fifteen feet from the front of our driveway on the other side of the road, towering over this road, is a very steep ridge with no inhabitants. If ever I found there wasn't a reason to go on in life, I would shoot myself on top of this ridge.

Our home is on a triangular shaped piece of property at a twenty percent incline from the road. From this road, looking toward the house, the driveway skirt is the length of one car and the width of two cars side by side. Past the skirt is a seven-foot-high by eighteen-foot-wide pine plank gate, which spans the entire eighteen-feet of the driveway's entrance. Until a few years ago, the gate almost swung out onto Lookout Mt. Road. It made on-coming drivers flinch when I swung the gate out. It's funny how inanimate objects like this gate have significance for me. They've given me insights that I otherwise would have missed.

The traffic on the small, two lane road in front of our house moves fast. Dogs, cats, deer and raccoons have been splattered by cars here. When I was about to leave home, if I heard a car racing up the road, I'd push the gate open hard and fast. All a driver would see as they rounded the blind curve was eighteen feet of a wood wall swinging out almost in front of him. After my neighbor's Akita was hit and died in my arms, I began to push the gate harder and watched it fly out with an added feature of a large mirror bolted to it vividly reflecting the on coming speeder.

I made the gate over twenty years ago. My friend Tom Macgregor welded the steel frame that I had cut to size. My friend Glen Strode made four ornamental facade hinges that we put on together. Next, we had the task of putting up this eight hundred pound gate on the functioning hinges I made. Gillian never liked the facade hinges; they never had the rustic, distressed, large, tortured look that I unconsciously give to so many things. In Gillian's estimation, the fence or house will not be done until another pound of my flesh is butchered over this gate. Putting the gate up was not an easy task; the size and weight made it hard to get it into place, but Glen and I persevered. I left Glen's hinges just the way they were, un-bloodied.

I bent a draft horseshoe into a handle and made a trick lever to unlock the gate. By pulling the lower one of three old carriage bolts halfway out of a rusted steel faceplate, the lever on the other side was released, freeing the gate to swing out. It swung all the way out onto a large piece of steel that I turned in my shop's large coal forge.

The gate no longer swings out, but rolls on a track to the side and is now powered by an electric motor. If I add up all the times I've had to wait to have it repaired or the late nights fixing it myself, it's equal to the time getting out of the truck to swing it open when it was a manual gate.

This gate opened me to a new revelation years later. At two in the morning, after one of Berrigan and my Thursday midnight rides on mountain bikes in the Santa Monica Mountains, Berrigan, (eighteen years old at the time) and I came home dirty and muddy to find that the gate was not working. Normally, I would be the one to figure out why something was not functioning. This time, Berrigan found the problem: the keys in the motor shaft had slid out, and now the sprocket, not anchored to the shaft, was unable to turn the chain to open and close the gate. On this cold, windy, winter night for the first time I held the flashlight for my son, instead of him holding it for me. Berrigan loosened the motor mount nuts, wiggled the motor to one side and pulled off the pulley's belt, so his hand had room to fish the key back on. Meanwhile, I found the other shaft-key that had fallen between the motor's brick and cement foundation. Berrigan put it back in, retightened the bolts and adjusted the belt. The problem was resolved in just a few minutes.

There and then I knew my son was going to make it in this world on his own. Within the subtlest movement toward autonomy in a young man's life is the recognition that his father doesn't always do things the right way. Berrigan not only felt a sense of accomplishment, but he had earned the right to see me through critical eyes, which he had not done before, or at least not consciously. A new feeling of obsolescence rested on my shoulders like a feather. Berrigan turned the switch on and bolted the motor cover back over the whole mechanism, then pressed the button, opening the gate.

A few years later a fast moving Mercedes rounded the blind turn hauling ass down the hill just as one of Gillian's friends was leaving our driveway. To avoid slamming into the friend's car, the Mercedes went up onto the high curb and ran over the fire hydrant. The driver got out as his Mercedes started to fill up with the hydrant's water. Gillian's friend pulled over and ran to see if the person in the

Mercedes was all right. It turned out to be her ex-boss who had fired her, whom she hated. He instantly started to yell at her, even though she really wasn't involved in his accident; she only wanted to see if he was OK. Moments later a motorcycle cop showed up. The Mercedes owner acted as aggressively as he drove and started in on the policeman. "Officer, she was in the middle of the road. It's all her fault. None of this would have happened if she wasn't there."

Unfortunately for him, a neighbor and Gillian saw the whole thing and told the officer that Gillian's friend had finished her turn out of the driveway. She was going down the hill when he came barreling down the street. The ranting man was unconvincingly pleading the guilt of Gillian's friend to the cop, who at this point looked at him and said, "She has a right to pull out of the driveway. Furthermore, the City is going to sue you for the broken fire hydrant, and you're going to get a ticket for speeding. It is obvious by the length of the skid marks and the damage to your Mercedes that you were going way past the speed limit." The driver started to argue again with the officer but he was interrupted by the hydrant's water filling the inside of his car. The unbroken, rolled up windows on the passenger's side made the car more of an aquarium than a Mercedes. Both the cop and the driver stood in silence and watched the car slowly fill up and roll over.

Gillian gave her friend a hug goodbye, closed the gate and left the mute, once animated Benz driver to the motorcycle officer. Maybe I should have painted motorcycle cops on both sides of the gate and then let it swing out instead of a mirror.

Past the gate to the immediate left was the dogs' area, when they didn't have the run of the whole place. A six-foot-high black imitation wrought iron fence and gate spanned the eight foot distance between the large motorized gate and my studio. When thinking about wrought iron, I envision the sight of solid, hot rolled steel that makes peace with the elements and will wear a patina of rust, unlike today's square tubing they dare call wrought iron, which rusts through and bends.

The dogs' area opened up from here into a twelve-by-thirty-foot space. At the far end of the thirty-foot area was a very large, wooden doghouse with the word "Claque" painted on the front over the opening. Our dog's home was previously occupied by either Rowan or Martin's dog. Rowan and Martin were known for their television show "Laugh In."

Past the front gate and dog area on the left was my studio which originally was a carport. I framed and enclosed it. Later the studio was destroyed when the next-door neighbor's giant sycamore tree fell on it. The wood studs splintered, rafters suffered compound fractures spearing the studio's floor. It was full of my sculptures. I pried open the garage door and crawled through the two-foot opening. The rafters that now stabbed the ground had missed all my work. A figure I had sculpted went through a major fire at a friend's house in Topanga where all of her work was destroyed, but this piece somehow made it through with just a whisper of singe. After the fire I called the sculpture "Topanga Man." I didn't change the name when it made it through the crushing of the studio, but twenty years later he still waits for my hands to finish him.

My next door neighbor was a contractor who only did reconstruction of destroyed or damaged property. It always seems that when you go on vacation things happen on the home front. I will never forget coming home from Big Sur where we spent a couple of weeks camping under hundreds of redwoods. Rolling up into the driveway and opening the gate, I saw my neighbor's tree in the middle of my studio, as a Dodger dog might lay in a small hot dog bun, or maybe it was a knockwurst.

The neighbors rebuilt my studio with my insurance money. They also put in a much-needed skylight as a gift on their dime. In turn I bought them a large, polished geode.

Later, three windows were put in by Berrigan's grammar school teacher's soon-to be husband, Buck. I made a Dutch door out of Douglas fir two-by-eights. Next I heated in my forge one-quarter-inch by six-inch hot rolled steel and distressed it on the anvil. I then bolted the steel to the front of the door and through two-by-fours on the other side and hung the door on the side of the studio closest to the house. It became a solid door. No, it was more than solid. It kept out ridicule, and the phantom hands of those who stole my childhood. Could this be what all this overbuilding is about?

I'm compelled each time I remember building something at our home to write it down. This self-acknowledgement stands in for self-acceptance. There are moments when relating to my wife I feel that I am not enough. So I'm compelled to prove myself—building for her and then bragging about it. This addiction to work erodes the time to create—to add my voice to other artists who have subdued their personal needs to participate in the orchestral sounds of creativity.

A few months ago, at my local hardware store in West Hollywood my friend Johnny, one of the employed mentors of the paint aisles, grabbed my hand. "Alan, come with me."

Pulling me past the utilitarian world of Koontz's paints to the candle area, he said, "Alan, sit down. Alan, listen to me now I'm going to have you look and smell candles."

As he waved candles past my eyes and nose, I smelled long, short, round, square, red, gold and black ones. We came to consensus.

The candle we picked was small and golden yellow.

Johnny had high arched brows and cheeks framed in an angular face and a jet black goatee. His combed back black hair had a lightning bolt of silver gray running through it. When he spoke I felt he was conjuring spirits, "Yes, this is the one! Now, Alan, what I want you to do is sit in your studio with the candle lit and the lights off. Let your mind rest."

Sitting with the lit candle in my studio, I wait patiently for my turn to dream.

But I'm not ready to give up proving myself to the world, forgetting that I already belong, and I don't need to do anything.

Roses now span the width and height of a post and beam arch that my hands constructed and distressed. I cut these twelve-by-twelve timbers and made a ten-foot-tall by ten-foot-wide, Western style arch. My son, and his friend/ hockey teammate, David Galley, both fourteen at the time, stood atop ladders that leaned against one of the two Douglas fir posts, which I had bolted into steel anchors and sunk into three feet of concrete. I love to overbuild things. I raised the end of the beam into Berrigan and David's strong hands; this freed me to go to the other side and wrestle my end of the beam up the ladder and onto my post. David was deaf, making idle chatter between us unnecessary. In this space, devoid of talk, David, although only a teenager appeared to be a man.

When I listen with my eyes, the outside world is quiet. During these moments, I see the absurdity of the lifestyle I have chosen: running around, pleasing my wife and son by being their indentured slave. David's passion for hockey took a second seat to nothing. Hockey had honed his concentration, and when he was off the ice, this gift was ever present. Of course, this is all my perception. Could it be I was reading into him what I thought my attitude should be?

Together we centered and marked the beam, then brought it down to the ground. I notched it with a circular saw and wood chisel. Once again I lifted the twelve-by-twelve into the hands of Berrigan and David. I then secured it in place for the final time, or at least until some other man's wife decides she doesn't like it.

We got the beam up with no one being hurt, except all these endeavors took me away from the real important things in life: sculpting, writing, the proverbial walk on the beach, which is actually precious to me, skiing, walking my dog, riding my horse, and sex with my wife.

I wish, though, I had done more of these constructing endeavors with Berrigan. It would have been another place to bond and lessened my load and, I think, strengthened him in a way that only constructing things can. But maybe then he would feel obligated to do these labor intensive things for his wife. Perhaps I have in some way liberated him.

The flat topped arch connected my studio with the rock wall that bordered the head or front of the driveway. This wall stands six feet high. Years before, I had hauled in rock to repair and fortify the original rock wall. Its stonework looked indigenous to Laurel Canyon. Those old rocks, jagged, dark and irregularly shaped, never showed the evidence of being polished down by raging torrents of water from rivers or creeks. This original wall seemed to only know an otherworldly peacetime that was still, marbled with black earth, hauntingly dark in patina. Fine threads of roots web around and through the crevasses, clutching at the wall's rock, caressing them in a petrified waltz.

I wanted stones enhanced by storm waters, the ones that catapult and roar down rivers, making them smooth. These original Laurel Canyon rocks don't show the signs of prehistoric torrential waters of a river. They are older than that, and their ancient past is seen through dark, sharp-edged decay.

The rocks that I added to the original rock wall had been made smooth over thousands of years by the waters of Big Tujunga River fifteen miles from our home. Big Tujunga Canyon is almost a dry riverbed except for those winters when the rain pours.

During these rains, as in our 1978 downpour, the earth rumbled with the tossing of thousands of boulders. We humans are a pompous lot; as I write this, a golf course is being built where hundred-year torrential rains fall. These waters never move slowly within their desert banks or cast a reflection of the landscape. Desert rivers disappear, going underground where they flow silently. That middle pace, where rivers move too fast to stagnate but slow enough for lovers to count the minutes away in the floating leaves never happens in these creeks.

There was a clean sterility to the new rocks I cemented in place. At the same time, a mortar was being mixed between Gillian and me. The desire to find physical love with my wife had been covered, smoothed down and made slick by her stories of bad relationships and the betrayal of her innocence. Now, love was unable to erode my solitude.

The then-new rock wall, when hosed down, glistened in the sun; it made our old house look new. During those first few years when we gave the wall a shower with the garden hose, it never occurred to me there would be a reason to rebuild our home, or that Gillian and I would become closer.

We discovered much later this house was not really connected to anything; it was barely even connected to the ground.

Walk the winding brick path, pass under the shade of the large redwood tree which guards our property, and climb the few brick steps: You'll come to the front door of our house. At times I have been ill with an indefinable sadness, fever and violent, teeth chattering, shaking due to city life. To stop this convulsive response when no one was around, I would tie myself to the large redwood tree. Thirty feet of thick-twisted, dirty, cotton rope that smelled of the horses it kept from rearing while I shod them, now kept me still. First, I tied a square knot tightly around my left wrist, and then I tossed the rope around the tree. Near the middle of the rope, I squeezed my right hand through a bowline knot's loop and ran the rest of the lead through an overhand knot's loop. I pulled the rope tight and held it with my teeth; the dried horse sweat on its threads tasted of salt. The violent shaking stopped, and I became the tree's son.

This tree, enduring and solid, knew she couldn't save me from the future. She stays where she's planted. Like all mothers she stays rooted in my mind.

Those times I've lashed myself to her red, velvet bark and smelled her scent have been my birth. But now I need more than a tree. The urge is strong in me to live somewhere else, where trees and mountains dominate the landscape instead of cars, houses and people. I will miss both redwoods when I move on.

Through her bark, I feel the heat of life. She silently asks me to stop and listen to my own song. The tree's beauty seeps into me. There is no time to lie. I must change my priorities.

Once inside the front door, to the immediate left, were the twelve steps which climbed to the balcony and looked down onto the living room.

The balcony has memories for me in the way that a junction or an overlook on a high mountain road might have memories for lovers, or for people who drive over the cliff at Dead Man's curve on Mulholland Drive and survive, or for those who just stop to think. This is where I watched 25 people migrate onto the balcony to look down onto Gillian in the living room for her surprise birthday party. I had summoned her to the telephone from the car, after we had just made the trek to Pasadena, about fifteen miles away, with the ruse that I had forgotten my wallet and would therefore be unable to pay for her birthday dinner at a romantic Pasadena restaurant.

We had almost driven the total fifteen miles one way to the restaurant and then turned around for home to retrieve the "forgotten" wallet, which would give everybody, including the caterer, time to prepare. After making sure everyone was behind shuttered doors on the second floor, I yelled for Gillian to come from the car to the phone with the pretense of an urgent call from her friend Miriam, who was upstairs along with everyone else. Gillian came inside, took the phone and became embroiled in a heated telephone conversation below the balcony in the living room with Miriam hidden above. Miriam, an acupuncturist, was collaborating with Gillian on the development of Chinese medicinal herbal formulas. Gillian is a drama heroine, which differs from a drama queen. They, unlike queens, thrive on the notion of a great evil in their midst, and like all great heroines, they have the wherewithal to steal the day's victory from the grip of Satan. Then they bow to applause for another great day's performance.

All addicts, including drama heroines, thrive on a need to fix something. An addict of alcohol would say, "I need a drink," implying that booze is an elixir to remedy a negative state of being, or a drug addict might say, "I need a fix." My own prosthetic emotional stabilizer is to try to make everything perfect. This is as plausible as driving down the autobahn safely at top speed, totally gassed on single malt whisky. The subject of Gillian's obsession – to bring traditional Chinese herbal medicine to medical doctors – was her herbal project conquest, but there was an oppressive thundercloud. Her impending challenge obscured her personal feelings of imperfection. Western medicine's scope is myopic and it does need heroines. But when one is intoxicated with a goal, there is no longer an urgency to focus on the broken concrete in one's own life.

Gillian was oblivious to everything but the critical urgency of "the herb project" to such an extent that 25 friends, including

Miriam, while still on the phone with Gillian just a few feet above Gillian, went completely unnoticed. Gillian continued on with the conversation with her herbal compatriot. She finally did a double take when Miriam, looking down at her with phone in hand, started talking directly to Gillian. Gillian, now aware of the people on the balcony, still tried to carry on the herbal conversation.

Finally Gillian got it when everyone yelled surprise and sang "Happy Birthday." The party went late into the night, but Gillian didn't. She fell asleep around eleven thirty on the couch still in a stage of shock. The rest of us drank, talked, ate and watched her snore.

One more word about throwing this party for Gillian: a week before the party I put a twenty-five-gallon galvanized tub in the living room by the front door to submerge the drinks in ice the night of the party. Gillian asked, "What's the tub for?" I told her it was for a horse. Her reply was, "Oh," which ended the discussion. Did she think I was bringing a horse into the house? In some ways, Gillian and I are a perfect match. In the past, I have brought home a 200-pound, half-Great Dane, half-Saint Bernard and assortments of many other half and full-blooded characters. More taxidermy animals and horns adorn our walls than in most Alaskan hunting lodges.

One night, I had old and young members of my side of the family over for dinner. Gillian was warm and friendly till about 11:00 p.m., when she went upstairs to sleep. I raised the level of the music; sounds of Motown's finest can keep the dead moving. Family members got up and started to dance. One thing led to another. Gillian's reputation for sleeping through anything was again established. Everyone formed a single conga line on our way up to the bedroom where Gillian slept.

When we traveled through the kitchen, a few of us picked up pots and pans as percussion instruments and attempted to keep time with the music. Only after some minutes standing over the bed, moving and beating our culinary drums did Gillian awake. The pleasant thing about Gillian is that with little effort I can make her smile when she wakes. Gillian is, for the most part, oblivious to her environment, and I tend to be acutely aware of mine. She carries herb books; I, at times, have carried a gun.

My parents were at this party. I was attempting to forget the past and make a new relationship with them. I went to a hypnotist, who cast a hypnotic shroud over my memory of my mother and father's brutality. But it catapulted me into old childhood feelings that I had erupted into this world from hell, and my parents were the victims of my birth. My mother took this time to reinvent the past for herself, saying things like, "Wasn't it wonderful that your father took you on a camping trip?" I was astonished at how she still needed to be perfect. My father did once take me on a camping trip. On that trip a constant flow of verbal abuse poured from his lips. I feared being beaten when he would blow into one of his rages.

These memories of guilt I've carried for every fear my phobic mother had, her compulsion to have everything perfect including me, came in flashbacks, like an old suit, threadbare and revealing what's underneath. The pain started crawling into the numb void where my emotions had been in a coma. Sometimes I wish I could have stayed in that hypnotic stupor, to think of them as wonderful, so I wouldn't have to write this.

At the front door, when you peered into the living room you saw a large fireplace against the opposite wall. It had a great draw. For me, a house must have a fireplace to be a home. A good draw means that when you light the fire, the smoke is quickly drawn up and out the chimney. The house's voice comes to me through the hearth. Warmth, the smell of wood and sounds transport me past the Department of Water and Power, whom we pay to keep our families warm. The flames are souls that speak to me. They, like the ancient rocks around my house, guard us in a language foreign to my lips but not to my flesh. Contained but never tamed, this wildness keeps my family warm.

The textured walls of the living room rose twenty-four feet to meet the ceiling and were held together with exposed wood beams and trusses.

To the right was a large picture window with thirty-five panes of glass, one cracked in the upper top left hand corner, which we purposely left that way for good luck. With the pressure of one finger on a center window's wood frame, the picture window bends. During the wild earthquake of 1994, we were in the midst of the remodel. Our living room was the only part of the house that stayed untouched, at least structurally, its wood and stucco held up and out by beautiful wood beams and trusses, like a rib cage and spine of a wooly mammoth. The room moved and shook but never stopped breathing. The rest of the house at this point had been torn down and a new wood skeleton was in its place. Soon it would be ready for the flesh of insulation, nervous system of electrical wiring, vascular systems of plumbing, and the skin of drywall and plaster.

On the left, six paces beyond the steps to the second level, past the ghost's closet, and under the balcony was a bar made by the set designer who built the sets for the movie "Rosemary's Baby" years before we moved here. Early on, the bar had very little significance to me. It was a Western, ornate style with a revolving, gilded liquor cage, inset in richly stained wood cabinetry. Now in later life, I ritualistically drink, much to the surprise of old friends from my teenage years. When we were young, these friends always had more reverence for booze-related rituals than I.

Some say, "Add a drop of water," to open up the essence of single malts, though for me there is already a tear in each glass of Scottish whisky, a remembrance of something very old that will never die.

Dogs, horses, women, the stars and the winking of the sun through macabre clouds: this is what I taste.

White and brown patterned tiles in terracotta grout make up the backsplash and sink counter. The backside of this bar almost touches the decomposed granite hillside on the other side of the wall.

Construction always brings destruction. This beautiful bar with the small, brown, porcelain sink, small refrigerator built into the counter, blender and cabinetry were created by this artisan of movie sets. It found its way out to the construction dumpster. Art was abandoned on this day, and the builders of the Pantheon wept for me. I have fought for things that have brought me grief and backed down from fights that would have given me victory. This was a fight with Gillian I backed down from. The simple truth is I liked the bar, and she didn't.

Next to the bar was a small antique wood door which opens to a large closet.

It was through this closet door that my life changed, along with the lives of everyone else who ventured beyond it. Walking four feet in, to the back of this closet, there was a loosely secured quarter-inch thick, four-by-eight sheet of plywood. Behind this plywood was the decomposing granite hillside of the Hollywood Hills. This is the land that our house now stands on, but used to cling to.

Backing out of the closet and to my immediate right, or to the east along the north facing interior wall of the living room, was a bookcase. The same set designer who made the bar also made this Western style bookcase, which ran the remaining length of the wall. The books ranged from Tolstoy's writings, to how to train a mule. Maybe if Tolstoy had read "The Misunderstood Mule" he wouldn't have had to write "Anna Karenina." Walking up the twelve steps of the staircase at the southwest corner of the living room brought me to the balcony overlooking the living room, where Gillian's birthday guests congregated. From this gallery, I looked through the picture window with its thirty-five window panes. On late afternoons, my eyes gaze upon hills that have never been built on. This theater of oaks, wild grasses, sage and laurel trees is where deer think they hide from my eyes, where coyotes wait for cats, and ravens wait for coyotes to leave so they can finish. This balcony goes the length of the living room. In the middle, there is a hallway which intersects the balcony, but when I had the party for Gillian, there were two pairs of shutter doors that opened onto the balcony. The door closest to the top of the living room stairs opened to our bedroom; the second door opened to a small dining room. The kitchen also was on the second floor at the other end of the dinning room.

We didn't make any improvements to the kitchen before the major remodel; for that matter, we didn't do much cooking here either. The room was narrow and small.

The old wallpaper looked like greasy confetti, and the wood counter looked as if it would be soon spouting its own life form. But I didn't want to be bothered with working on the house. At that time, Gillian and I were not into cooking so why improve anything? I did do some wonderful woodwork in the kitchen unrelated to repairs though.

On Halloween's Eve, late at night, I decided to attend a Halloween party dressed as Frankenstein's monster. In the kitchen, I cut two-by-fours, then nailed, screwed and attached the ends to foot patterns of plywood. I inserted these into my old, large rubber boots, to make two-foot-high stilts. I learned to walk on them by bracing myself with my hands against the kitchen's eight-foot ceiling. Amused by my newly gained height, I could not stop my late night laughter. Most of the women at the Halloween party wanted to talk to me, now that I was 7'8" and green. If only I'd known this when I was in high school. I guess that night I looked like a strong provider.

At the end of our bedroom was a bathroom with two doors– one entered the bedroom and the other to the hallway. At the end of this very small hall and bath was a space one could loosely call Berrigan's bedroom, when he was about two-and-a-half years old. The room had a row of high, narrow wood-framed windows. These windows gave the effect of a walk-down apartment, because the top of windows met the room's twelve-foot ceiling. Out the other side was a patio at this level. I remember the room's musty odor and damp coldness, which during the summer was just dank. The room's tile floor had been laid on a thin layer of cement over dirt. It had no real barrier to keep the room from dampness. A good structure is one of sight, smell, sound, light, and how air finds its way through the front door to the last rooms of the house.

Facing this bedroom with my back to the rest of the house was a single bed on the left, in an elevated cubby five feet above the floor. Above the bed was a small pane and sash window, reminiscent of a room the cartoon character Tweety Bird would have had in his house. The window was centered above the bed's length. A small antique wall lamp arched above the pillows. At the foot of the bed on the wall I had hung a small oil painting; pale blue moonlight reflected on deep blue waters embraced by legions of ponderosa pines cradled in rocky peaks, where northern exposure keeps the wind and snow forever. On the still waters of this midnight lake, a young Indian woman sat in a canoe, held my dreams and waited for me.

Laird Macgregor gave me this picture.

I see the women around me now and realize that I am only touched by good women, not by the hands of a betraying mother.

The Tweety Bird window and shutters faced the outside walkway. This walkway went the entire length of the house and ended up in the small backyard behind Berrigan's bedroom. Large folding shutters closed off the opening to the cubby from the rest of the room. To transport my son to this lofty perch was a four rung, wooden ladder that could be moved but fit nicely in the center of the small elaborate opening to the bed.

I caught a glimpse of Berrigan's autonomy when he climbed the ladder to his bed, unassisted, at the age of two-and-a-half. Berrigan was growing up, and until that moment I felt that he would always share his experiences with me; I hoped we would never be apart. But I am from my time, not his. As I grow old, I watch him grow strong, and the glow of his shadow is cast on my blurred thoughts. My feelings of respect ever deepen for my son.

This was Berrigan's first bedroom, and he did not spend much time in it. At some point during the night, he'd find his way into our bed and would stay with us till morning. Why should it be any other way? In our small bedroom, three people slept deeply along with a ninety-five pound German shepherd and a forty-five pound Australian shepherd.

When I think of Berrigan at this age, I lament that Gillian and I both worked many hours. Some of the time my curly towhead was delivered to a friend's mother, who also watched her grandson, my friend's child, who was the same age as Berrigan. Opa was the epitome of Albanian motherhood. She looked like a hard seventy-five but was probably sixty. Twelve times pregnant, she had gone down to the creek in her Albanian homeland and delivered all of them by herself, losing only one of them in the birthing process. Opa shod her own horse as well as friends' horses.

For those who are embarking on parenthood, let me risk saying this: Live below your means and fill those empty places with your lover, friends, sunsets and sunrises. Only read books you love. Feed your children good food, and don't be weakened by their initial whimpering desires for fast foods.

I am not certain how Berrigan actually felt about his relationship to Opa when he was young. I did notice a subtle acceptance of

Eastern European enunciations in moments of elated rapture; long monosyllabic nonsensical diatribes would elastically reverberate from the echo chamber of Berrigan's throat. His ability at this sing-song was so good, strangers thought he was speaking a real language.

We named Berrigan after Father Berrigan, a Jesuit priest who was well known in the 1960s. The articulate Father Berrigan took a stand in the Catholic Church, and his voice resounded farther than his parishioners to non-Catholics like me, giving solace to all of us who objected to the Vietnam War. Gillian wanted her Uncle Jeremy to be the other person our son was named after. I cared for Jeremy and remember him as strong, self-reliant, generous and kind. I have always taken Gillian's heartfelt requests seriously. She let me know how important it was that I meet and spend time with Uncle Jeremy, for he was the only loving member in her family. So Jeremy became Berrigan's middle name.

Gillian comes across as tough, but she protects an inner tenderness by her hard outer shell. I find Gillian clutching at love in her dreams. In her midnight reverie she becomes a pre-adolescent, sneaking out into the moonlight to play with others who share the same innocence. There are other nights when nightmares fill her sleep as violent men on horseback raid our farm; our dogs protect us, and then she wakes. Gillian's parents were hateful; her mother Renée was always throwing hostile jabs and insults at Gillian. Most memories of these interactions have faded away with her mother's passing. Renée has been dead for many years.

There is one memory that stands out, not because it was the worst thing Gillian's mother had ever done to her daughter, but for the pure malice of it. Gillian's female dog Calypso was in heat so she left her with Renée and brought her male dog Arden to my house when Gillian spent the night. Gillian let Arden out to take a pee, and

when he didn't return a few minutes later we started to look all over
the neighborhood for him. The next morning after looking all night
long Gillian called Renée. So as not to alarm her that we couldn't
find Arden, Gillian asked, "How's Calypso?"

"Just fine, is there anything else?"

"No, well um, Alan and I have been looking for Arden all night
long."

"How could you be so irresponsible to let him out like that?
What kind of mother will you make if you can't even take care of
your own dog?"

"Renée," Gillian always called her mother by her first name, "I
don't want to get into it, and I'll come by this morning and pick
up Calypso." It was only then that Renée admitted that Arden had
shown up at her back door at ten o'clock the night before in Ocean
Park. He had trotted from my house in the Hollywood hills to her
place, approximately twenty miles in four hours.

This was normal behavior for Gillian's mother. All of her mean-
ness was pale in comparison to her vicious silence when Gillian's
childhood innocence was being stolen by her husband, Gillian's father. So when Berrigan was born I felt happy to name our son after
Uncle Jeremy. In a way it was protecting Berrigan from his grandmother and grandfather's legacy, for Uncle Jeremy, Renée's brother,
hated Don, Gillian's father. While writing this I realized that a few
times I have tried to prove Gillian wrong for things in a remotely
similar fashion to her mother. Ouch.

Years later, our son Berrigan recounted his daycare days with
Opa. When things got out of hand between Berrigan and Opa's
grandson, she would turn off the electricity to the house. Opa was
a sweet woman who could have knocked the shit out of Attila the
Hun. She had dark rings around her eyes, weathered hands that were

capable of ringing more chicken's necks than ten circus geeks, and she had the agility of Quasimodo.

She enjoyed making a fuss over Berrigan. Her affection for him was reminiscent of Boris Karloff's portrayal of the monster in the movie "Frankenstein," when the monster, with his huge stitched-on hands, stroked and held a small kitten. Opa was multilingual in that she also had the intonation of Bella Lugosi and Igor's Yugoslavian and Carpathian speech patterns. "Oh, Baarriginn (Berrigan), oh, Baarriginn, yoou so guood," she'd say.

Her dark ancestral past had been recast into deep Catholic belief, most likely to ward off ancient fears and unexplainable awareness, uncontrollable experiences, the power of her sex drive and the call for death as a solution to disputes. This was Berrigan's first childcare person.

Behind Berrigan's bedroom was a small backyard, which ended in front of a steep hillside of wild grasses and flowers. If the roof was off our house and we looked down into it, the appearance would be that of a well-used rat maze. Berrigan's bedroom, the kitchen bath and our bedroom were fused together more by memory than by nails, although when it was built in 1923, a two-by-four actually measured two inches by four inches, not today's two-by-fours which measure one-and-one-half by three-and-one half. The rustic, beautiful living room entry door still is the greeter to our home as the fight continues between Gillian and me about its future.

In the kitchen, old decaying wallpaper dripped from the walls in homage to a strident monastic life that I strived for without the help of a conventional deity. At an unconscious level, I had hoped by waiting long enough that the house would self-consume and until that time we could just do some simple things. I argued: "All the house needs is paint and some new trim." Gillian disagreed that just doing a few cosmetic things to the house would have been sufficient.

A phoenix, which through total destruction becomes anew, was perhaps Gillian's intent for a major house remodel. I didn't know then this mythological bird's trial by fire would not have been overkill for Gillian's idea for redoing of the house. I know now. It would have been easier to burn it down.

Instead of using a flamethrower, years later I smashed the walls apart with a sledge hammer to rebuild the house. I didn't want to burn down the neighborhood.

As I ripped apart the ceiling in our bedroom with a crowbar, I discovered that life can be a fragile thing. The ceiling fan was a lethal air mover that weighed seventy-five pounds and probably had an industrial past. It was barely fastened to the ceiling over the middle of our bed. On hot nights, at full speed it wobbled like the predecessor to the Kitty Hawk. If I had only known that thing was so heavy I would have put the bed somewhere else.

15

THE HISTORY
OF OUR HOUSE

Our house was originally built in 1923 and is situated on the lower end of a steep mountain road. The narrow asphalt snakes its way between high, steep hills which keep the canyon cool and dimly lit, even on summer days. The road twists on this former hunting path and climbs up and out to an overlook. At the end of the road at the top of mountain, eighty years ago sat a restaurant, the Lookout Mountain Inn.

"Lookout Mountain Ave." is what the road sign says now. For me it will always be a simple mountain road.

A small trolley, long before my mother was born, carried guests to this restaurant and lovers to neck while they looked out over the rural skyline of Hollywood and the distant lights of Los Angeles far to the southeast. Hollywood Boulevard wasn't even an orange grove yet, just plots of land waiting for the first wave of developers. Deer crossed these barren stretches between Los Angeles and the coast. Ocean breezes carried the smells of the Pacific, and on stormy days the winds brought in the gulls, like immigrants from the sea. Bobcats on the desert floor hunted mourning doves, and jackrabbits ran from coyotes. Grizzly bears lumbered across this prairie leaving only their paw tracks in their wake.

Lookout Mountain Inn is no longer a retreat and respite from the city. Not a trace of burnt ash of the 1918 fire that destroyed the eight-year-old mountaintop inn can be found, nor is there a place to share hot lips and warm arms anymore without being cited by the Los Angeles Police Department.

When she was young, my maternal grandmother would come up on the slow, trackless ten-cents-per-ride trolley to neck with a suitor. My grandmother settled on a man who brought her very little happiness, one of the traditions of my mother's side of the family. My grandmother was a beautiful woman, whose only liberating acts that I know of were being a flapper and participating on a women's softball team. "The American Heritage Dictionary" defines a flapper as "a young woman in the 1920s who showed disdain for conventional dress and behavior." There will probably always be women like my grandmother.

Why in current times do we need a reason to have disdain for conventional dress and behavior? I have disdain for everything at times, and I don't have a reason.

Sports that did not have a possibility of death were only unsporting games to my paternal grandfather Will, who I spent much time with as a child. So when my mother's mother threw a baseball to me, and I caught it and threw it back, I was only doing it to amuse her. A sporting endeavor to me was and still is chasing a black bear. God, I hope I am raising my son differently.

While writing this, my grandmother's spirit is around me. The truth had better be told. For me to talk so cavalierly about this woman does her memory and my karma no good. She seemed to be a kind woman – slender, beautiful, with an aristocratic but open face and a memory of Los Angeles's past that could have brought her California historian status.

For the record, it has been said by female family members that my maternal grandmother must have been a saint to live with my grandfather, who wasn't generous when it came to giving compliments. Later on when he was in his nineties, he did give me a kind-of compliment, "Alan, you work too hard." What sticks out most for me as a child about my mother's mother is this: My mother was sick, and my grandmother came to our house in the Hollywood Hills. At the front door my grandmother was confronted by the neighbor's butting billy goat. Even while being rammed, her calls for help were sedate and punctuated with demure whimpering. In many ways, I must have been like that billy goat in the eyes of the females on my mother's side of the family.

At times, I've wondered if I'm 100 percent human. Doctors concur that my heart is a little different and actually functions better because of the direct route it takes its beats, similar to that of a lightning bolt, and I have one less vertebra in my lower back than most people. I am an Aries.

As for my mother's treatment of my father, she changed the pattern. She showed her displeasure with me instead of my father. He was always at my mother's beck and call. He provided a wonderful, large safe home for my mother. Did this house create a strong feeling of support that reverberated for my sister and me? No. Therein lies the unrealistic view that a house will make the difference in how secure a family feels.

Women will always look for that special provider, and men will always pretend that they are never lost when maybe all there is to do is hold each other in the middle of this darkness we call life.

My father verbalized very few desires, other than proud statements about maintaining a balanced checkbook and a thrifty budget. The difficulty in being a breadwinner is that no one does it right. Within this struggle to buy or not to buy, I sometimes take less than what I need. The result has been a life not fully lived. My mistakes have been made by saving something for a rainy day and not realizing it was raining, or making uneducated "frugal" purchases, which fail when needed most.

In keeping with my heritage, over twenty years ago in 1977, the then-new, backpacking hammocks that we received as wedding gifts, per Gillian's and my request on our gift list, were left at home when we went on our honeymoon backpacking trip. Other new backpacking equipment was also left and instead, in the thrifty tradition of my father's father, I opted for my old, seasoned hammocks, which I used when I didn't have a care.

Gillian and I were tired and sleepy from the eight-mile hike on the first leg of our Sierra backpacking honeymoon. The trail over Bishop's Pass is steep and goes up to 11,972 feet before it drops to the other side. The path winds its way into the deeply shadowed mountains, under rugged peaks, past hidden lakes and a multitude of stream crossings. They are the reward for a walk up and over the pass.

I set up my single man sleeping arrangement for the two of us. It consisted of a tube tent, hammocks and down sleeping bags. Both tube tent and hammocks were suspended between two trees, with the tube tent enveloping the hammocks and sleeping bags. A tube tent is what it sounds like, usually orange in color, made of lightweight plastic, but thicker than a plastic trash bag. This seven-by six-foot piece of plastic is hermetically sealed at the shorter ends to make a flexible tunnel and is normally set up on the ground. I like to swing from the trees in the wind and rough weather while sleeping. This architectural feat is executed by first running a nylon line through the tube tent, then tying the ends of the line between two trees, about twelve feet apart and about six-and-a-half feet up. The hammock is then strung through the tube tent and secured to the trees in the same fashion as the tent but at about the six foot level. Then the sleeping bag is laid out onto the hammock within the tube tent. This arrangement had sustained me and my Shetland sheepdog, Curry, for seven months while living in Alaska.

You might ask, "How does one get into this cocoon?" It's easy. First, I'd draw back the tube tent as if I were sliding back the curtain to get into the upper berth on a train. Next, I lifted my dog Curry up and put him at the foot of this swaying bed. I'd grab the hammock's rope where my head would be resting, then swing onto the hammock. All that was left was to zip up the bag and call Curry, who would then rest on my chest. I was warm in Alaska. I hid from the rest of the world up there and tried to heal.

Apparently, Gillian had never slept in a hammock before. She was also bigger than a Shetland sheepdog. With coaching and help, after a few spills and flops, my bride was in her hammock and sleeping bag. Then it was my turn to get into my hammock and sleeping bag. Within the shared orange, two man tube tent, we probably looked like two humans in a festive condom.

Snow started to fall. We were cozy. Wind gently blew, and the sound of light snow on the plastic was rhythmic. Cymbals were the leaves; the ground was the drum for the weighted snow and hail. Within this torrent of sounds came a violin string plunk, a very faint plunk; it came and went, not with the ebb and flow of weather but with the movement of our butts.

"What's that noise, Alan?"

"What noise?"

"That noise."

"I don't know."

"Alan, how old are these hammocks?"

"Old."

"Alan, I think the threads are breaking apart."

"If you stop moving, it will hold till morning."

"I am hardly moving, and they're still snapping."

"OK, just hold the sides of the hammock and keep your ass off the hammock. Sunrise is not that far off. We'll hike out at dawn."

I weighed more than Gillian, so my hammock fell apart faster. About an hour before dawn, I gave up my hold and just let it rip. Still in the sleeping bag within the now over-stretched tube tent, the feel of the ground's cold and dampness started to creep through the tear in the tube tent, where my butt rested on the ground. In the dark, soggy, early morning cool, the need for companionship overtook me. With Gillian's rear end hovering over me looking as if it needed to be grabbed, I pulled at what was left of Gillian's hammock. She fell onto me. We did not sleep at all, but at least I was now warm, lying on the ground holding her till the sun thawed both of us out.

Many hiking trips and years later, I think there has been a deception acted out by Gillian. The camping and athletic things we've done together have more and more been substituted with café lattes and hotels. It took a turning point when I had packed our tent, sleeping bags and all the rest of what we needed for a winter camping trip in Big Sur. With the falling of each night came Gillian's excuse not to camp, as certain as the sun going down.

"Alan, I have a little chill tonight; I need to stay in a hotel." Or, "It looks like rain. I don't want to be in the tent when it is raining." The best time to be in a tent is when it's raining.

On this trip, we never found a place to set the tent up for a night of unencumbered sleep under the relentless dark sky with the peaceful sounds of my own thoughts. Inside a hotel room the thoughts are "When is check out time?" And the ice maker down the hall will never duplicate the sound of a rushing stream.

If life is about anything it's about redemption. If our relationship was to go forward Gillian would have to redeem herself. The redemptive act came in the form of a backpacking trip two years ago into the high Sierras. After thirty years of being together, Gillian has become exhausted by and a disbeliever in my short cuts. I needed help, so I called on my favorite person to hike with, Tom Macgregor.

"I want to hire a motor boat to take us to the north end of Saddle Bag Lake, then we'll hike over Shepherd's Pass and down into Tuolumne Meadows. It's about a four-and-a half-day trip. Do you and Taylor, (his son) want to go?"

"Yes," Tom answered.

On day two, at ten thousand feet with two thousand feet to go before reaching the top of Shepherd's Pass, I carried a seventy pound pack and chose a route that was up a 60 percent grade of shale.

Watching from a thousand feet below, Tom laughed, Gillian smiled and Taylor couldn't believe it. Tom and Gillian's simultaneous comment through their laughs were, "We're not going that way." In times past, Tom and Gillian have always overridden my rambling.

Gillian and Tom had the guide book and maps and actually pulled them out. The route they chose took them on switch backs between boulders and came out on the trail leading down into the valley, five miles away. I ended up about two hundred yards above them. Tom and I met at the same time on this trail, just in time for him to tell me I had to go back down their path to bring out Gillian's pack. Their trail led around treacherous boulders, and at one point was only a few inches wide with a six hundred foot drop-off. Tom helped Taylor over this spot. The most amazing thing to me was that Taylor did the entire trip in skateboard sneakers and with my old hiking gear. On this hike, my feelings of love for Gillian grew with each step.

Before we owned this place we call home, and for that matter, before Gillian and I were born, our house was flanked by a log cabin brothel on its uphill. On its downhill, there was, and still is, a version of our home. It was once the larger of the two homes. Both were built by the same man. Looking at these almost twin dwellings, thinking about when they were built leads me to certain beliefs about human beings.

In this dark, cool, steep scrub oak and laurel tree canyon, eighty years ago when there was nothing on this plot of ground, there seemed to be a need for men to tame this land, far beyond just creating a safe shelter or what would be aesthetically pleasing. There is and will always be a struggle between conformity and individuality in home design. Is it a fear of the land and at the same time something else unknown? Maybe fear of being noticed or singled out by some ancient, celestial predatory animal? So we build houses which all look alike and we conform in dress and thought with one another in the hope of not being noticed or noticed just enough to attract the opposite sex. I believe that before building on the land one should sleep against its earth, to feel the ground. It's not that I find my house's facade ugly, but it doesn't belong to this land. Glass, wood and mud dug into the hillside is the kind of house this land calls for, not a home of Spanish and Italian descent. Maybe I wouldn't feel the striking contrast of life indoors from that of the outdoors if both were made of the same things. This sister to our house has gone through many owners but has changed little since both houses were constructed in 1923. But now with the home's most recent owners, Kent and Steve, it's going through a kitchen expansion and other major remodel improvements. Though our house was the smaller of the two when first built, we had a fireplace and they didn't, but Kent and Steve have corrected this.

Looking out my office/guest bedroom window, one of only a few original windows remaining in my house, the visions through the wavy glass haunt me. An earthen tower hovers over my good neighbor's small backyard.

In the course of their new excavation for a larger kitchen, they've fallen into a mire of bureaucratic red tape and nonsensical thinking, which the city's building and safety department loves to dish out. I know only too well.

To please the city, Kent and Steve cut the natural slope of their hill away, creating a cliff. Then a pit was demanded by the city for a foundation of the now needed thirty- foot high retaining wall. If Kent and Steve would have been allowed to keep their hill, instead of making it into a miniature Yosemite's El Capitan, all they would have needed was a wall a few feet high and proportional footing— something to sit on during a weekend barbeque, instead of a practice wall for a Matterhorn climb. In the Hollywood Hills, to make houses bigger we dig into the steep ground, and why not? But this digging was unbelievable.

Bad luck fell on this small back yard of Kent and Steve's. L.A.'s winter rains washed down large mounds of rock from the decomposed granite tombstone wall punctuating the ground between their house and the dirt precipice. Now thirty-by-thirty feet of tortured ground, freshly excavated in preparation for the kitchen's foundation waits for the city's OK, so the retaining wall can be built. The cliff would become an avalanche if the wall wasn't built soon. The entire cliff waits impatiently out of balance, only held together by its weight and memory, as it is with all decomposing granite rock. I think about telling my neighbors to look for some help to speed up the process, but I don't want to intrude.

Looming above their digs, a fifteen-foot, old, and green, wooden set of steps clings to the house and is tied on the other end to the cliff's oak tree. The steps used to connect the second story bedroom above their old kitchen to the patio at the top of the hill under the shade of the oak tree. The steps now span the space like a dangerous foot bridge to an island. Sand castles and abandoned eagle nests in the crotch of rotted tree limbs over water will eventually disappear and so will these stairs as the cliff slowly crumbles. If and when this bare ground tumbles, it will miss my house, but it will devour their small, old kitchen. Each time I look out my vintage window I say a prayer that they can subdue this tidal wave of granite.

It was either Steve or Kent who said, "We are just waiting for the city to approve the next part of the plans." I bit my tongue. Maybe I should say something. I think I will, but I'm too late.

Another night of pouring rain came down, and the sound and tremble of a crash brought my sleep to an end. I ran down the stairs from my bedroom into my office fearing Kent and Steve's cliff had finally let go. The window felt wet from the inside as I struggled to open it fast. There, like two captains on two ships passing in the night, Kent and I yelled in the wind and rain through tree branches that were like a wave of oak bark and leaves crashing against their home. The branches, big and thick, pressed hard against the house. It looked like the tree was going to make the house double over, and the old green steps were now more of a ladder hanging from the sideways tree. Then the hill let go again and the fallen tree's roots unclenched their grasp. The stout limbs rammed their way through the upstairs guest bedroom.

"Kent, are you OK?" I yelled.

Kent bellowed back. "Yah, I'm fine. Are you OK, Alan?"

Filling my lungs, I hollered, "Hey Kent, I guess you don't need to worry about the tree anymore."

"Alan, did the tree get your house?"

"No, I don't think so."

Kent shouted through his soaking wet smile; "I guess the worst is over."

I bantered back, "You're right, I'll help you in the morning"

"Good night, Alan."

"Good night, Kent."

The next day I helped Kent shore up and cut things and made a new window for them out of a sheet of plastic and duct tape where the tree had punched the hole into the house. From that point on I became involved, helping in any way I could but mindful this was not my project, and I could get in the way. The truth is I've avoided my life's work by my need for approval and through assisting others. I wonder where I would be with my writing and sculpting if I had let someone else change a stranger's flat tire.

There are boulders that dwell just beneath the surface in these hills. At some point we were able to incorporate them into the retaining wall of our house, saving many hours of work trying to extract them like dinosaur teeth, but Kent and Steve did not have that luxury. Their workmen used circular saws with diamond blades and jackhammers on the huge boulder imbedded in the ground where the horizontal part of the retaining wall was to go. Nothing seemed to work. They asked me to take a whack at it with a hammer and chisel, thinking since I have sculpted in stone it would be worth a try. But there was no small crack or fissure in the rock to get a start with. After a few months, with many diamond saw blades used by their workmen, it was cut and jack-hammered to ground level and was then incorporated into the retaining wall.

The question I have now is, "Will I finish the rewrites to this book and get it published before their last door knob and faucet handle is installed?" They might beat me, for although the sandblaster's scaffolding still surrounds the entire house, they planned now to use it for painting the house. I wish us all good luck.

I have been blessed with good neighbors. Years ago in that same house, Price and Stewart were my neighbors and friends. During that time, the Department of Water and Power, to put it politely, operated poorly. In the scorching heat of a rogue summer day, our normally cool canyon was hot. On the other side of my house, I share an easement with the house that flanks the west side of ours. The narrow easement leads to a small home farther up the steep slope. The access road is steep, approaching forty-five degrees. It was a sweltering summer day, and a merry band of "red-nosed, stumbling, drunken

DWP workers," as described by Price, attempted an ascent to the top of this unkempt, broken asphalt trail in their overloaded two-ton truck. After many tries they continued to end back at the bottom of the easement.

From the neighbors' accounts, they were all too drunk to walk up the hill, and the truck finally overheated and vapor-locked. With only gas fumes making the journey to the carburetor, they switched tanks. At that moment something under the hood caught fire, and the truck burst into flames. The fire spread to our wood fence. I was not home at the time. I did see smoke from where I was down in West Hollywood, but, of course, I didn't think it was my house. If not for Price, coming over and taking our garden hose and fighting the fire single handedly, our house would have been lost. All the while, the Department of Water and Power guys were desperately trying to call the fire department with the same lack of awareness they showed while driving the truck; they couldn't understand that there was no two-way radio reception in the canyon. Their attempts to call the fire department just took valuable time away from fighting the fire.

I believe that the ghost of our house somehow shared in saving that day. More than thirty years ago, there was a fire in the same area. That time the fire was under the second story floor. It burnt the floor joists, and the area around the burn had the visual appearance of a backfire without the signs of opposing flames. One of the functions of a backfire is to suck up and burn all the oxygen. The question I ask with no desire for an answer: "Did the ghost suck all the air away from the fire long enough for the flames to die?"

The following day, the DWP men were back up there. As I walked by the easement at street level, I saw it – big, wooden four-feet tall and bounding in the air as it wheeled toward me. I threw myself out of the way as this huge empty cable spool hurled past me, just missing a bus full of grammar school students. Running up the easement to them, I exploded, "What the fuck do you think you're doing? You almost killed me and took out a school bus full of kids." They started to laugh, and one of them, a big fat unkempt version of Santa, said; "OK, OK," as he tried to hand me a beer. I didn't know until then that someone could slur the word OK.

Our home was singed from the fire but did not burn. I made a phone call and asked the DWP authorities to replace my fence and paint the house. Their lawyer's reply was, "You have to sue us first."

"But I don't believe in suing. I just need for you to repair my house."

"You don't understand, Mr. Claymore. Before we can do anything you have to take legal action against us."

"Look, you know that your men started the fire with their truck, so just pay for the painting of my house and a new fence, and that will be the end of it."

"That's just not the way we do things."

"If I take the time to sue you, that is more money out of my pocket and I am self-employed. So please just take care of your Department of Water and Power responsibilities, and you'll never hear from me again."

"I'm sorry, that's not how it works."

"This will cost your department more money and these tactics only end up being reflected on consumer's bills each month." In the end; I refused to initiate a lawsuit; my homeowner's insurance paid for the repairs.

I've seen many a folly in our easement. I heard the sound from outside my bedroom window of a gardener's truck rolling down the path, out of control, onto Lookout Mountain Avenue and hitting something. I went down to see if an ambulance was needed. The gardener was shaken. He had clipped the side of a flatbed truck with the side of his mini-truck. If the gardener's truck was a second faster, the steel diamond plate corner of the flatbed would've gone through his windshield.

Impractical feats of construction have been attempted in this bowling alley of a road. A man who once owned the dwelling on the west side of us where the brothel used to be decided to dig a swimming pool; he found it necessary to shovel the same dirt three times. He first dug the hole, throwing the dirt into a large pile on his property. Then, with a small Bobcat tractor, the dirt was shoveled into the easement. Once again the dirt was shoveled, this time into a dumpster in the easement. This all seemed like a new version of the old line, "Build it, and the stupid will use it."

On the other side of our house, and on the opposite side of the steep easement, a log cabin / brothel was built in 1905. Although it hasn't been a house of ill repute for seventy years, and you would not recognize it as a log cabin anymore, it is the same structure now hidden inside the cocoon of a larger home. Within these last twenty-some odd years, this log house had become a landmark. For that reason its new owner can't tear it down to build something new. I have never been able to understand how it happens: you can change the size and entire look of some of the city's historical dwellings, as long as you don't tear them down. In the case of this brothel / log cabin, it no longer looks like the rustic red light district, hunting lodge it once was.

Even though many years have gone by since it was a brothel, I still envisioned silhouettes of its past on moonlit nights. Gillian would be away as I lay in bed. I dreamed and imagined dim red lights cascading off white cotton gowns begging for men, and the sounds of laughter from these "educated" women against the pale contrast of men's momentary innocence. The smells of those years seep through the chink in the old log walls outside my bedroom window. This was what I stared at for the first few years, living next to this dark timber palace before it became just another big home.

I believe the powers that be intended me to live next door to this shell of a whore house. Within the shadows of its loving glory, I felt justified in having sexual fun in my own life. I think Gillian sensed the pure and raw, sexual ghost running through the log home and was jealous of the cabin before it was transformed. A few years later it was turned into a multi-million dollar, hillside retreat and lost its charm and character. The retreat had grown in size from its original 2,500 square feet to over 6,000 square feet of modern, cedar shingled house.

Building over old beautiful places is just another version of historical and architectural betrayal. Architects who transform beautiful structures into buildings that conform to contemporary design standards believe that big and new is better. That is their explanation for destroying something beautifully built by men whose craft died when they did. The fear I have is the farther we get from the natural order of things like wood, earth, sun, water, the more alienated from love, sympathy and the appreciation of simple things we become.

To get around historical committees, these purveyors of sterility leave some wall of the old structure intact, and with a little bit of greenback greasing, a builder can circumvent city laws. Then they are able to call these new monstrosities "preserved historical buildings." I remember a wonderful building that I loved while growing up. Humes Sporting Goods was a tragic example of how one was able to keep an historical site "historical" and at the same time destroy it.

The way it was told to me, the Humes family in the 1930's had disassembled a Maine hunting lodge and shipped it across the country to Burbank, California, along with its contents that had been collected by trading with sportsmen and guides since the early 1900s.

Enormous logs, which today would be put on exhibit as logs from old growth forests, made the four walls of this two-story log church. (For those of us who worship the Gods of Wilderness.) This structure was from a time when good sportsmen were more like naturalists, and good naturalists were more like good sportsmen. Both groups knew that wild meant dangerous and not necessarily romantic, except in the telling of their exploits. The sportsmen could see the interconnectedness of all things wild, including themselves, and from this awareness they could thank the animal for its meat. Within this enlightened state, hunters shared willingly with those who were having a rough winter. Reflecting on how things were and still are in some rural parts of America magnifies my own feelings of alienation from life's harsh truth. Death and life are one and the same to nature; everything is recycled.

A few years back, Gillian ran over a mule deer that rolled onto our side of the road after someone speeding in the opposite direction struck her. They did not even stop. I told Gillian to pull over. I grabbed the doe up in my arms while the doe looked at me. I put her in the back of Gillian's large station wagon and got into the driver's seat. Gillian tried to keep her calm as I rushed to the nearest 24-hour veterinarian hospital where I put her on the vet's examining table at once. The deer breathed her last breath, and the vet pronounced her dead. As I touched her soft amber and gray coat, I noticed she had not a flea or any visible parasites or flaws. I didn't want to waste her meat; I wanted to take her home. That desire became the catalyst for my tears. "Are you OK? Did you hit the deer?"

"No," I replied. Nothing else was said. My tears were for how beautiful she was. If I were someplace other than L.A., I'd dress her out and feed her to my family. I'd season her hide with my tears for the loss of such a beautiful animal. I'm sickened by the strong chains of a city's "appropriate" behavior, which I let manacle my ethics. Waste not, want not. To eat something that is already dead means I don't have to pay someone to kill an imprisoned animal to feed me that day. Life is bittersweet. The deer's death would sustain my family for many days. And in turn, when my death comes, I will give sustenance to something else. For all those vegetarians who feel you have fled from the guilt of sustaining your life by killing something, I dare you to smell and feel the quiet power of a large spruce or California redwood. Then get down on your hands and knees and look at an ant making its way through the timbers of grass shoots. After you have learned to hear the tiny forest of the ancient insect, tell me that you don't kill to sustain your breath. Remember this: the goal of self-preservation is only a facade. Our killing and our death have everything to do with everything. Almost everything we eat has to die, and so will we.

I wanted to share the beauty of Humes Sporting Goods Store, but these memories go to a deeper place in me. They even go back to my male mentors, especially Laird Macgregor, who introduced me to this store and who contributed so much to my appreciation of nature within me and in the world.

The massive timbers of this lodge's exterior almost asked, "Are you ready to risk another day on a journey with no trails?" Humes took up a whole block. The front door was imposing, appearing to have been hung by a blacksmith. It was equal to the rest of the exterior, and so was the porch that ran the entire front width of the building. Once I went through the front door, it was too late; there was no turning back from my imagination.

Inside, Timber Wolf heads snarled. Wolverines, moose heads, deer heads, whole lynxes, Roosevelt elk, tule elk, grizzly and black bear all found their places on the walls, along with bear traps, snow shoes, rifles, pistols, Indian baskets and blankets, Hudson Bay blankets, canvas desert bags, double bladed axes, wagon wheel chandeliers, kerosene lanterns, hunting bows made by the famous archer Fred Bear, birch canoes and more, all echoing the past within the un-milled log walls, beams and ceiling that rose at least forty feet above the flagstone floor. A large fireplace at the back right corner had kept Maine winters at bay a long time ago. These relics came alive!

If only I could buy the wool shirts, pants, hatchet, 12-inch Buck knife, snow shoes, hunting boots, hunting coat. Then I'd cross the cement and flagstone floor, go underneath the stairs and balcony: here I'd make my final ground floor purchases. I would know that my place in the past was secure.

Under the steps, before making that final purchasing ascent, there was something far finer than the Queen's royal jewels. In a thirty-five foot glass display case was a panoply of arms. Beautiful, pearl handled matching Colt .45s, single action revolvers, new Ruger high caliber Black Hawk pistols, Browning shotguns – so many rifles, handguns. On the wall, the holy covenant was revealed to me: shotguns, car-bines, high powered, small caliber, high velocity varmint guns, 308s, Marlin 444 magnums and Weatherbys, even Rigby 416s, one of the most powerful calibers ever designed. You might as well have shot me with all of them, for I was in purchasing heaven of down sleeping bags, down jackets, and tents made of Egyptian canvas. I knew if I could buy all this crap, I would walk out the back door and enter the wilderness. But as I started to hike and spend time in remote areas, I realized that all that paraphernalia would just weigh a person down. I'm glad I didn't have any money for this equipment. It took very little gear to enjoy nature; less truly is more.

Years went by, and the Humes family sold the building. The way it was explained to me was that the city had a stipulation, since it is a registered Burbank city historical building, "Whoever bought it could not tear it down." The plan of the new owner was to change the interior into individual office space, without changing the aesthetics of the building inside or out. But all of a sudden the city said that the old front windowsills were too low. The best way to bring this magnificent log lodge up to code was to frame in the windows and stucco the whole building so it looked uniform. Uniform to what I don't know, but that's what they did. No longer is it the place of my youth. It would be as if Daniel Boone and Davy Crockett changed their identities and were now Siegfried and Roy.

I visited Humes when it was no longer Humes, during its reverse metamorphosis from butterfly to moth. In the heap of things being thrown away in the parking lot were the large wrought iron fire screen and its doors. These had adorned the front of the lodge's rock fireplace which had kept things warm for so many years. I asked the contractor, who was destroying this rustic chapel of sporting goods upon Burbank's request.

"Do you mind if I take this old, rusted screen?" I asked, not telling him it was a priceless possession. He said, "No, go ahead," glad that his pile had just been made smaller.

Though ill-fitting due to its large size, it has been in front of my fireplace for many years, keeping my childhood memories warm. I contemplate making it into a coffee table, where it might rest in front of our fireplace. I could weld the sides of the fire screen into legs then insert beveled, green hued glass into its wrought iron frame on top of the rusted screen. Perhaps, one day.

16

APPARITIONS

Under the steps in the living room that rise to meet the balcony, is the closet where our ghost lives or, should I say, exists. Do ghosts live or exist?

A year or so after moving into our home I discovered we had a ghost, or maybe she discovered me. Late one night, Gillian and I had an argument, and I went downstairs to sleep on the couch. I managed to fall asleep, but at about one in the morning I woke up. Hovering over me only a few feet away was a ghost that looked like a finer featured version of the actress Meryl Streep: long, light, fine blond hair. Willowy and composed, she loomed over me with a look of curiosity, levitating above the ground a foot or so in a white linen dress. Being a brave soul when it comes to life's issues, and this not being one, I ran up the steps as fast as my feet would take me. At the top of the stairs, I glanced down over the balcony and looked at her, and she at me. In the next moment I was in bed next to Gillian, liberated from all resentment I had for whatever great injustice Gillian had perpetrated against me. For that moment the sexual frustrations in my so-called intimate relationship with this living being were quelled. The sight of the ghost paled my dissatisfactions for that night. The odd thing about this interaction with the ghost was the telling of the encounter; it brought questions from friends and family.

"Do you think she is attracted to you, Alan? Are you attracted to her?"

I have always liked my women with warm flesh on their bones. Would it be considered cheating if it were possible to have sex with her? What would it feel like? Would I fall into some sort of hellish abyss while having an orgasm, or would I just scare myself to death as I came?

On that night back in bed with Gillian, my head under the covers, I found rest. There were other days and nights when I could not simply run from the ghost.

REBUILDING: THE SHORT VERSION

I have always made things. My sister Mary is four years my junior. When I was nine and she was five, we played together. I, so much more informed about life, invented the forms of play. We constructed tunnels, rooms, hidden passages out of blankets, linens, card tables and other furniture in our parent's converted attic in the Hollywood Hills. I would do this when they weren't looking.

My sister's four-year-old eyes sparkled with amusement and surprise when she entered these structures. She did the exploration, and I did the construction. So it came as no surprise that my skills would be called upon once more in my late thirties and early forties to build another house. This time, construction was not with my sister Mary, nor with blankets, card tables or joy, but with my wife Gillian and our nine year old son, Berrigan.

There were others involved: Some labored on our behalf, and some labored against us. As I write this on January 29, 2002 no one has died or been permanently maimed in the endeavor of building my house. There have been at least two nervous breakdowns that I know of brought on by this project and a large area of scalp deforestation on my head, due to assumptions I made about workers, city codes and family members.

Shortly before starting construction on our house in 1992, Gillian and I made a family declaration: I was to quit shoeing horses and increase my time sculpting and writing stories and poetry. Then as now, art and words help to seed and express my passions for beauty, sex, love and my desire to understand hate and inhumanity within all of us.

Gillian and I made promises to each other. I would help her start a new business with her old boss, and assist her in any way I could with finishing her PhD in anthropology. In return, she would support me in my endeavors, with one proviso: "Alan, if you quit shoeing horses altogether, you will become morbidly depressed." Her statement is no longer true. I do need the company of horses, not to shoe but to own one when the time is right. Gillian understands my need to contribute to the family in a way that is not compromised by fashion or fad. That is what led me to shoeing horses in the first place. She also knows the love I have for horses, the outdoors, and my need to be free. It is what keeps me alive. I hate being indoors, even in a barn.

In the past I did not have to buy a horse; they were just given to me, whether I wanted them or not. The love of horses has only eluded me in the brief moments when I have been kicked. While convalescing in front of the TV watching Emily Bronte's "Wuthering Heights," I wish for a hard, rainy ride on some steed, over the English countryside to Scotland. At the end of this ride, I'd sit in my small thatched roof farm house by the hearth's blazing fire and rest. While flanked by a hot-blooded Scottish woman and my dogs, the cold, wet night smells and music creep into our warm room. This reverie rekindles my fondness and need for equines. A rerun of a "Bonanza" episode in my more vulnerable moments saves me. Hop-Sing makes me chicken soup, and the Cartwright's take care of me, because I am Ben's closest friend. It brings back my feeling of security with horses and life in general. I am probably not the most rational person when recovering from a horse's kick.

Gillian knows that for me to feel worthwhile I need to work, and she has used this female knowledge to drive me to build this place we call home.

Somewhere inside me there is a push for change. The truth about my existence is as incongruous as the flower I visit each ski season while taking a chair lift at a ski resort in the Sierra Nevada Mountains.

The flower's home is a northern-exposed jagged cliff that would not make a suitable home for anything. This fragile flower perhaps can only survive at this altitude, in the cold and rock cliff.

Like that flower, I survive at times spiritually, physically and emotionally by way of a harsh life that tells me I'm alive.

With the roles changing between Gillian and me— her holding down the home fort and me concentrating on my art— I felt as if a father figure dressed like a jockey was whipping me toward my goals. For some reason, there was a need now to push and shove my way through my resistance toward the things I dearly love: sculpting and writing.

The resistance came in the form of internal dialog, "I will starve as an artist, I'm self-indulgent and real men don't write or sculpt." The patriarchal jockey tightened its grip on me demanding immediate emotional and monetary gratification.

Then there were those other words I spoke to myself: "You need to court the muse. Take a breath."

We switched roles. But I was lying to myself. Instantly after the change of guard, we both felt the need to investigate the possibility of doing some much-needed work to the house. In my mind, whether admitting it or not, building a home was far more identifiable as a clear path to masculinity and prosperity than sculpting and writing.

To avoid the hassle of moving and to show Gillian I was "a man," I agreed with her decision to build a kitchen downstairs. The reasons for the remodel were obviously flawed, but I couldn't see that at the time.

When we bought the house, the kitchen was located on the second floor instead of downstairs next to the living room. This limited the house's living space. As with my sister's make believe house, Gillian and I felt we had run out of metaphorical blankets and sheets for our home.

I could tell that in the past the house's second floor had gone through quite a few metamorphoses, and they all seemed to replicate a vermin hovel when you scratched the paint and pried apart the wood. While peering inside the walls and under the floor, I saw each previous homeowner's faulty version of a remodel. Two-by-fours seemed to miss their targets, nails didn't quite make it all the way in, water pipes dangled in midair. All this suggested that something, at some point, needed to be done.

The transition from shoeing horses to sculpting was not going well. Delayed gratification was well and good while I was single. But being married gave life to the lies about being a man; hard and unenlightened work that would make a breadwinner rich was the sign of manhood in my family. Whether the choice was to be a lawyer, businessman or blacksmith, the order of the day was to fulfill some sort of patriarchal image. The fact was, no matter what manly gauntlet I ran through there was really nothing to prove to anyone. And the reflection I hoped to see of myself in others' eyes could never replace the joy of just being alive. Gillian being attracted to me had nothing to do with what I did for a living, but how I felt about her and me.

But, I was ready to try to do what I thought I needed to do to be desirable: build a house. I would like to blame my father, but he cannot be faulted for mentoring my future. He was also mired on man's muddy road, passing others only to find himself stranded and watching as other men pass by, pretending to be going somewhere else. They, like my father and I, are on this same conveyor belt, soon to be stuck in the same precepts about a man's life when we finally look in the mirror and see the gray paleness of age. Some of these false answers that are given to subdue the pain of living a life unfulfilled, have been, *"cause that is the way it is; your father's father did it that way; and that is who you are;"* or whatever else we say to our offspring to induct them into "group think."

I have seen my father's college books and the notes he made on the pages. I know he dreamed and aspired to find his loves and innate gifts in life. I feel tears as a father would for a son in conflict, for I am older in thought than these notes my father made in his college books. I ask myself, "Where does peace really exist?"

The answer comes to me in a vision of the day after the American Civil War ended: men, tired and blood-stained, limping home on tree-covered, rural roads.

I have been asked, "Did you ever get your turn to follow your dreams of being a sculptor and writer?" Not totally yet, but it is entirely my fault. To listen to the sometimes faint voice of the muse, to say "no" to life's distractions: that is what I'm learning.

To fit the profile of what a man is supposed to be, I started the task of rebuilding our house in 1994.

17

FEATHER, BONE AND ROCK

I was happy with the anxiety of ownership. Originally, Gillian didn't want to buy a house, but I did. When it came time to sign the papers, I didn't, and she did. Lying deep under the surface at a level that scares me is how much Gillian trusts me. At times, it could bring me to tears, for she believes in me. The tragedy is that I feel sad for her and her belief. Years ago I wrote a poem for Gillian. It wasn't a love poem. In one of the poem's stanzas, I wrote the words, "She believes in kites that have no tether." Sometimes I am a kite with no tether, going off on total impulse, but trying to make it look like I know what I am doing. This is the guilt that I feel. While I moved us into a tent, took stands against men who were beating their girl-friends or chased a bear with an axe, Gillian has watched in horror but stayed.

My encounter with the black bear which friends and family wit-nessed was three summers ago in Mammoth Lakes, California. The bear was having a stand-off with a group of other campers and win-ning by walking slowly towards the people with their weaponry of clanging pots and pans while he ripped tents and tore out car win-dows. The campers slowly retreated, walking backwards as the bear slowly advanced on them.

I couldn't find my shirt, boots, or .357 magnum, and now the bear was finding little kids in the campground interesting, with their fresh caught trout. I grabbed my axe and ran straight at the bear more

like a Russian Bear Dog than a human. I chased the black bear up the
steep, forest trail away from the children and adults. Thirty yards up
at its rich stash of camper's supplies, the bear stopped. It was a messy
heap of food, paper and plastic bags, reminiscent of an adolescent
boy's bedroom. I felt sympathy toward him when I saw these meager
possessions. This is where the bear stood his ground. On all fours,
he stood sideways to me and breathed heavily with a low growl, pretending not to be looking at me. The signs were clear; he was ready
to fight for what was his. I backed off slowly while growling back at
the bear, hoping he'd know I would fight, while I swung the axe in
preparation for his attack. If I had taken one too many steps toward
him there might have been blood, his and mine. I've pounded cold
steel on the anvil for 35 years, making it easy to swing an axe accu-
rately and fast, and the night before, by the campfire I had sharpened
it, but I could feel my heart beating in my hands pressed against the
hickory wood. Moving slowly, so I wasn't the one being chased, I
made it half way down the trail without the bear. I turned around
and put the axe over my shoulder and took a deep breath. When the
group of people saw me walk down the trail, bare foot, no shirt and
humming, their mouths dropped. Thinking that all the growls came
from my furry friend, the consensus was I'd been eaten.

I can say this about Gillian: she's got guts to be with me, but I've
always complained that she has no common sense. I'd like to think
that I did this to save the other campers, and there is truth in this,
but I think my son Berrigan said it best: "Dad just felt like chasing
a bear today."

In 1982, before the remodel of our house, I was thirty and totally turned on to my wife; it was not reciprocal. Because of years of
shoeing horses, teaching riding, sculpting and observing animals that
have become my subjects of sculpture, I have come to a temporary
conclusion. Everything is temporary except change, and I am not

even certain about that. My feeling was and still is that if I did or do one more thing, I would get the love that was not within Gillian's grasp to give. What does it mean to do all the right things for the wrong reasons? Unwittingly these "right things" pulled us apart. Not enough of the time did I take things to the wire with Gillian. There was never any consideration on her part about how something would affect the relationship or me. Things would come out of her mouth at times, like, "And if you don't like it, Alan, you'll have to make up your mind whether it's worth it for you to stay. I want you to stay but that's your choice." I found out years later she didn't mean what she had said and would have reconsidered things such as choosing working for a company which demanded more of a commitment than a marriage. Twenty years later she still works for this establishment.

I thought that by supporting Gillian's work it would make our relationship better. Instead what happened was that by putting the needs of Gillian's job ahead of everything, we lost time together in our young relationship. We have never recovered from the wasting of those moments of possible intimacy. Going along with things that were against my better judgment for the sake of keeping the relationship killed so much of that time reserved by angels for lovers.

Ever since I can remember, I have been looking for a home. I have owned property before, but never where I lived. I bought things for investment, so one day I could have my own home. In all the time I have owned this wonderful house, I have really never let myself enjoy it for fear I would lose it.

The work I did on the house before rebuilding was not done to make the house more comfortable but to ward off my fears of its destruction.

In the past I have sat out storms in tents and experienced the effects of such events as the Little Tujunga fire of 1977 where I lost one of my horses. Then a year later, in the same canyon, came the pounding of the so-called once every "hundred year rains" and the flood that followed. By this time I had developed a sixth sense for environmental change. A couple of months before the rains and flooding of Little Tujunga, I got the feeling I should tow our Silver Streak trailer we'd just moved out of to the higher ground of the cabin we were just moving into.

The rain came down hard for two weeks, and one late winter night the sound of a freight train shook us. It was the rumbling river water crashing over its banks, and it roared by at eye level. Just a few minutes before, you would consider it "higher ground."

That premonition to move the travel trailer close to our cabin saved it. After a week, the raging river mellowed into a deep, fast moving creek. On the shore by our cabin, an old bathtub beached itself. It was Saturday and I love boating. I cut a solid limb, boarded and gondoliered my way down to Hansen Dam, more than five miles away.

The first step to secure our new home from erosion brought me back to the flood of Little Tujunga and the thought that someday, maybe, I could boat down to the Sunset Strip.

To build rock walls and borders for our house on Lookout Mountain, I rented a 1950s ten-ton dump truck and drove it to the Hansen Dam rock quarry. There I paid the man operating the loader $25 to dump ten tons worth of rock and boulder into the back of the truck.

A five speed transmission with a split axle gave me ten gears forward. No problem going the twelve miles home until I got to the steep descending section of Laurel Canyon. In third gear low range, my foot lightly touched the air brakes, then not too lightly. Suddenly I wished I weighed more than 160 pounds. Now I know why truck drivers are usually big; they can put more weight on the brake pedal. Gears grinding, then double clutching got me into second gear low range. Maybe I had 12 tons of rock in this piece of vintage tin. I could not get the truck into first gear, and 12 tons of rock pushing against my back made the brakes almost useless.

Fourteen miles an hour was never faster. I got close to the curb and began rubbing the right front tire against it. My plan was to get my speed down to about a half mile an hour, so I could negotiate the turn up Lookout Mountain Road. Traffic was light on Laurel Canyon that day, but I still managed to get over the legal limit of holding up five vehicles behind me. I'd guess I was holding up twenty. Finally, getting down into first gear and making it to Lookout, I made the right turn and headed up the hill. As I drove past my driveway with no flashers on this ancient model, I must have pissed people off again. Drivers now waited for me to take the truck up my driveway backwards without the help of power steering.

Twelve tons of rock is a lot when it is in a 1950s truck made for ten tons.

When the rock was dumped in my front yard, it looked small. An extra eighteen tons of rock was needed. On the way back to the rental yard with the now empty truck handling like a new sports car, and I twenty years younger than I am today, I entertained the thought of doing it all over again. I thought fate was on my side, even though discretion hardly ever is.

Instead, a man who fit the description of a truck driver more than I, hauled eighteen ton of rock in a truck made for hauling eighteen tons. He charged me ninety dollars, which was cheaper than renting the rust bucket again, if I were going to do two more conservative nine-ton loads.

Now that I proved to God-only-knows-who that I can, if there's a need for more rock, I'll get the truck driver to haul it.

Manhood is constantly repeating the same message to me, "I can do it all." I have wasted my time with this sport and no score is ever kept, so the inning is never over. I'm going back to Scotland to drive again on small roads; fast, with the stick on the wrong side, hoping in moments of reverie the vehicle will still be on the left side of the road. The last time in Scotland I was told about an Italian driver who a week before died doing just that. What's with me? Will my son and wife be any prouder of me?

After I had gotten the needed rock for the walls and the aesthetics called for by the yard's voice, it was time to cement the rock together. I asked Ingrid and Vance, my neighbors on our uphill side, if they could recommend someone to help me do the cement work. They suggested Rodolpho.

Rodolpho's name will always bring a grin to my face. Ingrid and Vance had Rodolpho and another man work for them around the house. On certain days these two men worked there at the same time.

During those days I could hear Ingrid gently call out, "Enrique," then yell out in bellowing tones of frustration, "Rodolpho."

Ingrid had a parrot named Omar. This bird was selective in his utterances. Omar, in his desire to keep the planet Earth humorous, seemed to pick out the most important things relating to the human pecking order to speak on. He was a bird of few sentences. Mantras were his forte. I found great joy in his soliloquy, "Enrique, Enrique; Rodolpho!" This was performed to perfection in Ingrid's German accent and voice. Berrigan's five-year-old cries to Gillian at our house sometimes echoed in and also rattled Omar's cage.

Berrigan's demands apparently were of significant consequence to Omar, for I could hear the parrot calling "Mommy, mommy MOMMIEE," in Berrigan's voice. There is no accident that Ingrid and Berrigan were chosen as the foil of the raptor's utterances.

Knowing where the power was, Omar spoke their words as if they were his own. I wondered at times: Did Enrique and Rodolpho think they had two employers, or did Gillian think she had twin sons? I enjoyed listening to Gillian's motherly conversations with potential poultry. It was just as much fun to watch "MOMMIEE" run up and down the stairs for the concerns of her feathered second son. I never yelled Rodolpho's name or called out "Mommy," even though I wanted to.

Years later, my old friend Robin inherited Omar. Ingrid and Vance, who were no longer living next door, called me in a panic, saying that the bird was not safe to have around their newborn daughter.

I called Robin and asked her if she wanted another bird. She asked me what type it was, and I told her that I didn't know.

I originally met Robin in Griffith Park when I was about fourteen years old. Each day I would take my dog Curry to the park after school. One day a beautiful early twenty-something woman drove up in a new 1966, dark green, Cadillac convertible, with a brindle Great Dane and a Saint Bernard in the back seat. I was in love. She told me she was the Smirnoff poster girl on the Sunset Strip after we got to know each other. I never took my crush seriously, or at least not for very long. In spite of that infatuation, we became friends.

As time went on, we lost touch with each other. Two decades later, a horse trainer asked me if I would take on a new horseshoeing customer. I agreed. Twenty years is a long time and I did not recognize her, but she told me a few times that she felt she knew me from somewhere. Mind you, I was about fourteen when we'd first met, and when we met again, I was thirty-four. We picked up our old relationship where we left off. I fell in love with her animals again. This time, she had beautiful quarter horses and Rottweilers. One of her Rotties was about thirty inches at the withers and weighed more than two hundred pounds. Here and now I promise to write about them someday. I share the same birth date with one of her stallions.

Robin also had a motley crew of birds. One day over lunch at her house after I had shod a few of her horses, we talked about our past. In this conversation we uncovered our old friendship of my early teens and her early twenties. "I knew it, I knew I knew you," were Robin's words that day.

Robin came to my house first in her old, Chevy one-ton dually pickup on the day she was to pick up Omar. From our house, Berrigan, Robin and I drove over Mulholland Drive west for about twenty minutes to Ingrid and Vance's new home. We pulled into the driveway that went about a quarter of a winding and ascending mile. At the end of the driveway was a house disguised as a department store, or was it a department store disguised as a house? Not only was it one of the biggest homes on Mulholland, Vance also mentioned it was on the highest piece of real estate on Mulholland Drive. We saw their baby girl and got the tour. The first thing we found when walking into this structure was a living room the size of a ballroom with a forty-foot ceiling. At the end of the living room where there should have been a wall was an electronically automated glass door, about twenty feet by thirty feet wide, which glided and disappeared into the dining room wall. This glass separated the living room from an equal-in-width outdoor swimming pool, and there were only inches separating the pool from the living room. It appeared that the glass door was the only thing keeping the pool's water from coming into the living room. The kitchen and guestrooms on this first level were all monstrous in size. Even the doors to the bathrooms were well over standard height. After the first floor tour, we all got on the elevator. I could not contain myself. Out of my mouth came, "Ladies lingerie and children's toys." Exiting onto the third level we walked to their master bedroom and into the bedroom's closet. Within this closet were many expensive looking suits encased in high-tech, clear plastic condoms, organized like space suits on some duke or magistrate's outer space yacht. The closet was bigger than our bedroom before our remodel. Well, if you have seen one Nordstrom department store you have seen them all, and that was the impact their home had on me.

What happens to me within these walls of things we as a society pay homage to? Am I guilty of avoiding the honest struggle of making huge amounts of money? I found peace from that struggle for awhile. From the age of twenty-one to twenty-eight, when I was a riding instructor, there was no conflict for me; loving what I did was more important than a big salary.

When I fell in love with Gillian, the only woman I ever got jealous over, I changed my behavior. My father's words echoed in my head: "Alan, when are you going to get a real job?" He didn't think teaching horseback riding was a real job. If only I told my Dad that I was an instructor of equitation, things might have been different. To say it that way, I would have had to be coming from a different place within me. Probably if my father could take back those words, he would. As fathers, sometimes we forget the impact we have on the young men who carry our names.

For Berrigan will it be more of the same burden of carrying out family history and its falsehoods? Or will it be a chance to stand on the shoulders of a patriarchal past, to see and understand the importance of listening to one's own song? I hope I've broken the cycle for Berrigan and he'll hear his inner voice; the voice which lends itself to a full life.

Looking at Ingrid and Vance's house's interior walls, I knew that I wouldn't give up my icons of status. I could move to a place that would be beautiful, but less pricy and more modest. I could drive a work truck with vinyl seats instead of leather. (Do they still make vinyl?) Is this the closest I'll get to living a simple life of art and nature, the dream of it? I tell myself there is nothing to prove. These acquisitions—a large house, fancy cars—do we really need them? The illusion of following a trail of working till I die, looking to quench my thirst on the nothingness of success, whether it's a medal or recognition, means nothing.

Now finished with the tour of this monstrosity, we went down to the gargantuan garage. In the middle of the spotless cement floor was a large, black iron cage, old and ornate, on four wrought iron legs. From the entrance door of this empty auto auditorium, I could make out something small and green in the cage. It was Omar. At closer range, he glared at us with wild, black, attention-deficit eyes. Solid green instead of the normal array of parrot colors, Omar took on the drab appearance in his feathered fatigues of Fidel Castro or Mao Tse-tung. All three shared what could be called a lethargic, posturing dominance. I really don't know anything about parrots. He was bigger than a parakeet but smaller than a macaw. Even though I was ignorant of bird behavior and didn't have anything to base my negative feelings on, something wild in the bird bothered me.

Ingrid, Robin, Berrigan and I stood around Omar's cage in the middle of the neo-Gothic bird hangar. Ingrid, with her German accent, talked about this mid-size bird. "You haf to be very careful vhen you handle him." And with that, she grabbed a falconer's glove from under the cage, which dwarfed Omar as she waved it at the bird. On that day, he was left in his cage.

We loaded the cage and all into the back of Robin's Chevy truck. I lashed the cage to cargo loops inside the truck's bed with large, cotton horse-training ropes. These were the only ropes I could find before going off to Ingrid and Vance's.

Saying our goodbyes, we made our way slowly back to my house. As we exited Ingrid and Vance's long driveway onto Mulholland drive Omar started screaming; "FUCKER, ASSHOLE, MOTHER-FUCKER, COCKSUCKER." As we went down the road, these sounds echoed enchantingly through the truck's open rear sliding window. Evidently things weren't as harmonious as one might believe at the department store on the hill. For twenty minutes we drove on winding turn after winding turn, over the up and down dips and hills, almost in tempo with the sway and wind of the old Chevy. This glorified pigeon bantered out our society's vast selection of descriptive words. It was the beak from hell. Omar's "horny projecting mandibles," as described by the American Heritage dictionary, needed no elasticity for his utterances.

In sculpture, negative space is vital to give the work dimension. Foreground and background gives context and adds relevance to some sculptures. One can say the same thing of music: its negative space is the silence or space between notes. Omar knew this. To further dramatize his soliloquy on his pilgrimage toward bird Mecca, he would at times pause. When we thought he was done he would again start, "SHIT-SHIT-SHIT-SHIT, ASSHOLE-ASSHOLE-ASS-HOLE-ASSHOLE" By the time we got to our house, Berrigan, Robin and I could not stop laughing. Berrigan, nine-years-old at the time, was just starting to explore these words. He was red-faced; his laughter was unbridled. My son's guffaw was pure to the point his veins stuck out on his little, muscular white neck. Robin, on the other hand, tried at first to pretend for Berrigan's sake that she didn't hear it, then tried in vain to talk over the initial ruckus. She gave up soon and, as Omar started up again, Robin would say; "Oh no, here he goes again." I, at first, tried not to say anything, but I wondered what kind of opportunity I had laid at Robin's front door. Robin is a high end C.P.A, and runs her office out of her house on her two-acre ranch. Celebrities and other notables sit in her office and deal with their most intimate and pressing monetary concerns, not to mention visits from the I.R.S. Maybe she could build a place for Omar at the farthest end of her property away from the house. Perhaps she could tell clients that one of her neighbors suffers from Tourette's, or maybe there's a counterculture acting workshop at the end of her property? I assumed we'd have Thanksgiving at Robin's house at some point, and the main course would be Omar.

At our house, Robin decided to put Omar and the cage inside the truck's cab for the rest of the trip to his new residence. She was hoping to avoid being cited for vulgarity of the beak while driving. We unbolted the legs of the cage and squeezed the cage into the truck. Omar was now a true passenger. The next time I talked to Robin, she recounted Omar's first encounter with her. "I let the little son of bitch out of his cage, and he went straight for me. I caught him in mid-flight and threw him against the kitchen wall. He fell to the kitchen floor. Then I picked him up and put him on my shoulder, where he stood dazed and compliant."

I knew then that I had found the perfect home for Omar.

About six months later, Robin was looking for a person to help clean her house, I suggested Mia, our house cleaner.

Mia worked one day a week at Robin's. It is in Mia's nature to go the extra step. She's not afraid of toxic oil spills or hazardous pathogens, or teen-age boys and their dirty fathers, who think nothing of walking into the house with horse shit on their boots.

In a moment of cleaning ecstasy, Mia opened Omar's cage to clean it, going against Robin's warning. I never noticed what nice ear lobes Mia has. Apparently, Omar has a small, one could say fetish, for hanging appendages. Omar sunk his beak deep into Mia's ear lobe. Mia went through a metamorphosis. For Omar, she became an amusement park ride, an old merry-go round ride without wooden swings, suspended from chains. As she spun around, screams and shrieks came out of Mia's mouth instead of organ music. The centrifugal force kept Omar parallel to the ground but not fast enough for Omar to lose his grip. Utter joy and ecstasy was Omar's. Robin, hearing the ruckus, came running and then and there put an end to Omar's entertainment.

To get Omar off Mia's ear without ripping the lobe, Robin pinched closed the air holes on his beak and pried open his beak with a butter knife. For a couple of weeks after, Omar could be heard singing out the screams and shrieks of poor Mia, as one might do after going to an inspiring concert. The bird really knew how to entertain himself, I thought, as I inspected Mia's ear when next I saw her at my house. I have at times wondered about my ability to look civilized on the outside, but not too deep under the surface, I would think nothing about killing this bird who hurt somebody I care for. I resonate to a higher type of math. It's a form of math that has fallen out of favor with Ivy League schools since the turn of the last two centuries. Let me demonstrate how it works. Omar attacks me + my response= a feather adornment for my hat and a lo-cal, protein snack for my dogs.

When I hired Rodolpho on Ingrid's recommendation to work with me on the rock masonry, each time I spoke Rodolpho's name I thought of Omar bellowing it out in a German accent.

I picked out the rock and boulders from the tons piled high in my driveway, then made small piles in the areas where I wanted walls and flowerbeds to go. Sometimes I would do the mixing of the cement, and sometimes I would do the cementing. I found Rodolpho to be a good tradesperson and honest, which should be one and the same but has not always been my experience.

Los Angeles has prehistoric animals submerged in the La Brea tar pits, dead movie stars buried in Hollywood Cemetery and the bones of giant grizzly bears. While in preparation for the rock and cement in one area of the yard I was swinging my pick in glee, because I was in soft soil. Suddenly, my pick made a thud. The fifth blow telegraphed a twinge to my elbows that there was something very hard in the ground, and by the twentieth or thirtieth blow I knew it was big. Many swings later, I'd uprooted what I first mistook to be a casket of some forgotten pig-iron salesman. This sunken, cast-iron iceberg turned out to be a big, old, porcelain bathtub. It was comforting to know that those before me enjoyed bathing enough to dig graves for their tubs.

The Bradley dump is home to all things that no longer have any use. It's open twenty-four hours a day, three hundred and sixty-five days a year, which says something about the compulsive nature of humans. Ants and people, we're forever moving things.

At two o'clock in the morning, the Bradley city dump smelled and gleamed with trash. What I like about Alaskan dumps is missing in urban dumps: the potential visit of a bear, the whirling of evening stars above the hot blaze. The ugly Bradley dump was the new home for the exhumed, once-treasured items of my yard. Bathtub, old boots, indefinable metal objects and rotted boards that can no longer lie about the permanency of wood. This dump is where the truth is told about our old things that are guaranteed for life. As I shoveled and pulled things from the bed of my pickup truck, I fantasized that the Bradley dump was in Alaska.

Human bones are the only structural forms that are not allowed at a dump.

At this time, being of sound body and mind, I declare my bones to be willed to my son, Berrigan Claymore. I would like to make a few suggestions, though, on how to get good use out of my bones.

Berrigan, first off, I would like to see you make a good weapon of my sternum, sharpening it to a point and putting it under your pillow, in order to waste any intruder. What would then make me feel useful would be for you to take the smaller bones of my left hand and make a mobile to suspend above my great-grandchildren's cribs, for their amusement, and so they know that I'm still here.

Berrigan, like me, you are born of the dog and you know what that means, so I will not explain. I would like it if you let your dogs chew and bury a few of my bones that you and your children and your children's children have no use for. Sometimes bones make the best gardening tools. I would like it if you would avoid using my bones as a hammer or as a pry-bar; this would mean a lot to me. Feel free to use my humerus and femur bones as clubs. I would love to help you with this endeavor, but for obvious reasons, I won't be able to.

18

NEW AND IMPROVED

At the ten year mark of living in our house on Lookout Avenue, we realized we wanted more space. Unlike the simple purchase of an extra Porta-Potty for Gillian and Berrigan, this time it meant an architect, new wood, nails, plumbing, and electrical wiring. Gillian and I had just changed roles. She was now making the lion's share of the family income, and I was focusing my attention toward the art world, hoping to make it as a writer and sculptor. Knowing nothing about building a house, other than once helping to build a log cabin in Alaska, we thought we should hire someone with experience. Diane, Berrigan's teacher, offered her new love interest as the perfect person for the job. "Buck is an artist and builder and could build you exactly what you want."

We had dinner at their place and discussed with Buck and Diane what we wanted to do, while Diane noted the beautiful salad serving spoon and fork that Buck had carved. We told them the first thing would be to explore the possibility of a new kitchen downstairs, where the living room butted up against the hillside to see if it would be within our budget. Typically, homes in the Hollywood Hills follow the pitch of the hillside. If there is a second story, it will rest against that grade, and our home followed this tradition.

Diane, as Berrigan's grammar school teacher, was one of the cornerstones for his pre-adolescent intellectual and academic experiences. Unfortunately, this cornerstone was made of uncured adobe, and when wet with the reality of upper level, public school expectations, it turned into mud. Before it rained on his academic foundation he was exposed to the demands of junior high school and somehow manipulated the situation so that it was never revealed that he needed help. He had created an image in junior high school of brilliance and skills he did not own. The teachers bought it, always giving him high grades for God only knows what. Finally in high school it was discovered that he had only a blurred smattering of academic fundamentals. A less precocious child would have been perceived as being illiterate.

Gillian was the academic in the family. She decided on Happy Forest for Berrigan's preschool and grammar school education. Encouragement of the individual child to be free was Happy Forest's credo. It was a joyous milieu in which limit setting was not allowed; where a child could attempt to kill another child, and there'd be a "feelings meeting" to address the issue. Books and desks were looked on with disfavor. If you were unlucky enough to have a child with a learning disability, he or she would be in real trouble. Thank God, Berrigan did not have that challenge. However, Berrigan did enter junior high school almost unable to read but totally aware of his feelings.

When a parent would show concern that at age ten, his or her child could not identify even a few letters in the alphabet, the Happy Forest teacher replied, "All Happy Forest students do well when they graduate." We all draped our children in praise for their scholarly achievements, when in fact some of the grammar school graduating class could not read. When all the sprouting feathers of early academic interest had been methodically plucked from young students by well-meaning teachers with limited academic techniques, they were then dropped onto the doorsteps of the public junior high school. A child's exit from this humanistic institution could be quite harsh.

Happy Forest was where feelings came first, and reality was a thing to avoid. I imagined a day when there'd be a meeting on gravity. "Gravity is such an unfair thing; the children shouldn't have to deal with it at all," or at least not until they graduated from Happy Forest, when the unruly children could be somewhere else, my child being one of them.

Being a trusting person and not wanting to get involved, we hired Buck. The last words from both Diane and Buck were, "Don't worry, Alan, Buck always overbuilds everything, so you and Gillian won't have to be bothered with city codes." Diane was correct: Berrigan could be illiterate, and we could be homeless, and everything would be all right. It just depends on your definition of "all right."

The plan was that Buck would dig a little into the hill just to have a look around to see if we could put the kitchen downstairs. Access to the slope was by way of the antique door next to the bar in the living room.

I left the house in Buck's hands, and I went off to work. After shoeing a few horses, I wondered what Buck had found out. Was it economically prudent to put the kitchen downstairs by way of digging into the hillside?

I finished my day early. When I got home, I found a surprise similar to that of one of my customers, who forgot to chain up her timber wolf.

Upon my customer's arrival home from work, she saw that the foundation of her house had been undermined. Her fourteen-hundred square foot house was now about twenty-eight-hundred square feet. Quite an improvement, if you're a dog. The wolf had literally dug a basement under her house. Buck must have felt he had found himself a prime rib bone in us.

In 1923, there were no building codes in the Hollywood Hills. Our home had no foundation. Buck's conscious or unconscious plan was to have the whole house collapse. Then he could build it from scratch for us. He had dug under the house and into the wall at ground level. Some portions of our house were no longer touching the ground.

Over the years Gillian has convinced me that I am not a nice guy. What a dilemma: Berrigan's beloved teacher's husband was going to be killed by Berrigan's mean father.

I needed help. I prayed and received a miracle. It came in the form of a person who was immune to Gillian's wiles, understood construction and design and called things as he saw them. God was smiling on me. I got the idea to make a phone call to my mother's old grammar school friend, Everett Williams.

Everett was an interior designer who had crafted many interiors for the rich and famous. He had owned Doberman Pinschers, pit bulls, and boxers; he knew how to deal with the tenacious, stubborn and entitled. He exemplified strong, masculine elegance, was straightforward and wise to the bone. Although in his early seventies, his posture hadn't diminished, nor had his lean six foot two frame shrunk. It seemed fitting that Everett would exorcize our fever-flawed hiring, as Father Merrin (Max Von Sydow) did in "The Exorcist" by removing the devil living inside of Regan (Linda Blair). Everett even looks like Von Sydow._

At our dining table, with Buck's building plans in hand, Everett shook his head. "This is totally amateur, and he's drawn these plans on one-inch scale, furniture blueprint paper. This is totally unacceptable. Get rid of him. But before you let him go, have him repair some of what he did under the supervision of an architect."

This was to be the first of a few meetings with Everett; unfortunately, they always seemed to be too late in the game.

My next-door neighbors Ingrid, Vance and Omar the parrot were in the construction business. So I asked them to refer an architect, and they gave me the name of Louis Fuentes. Before I let go of Buck on Louis' recommendation, I had him build four-inch-by-four-inch Douglas fir supports to hold up our now undermined house. A four-by-four, like everything in construction, is not exactly what it seems. It's really only three-and-one half inches by three-and-one-half inches. These fibrous lies were cut and placed as one would do if making a miniature log cabin without notching out the logs. This procedure was continued until the supports were the height of the underside of the second story floor joists. They varied in height depending on the grade of the hill's slope. Doing the work would insure that the house would not immediately fall down.

My impression of these four-by-fours holding up my home was that of stalagmites and stalactites that had finally touched, and now the cave could collapse. A vision comes to mind while looking at these Lincoln logs: I have always enjoyed exploring abandoned mines.

I was in either the Turtle Mountains or the Old Woman mountains of California's desert, when I saw a mine unlike any I'd ever seen. The opening was at least one hundred feet across and sloped down, far into the mine at a thirty-five degree angle. My eyes traveled hundreds of feet down with the help of a powerful spotlight. The ceiling was about six-and-a-half feet high. Every twelve feet there was a large oak twelve-inch by twelve-inch timber holding up this gigantic slab of earth. This mine shoring was milled when a twelve by twelve was truly 12 inches by 12 inches. They were full heart, which means they came from the center of the tree, solid and strong. There have been few old mines I have refused to enter. I've always felt it was for a logical reason when I didn't venture in. This time, it was a sensation in my gut that held me from entering and exploring this man-made cave.

At five foot seven in his mid-thirties, Louis was a gentle, good-natured man, with energy in each syllable that left his tongue. Not a likely candidate to keep at bay the hostility of the skill-compromised tradespeople, who could and did darken our door, or at least where our door used to be. As a dream and design person, Louis was well suited for the task of designing our house. His persona was that of a competent architect, good person and strong in his own way. Louis' intelligence and straight forwardness was reassuring. First, I told him my thoughts. Then on paper I conveyed to Louis what I wanted in the way of changes made to the house.

By the next week, Louis had executed my visions onto paper, and generated another set: his version of what he thought we should have. Louis' remodel version was $300,000 more than my version.

Well, Gillian is pretty, and never really had a home, and I needed to show her that I loved her. I can feel my guts turning while writing this. Louis's version of the plans won. We had $60,000 to do the remodel; at that, it was a home loan.

We got three construction bids: $250,000, $300,000 and a $138,000 bid by a fledgling contractor, who had been the foreman for a builder of upscale, movie stars' homes.

I will not use his name. I want to keep him away; call me superstitious. This guy had just gotten his contractor's license and was completing his first solo construction job. Gillian and I went to see his maiden job in Bel Air. It was a small guesthouse on a slope above the main house; he looked well-organized, with his merry employees working right along. I asked the owner of the not-yet-finished guest residence, how was it going? He looked at me with consternation and said, "We'll see."

That was the first clue. The second clue was that after we hired him, he broke into my studio where my truck was parked and siphoned gas out of it. That was his first day on the job. I fired his ass. Gillian and Louis had him come back to me and apologize. My reply to this was "I do not want him back." Gillian replied, "I'll handle it, Alan, just stay out of it, and do your art and write."

So I did.

Two weeks later, Gillian, Berrigan and I went on our newly or-ganized extended family's semi-annual cruise pilgrimage, which con-sisted of about forty family members to some semi-exotic (cheap!) getaway, such as the Mexican Rivera. The Riviera, wow, just think about it, the Riviera in democratic old Mexico, just think about it, democratic Mexico, where years before I had been a prisoner in a commune.

The ship's main thing is food and well-engineered flushing toi-lets for the disposal of this lovely culinary fair. Cheryl and Philip are horseshoeing customers. Their old horse, Wooly, was the last horse for me to shoe before my family and all thirty-seven extended family members set sail. Cheryl is a nurse with a master's degree in psychol-ogy. She and I share an appreciation of the psychologist, Carl Rogers, I through his book, "On Becoming a Person," and Cheryl through actual course work with Rogers. My exiting words at Cheryl's that day were, "I'll be back in two weeks from Mexico, and the house will be half done, and we will live in the part that is finished." Years later, Cheryl told me that she felt that "I had really lost my mind and was living in la-la land, if I thought the house would be half done," but as a good Rogerian you don't say things like that. When we got back from the Mexican Riviera, the house was partially demolished.

With the help of gravity demolition goes quickly, so I saw prog-ress even though they had not done any rebuilding. At this time, we could still sleep in our bedroom, and my attention was far from any-thing to do with the house. I would get up in the morning, shoe four horses and trim a few that didn't need shoes. Around three in the afternoon I would start writing. After a few hours of writing, I'd go into my studio to work on a sculpture. This particular sculpture I was

working on was that of a lean, muscular, sensuous woman stretch-
ing: one leg forward and the other leg back, her torso gently reaching
over her forward leg. Under power of the female form, earth, stars,
milk, I fell deep into the holy abyss of the feminine. I lost sight of
my masculine duties. Each day, though, I would just peek at what
the construction workers were doing. They seemed to be busy; I had
left it up to Gillian.

Leaving the door open to my studio on a hot summer day, I
went upstairs to the house to use the bathroom; at that moment one
of the knuckle dragging, wannabe tradespersons entered my studio,
walked over and touched the wet terracotta of the woman's form I'd
been working on for the last month. Groping my mortally-made
daughter's body, he had altered my heart's work. I told him not to
come in here again. Now I was interested in the remodel. I was looking for a fight, but these so called "workmen" had already knocked
me out without a blow delivered.

As I inspected the construction, I noticed it looked like framing
from a Hollywood prop house. How can you take two-by-fours, nail
them to the old framing on top of old stucco to make a bay window?
As I write this, I realize those idiots had never done a remodel before.
It would seem common knowledge in the building trade to take off
the old stucco and nail directly to the existing house's framework.
Who knows what else this group was capable of? Maybe they could
silicon a new toilet on top of the old one and we could flush twice.
Given that these amateurs were swarming around my house in slow
motion, what else had we paid them to destroy?

The new two-by-fours were to be the supports for this not-soon-
to-be built bay window. Both were cut at forty-five degrees and attached to the wall at the bottom end of the two-by-fours. The tops
of the two timbers were flying in the breeze. It became obvious it was
time to meet with this "great deal of a contractor."

I told Louis and Gillian, "If there are not major changes in a week, I will fire him, and you and Louis are not going to hire him back again!"

Gillian, bless her heart, trying to keep her promise to me to keep me out of it, said she would deal with it. I could continue to focus on sculpting and writing while Gillian and Louis once again rearranged our metaphorical deck chairs on our Titanic project. Gillian said, "We're back on course, and things will be watched more closely." Well, of course, a week went by and I fired him. It was weird, though. I said to the contractor, "This is not working. I have to let you go." After the conversation, the next day the contractor pulled his truck up the street and in a sweaty frenzy started carrying his tools by the armful up the street to his pickup. He looked as if he needed some sort of psychological intervention, but it wasn't going to happen on my dime. I told him to bring his truck down to the house, and I would help him load it. It was either get him off the property, or find a place to bury him on it. I wasn't in the mood for any more digging.

It's been suggested that I describe this Pillsbury doughboy, brown-eyed Guernsey cow contractor but I just can't force myself to do that. There is one big thing I forgot to mention: my house, because of this guy's thorough demolition, no longer had a roof, floors or walls. There were, however, three walls still standing in the living room. Enough wall remained that I thought I'd be able to throw a tarp over the entire top of the house. I made my way down to a large surplus store, which deals with Armageddon and other paranoid-type things. There I purchased a seventy-five foot by one-hundred-and-fifty foot tarp. I knew the way it was folded from the factory that I would not be able to unfold it over the house. Instead of going home, I went to the park, which now felt more like a home. On a grassy hillside I unfolded what was to be my new temporary roof. It started to get windy, then very windy, and the smell of rain was in the air. I tried for about ten minutes to re-roll the tarp in such a way that I could unroll it over the make-shift rafters I had made to keep the flanks of the house from falling in on themselves. Unfortunately, the wind caught the corners of the tarp each time and lifted it off the grass, making it impossible to roll up. Luck was with me; my neighbor Kane happened to be at the park. With each completed roll, I on one corner and Kane on the other of the seventy-five foot width managed to get it rolled up. The smell of rain became more pungent. It got dark and started to rain as we finished the final task of folding the tarp, which would make it easier to carry up onto the roof and roll it out.

Kane asked me several times if I needed help unraveling the tarp onto the house, but for illogical reasons, I declined. There is so little in this world I have control of. The dramatic act of putting the huge tarp over the house in a wind driven rainstorm brought me self love. Would I be any richer, could I sleep in the next day, or did anybody really care? I cared. With all these attempts of trying to please Gillian, it was and always has been about me romancing me.

Now what? We had no more money, and no one to build our house. But we had good credit, so we used it to take out another loan. We also had credit cards. I felt safe under the tarp. Plastic was now keeping us dry and fed.

Gillian, Louis and I became the Three Musketeers. Somehow, it was decided that I would be the new contractor. I was going to lose my house if I didn't do it. I had a construction résumé that we could afford.

Alan Claymore, at the age of eight, built a house in his parent's converted attic out of blankets, bed sheets, bedspreads, card tables and folding chairs. I could use the memories of my younger sister's occupancy—she was four; I was eight—as an endorsement of my talents when I questioned my ability or sanity.

At twelve, Grandpa Will and Alan put up a punching bag in my parent's garage using nuts and bolts, nails, and two-by-fours. By twenty, Alan had built horse corrals, bookshelves, an array of toolboxes and a wood camper shell for his 1973 Dodge Power Wagon. Later, this shell became the top of a woodshed Alan made for the fifty-five acres he and Gillian leased in Little Tujunga Canyon. All of this was washed down stream, along with thousands of tons of boulders, trees and large sections of Little Tujunga Canyon Road itself in the "Tujunga floods." The camper shell found its way into the mire on the banks of the Little T, a mile down stream, where it became a sparrow's home.

It was obvious I was the right person for this now $350,000 rebuild.

I am blessed with the insight of knowing that I don't know everything about construction. I needed to rein in my ego and hire a good journeyman carpenter. Laird Macgregor's words, "Look around your feet for firewood before walking all over the forest," are so true. While driving around the neighborhood, I spotted a man working on a small, but well-constructed, brick wall at his own house. I asked him if he was a carpenter. He said, "Yes." I told him what I needed and asked if he would be interested, and if he was, would he give me some references?

Unlike the contractor who we originally hired, I say the name Martin White with great pleasure. He was about six-two, slender, and wore his long brown hair in a pony- tail. Weeks later, he told Gillian that "we," meaning he and I had something deep in common. I understand now what he meant.

I got the references from Martin and gave them to Gillian. She made the trek up to Ventura to look at a Victorian house that Martin restored and met the woman who owned the house. Gillian came back impressed with the work and what the woman had to say about Martin. Victorian homes find their beauty in precise, ornate design, leaving very little room for inaccurate measuring. What sold me were the pictures that Gillian took of the finished home; Martin was hired.

Next came the meeting between Louis, Martin, Gillian and me. Together we all looked at the plans. Gillian and I now were making the decisions together on the construction of our home.

The first thing that needed to be addressed was the architect's roofline design, which to me looked like something out of the pages of a coffee-table edition of Escher's works. Escher masterfully stops and begins lines and in doing so plays with our visual imagination. We end up seeing things that are not really there. Sure enough, Martin, with some hesitation, said, "The roof line design will not work."

Louis, without batting an eye, said "No problem. What do you need to see?"

Martin explained what was missing: "Well, Louis, the roofline stops here and will not provide adequate water drainage."

"No problem Martin, anything else?"

"Well, the roof for the master bedroom is also pitched in not such a great way. If we were to leave the roof here in the back like this, it would mean a lot more lumber and the water this time would drain on the other new roof below."

"So is that it, Martin, or is there anything else?"

"No, that takes care of it for now." Within a short time, I had the new set of blueprints.

I was apprehensive during this first pissing match between the carpenter Martin, and the architect, Louis. I sensed a little hostility from Martin, maybe because he was a journeymen carpenter, and wondered why he was doing the architect's job?" But I was extremely grateful for Martin's professional eye and Louis's lack of ego.

I recall wondering, "Will the house ever be finished?" I should have rebuilt the house when the energy of youth overwhelmed me. For that matter, at the age of twelve, I should have taken a vow to be an artist and writer. The schism of what is and what I want is quieted by the fact that Frank Lloyd Wright's buildings notoriously leaked; Mary Shelly wrote "Frankenstein" in Lord Byron's castle, but never saw a good review. Just possibly, the path I'm on leaks and will never get applause, and maybe that's OK.

Last Sunday, a large group of neighborhood friends from my childhood got together to celebrate one of our friend's fiftieth birthday. While reminiscing with this old group of friends, the conversation wound its way to the exploits of our youth. One story that came up was an idea that I had had of using shovels, picks and other hand tools to dig caves.

In our fourteenth year, Dane, George, Carl, Tim, a few others and I participated in the making of these caves.

The excavation took place on the edge of Griffith Park in a new housing development, which went up in the early 1960's. I lived in one of these homes with my parents and sister from the age of thirteen to sixteen. The houses were built on a 45-degree slope on the southwest property line of Griffith Park, almost under the park's observatory. At the top of this slope, the more expensive real estate with views of the city bordered Griffith Park. We decided to build our tunnels on the backside of these lots. Could it be that this was the prelude to our homes in the future, or maybe this was our true home? Would you expect anything other than a cave?

Our young bodies were ravenous for change, but how and for what?

We dug holes.

If you are a woman reading this now, you might think young boys are strange, but if you actually bought this book, you might call my friends and I at this age "eccentric." And that is how women are strange.

At fourteen, we'd rise before the summer sun. We didn't want to be seen walking up to the top of the hill with picks, shovels, crowbars, sledgehammers, flashlights and axes. Like the seven dwarfs, we went off to work. I can only speak for myself, but if only I could have found shelter under Snow White, I would have.

On the backside of these freshly bulldozed lots at the top of the steep hillside, we had a view of the park's wilderness. Years later, the famous trial lawyer, Johnny Cochran, lived in a home on one of these high-priced view lots. Not one of the ones we had dug, but one that was built by a high priced contractor.

Always remember one thing: LOCATION. So we dug on the dirt backsides of these lots facing the park. Each of us made our own dwelling. My cave started with a very small opening that I could hardly squeeze into. Past the opening, I crawled on hands and knees for a few feet where the tunnel made a ninety degree turn. There the first room was out of sight from the opening. The cave opened up to approximately six feet by eight feet and was about four feet high. The room's walls undulated in the glow of a candle. I sculpted the back wall of the first room to contour and bend into itself. This way I could hide the entrance to the second room as just an indentation in the wall. This rear room's opening was always in the shadows even when you shined a flashlight on it. I built another tunnel behind the second room, and it led to another room. This next room was a little larger than the front two rooms.

Carl's cave was more geologically noteworthy than mine. What made Carl's place so special was that he put up wooden shoring and placed candles in carved out alcoves. He had genuinely executed the look of a gold mine. He even dug out a shelf for a sleeping area.

He constructed other shelves for tools, water and even food. I was amazed at how he had immersed himself in the project. The other members of our group had other themes. We all had different needs: Carl's were apparently structural and geological, and mine were the allure of the mysterious.

Dark rooms, hidden passages: it is the alchemy of life that intrigues me.

Carl now lives in a remote part of Nevada and is a geologist.

A few years before the rebuild of our home, I had done a favor for a second cousin on my father's side. Unfortunately, she felt the necessity to repay the favor.

With a smile and excitement in her voice she said,"Alan, I insist that Berrigan, Gillian and you move into our house. We have a guestroom that no one is using. It has its own full bathroom and is separated by a hallway from the rest of the house. I won't take 'no' for an answer." I told her it was a great offer, but I preferred to stay in our home. Years ago, I learned not to trust family.

Not one to take "no" for an answer she went directly to Gillian, who was more than glad to vacate our house that was cluttered with tools, sawdust, a roof made from a tarp and occasional visits from opossums, raccoons and skunks.

Gillian pled her case.

"Alan, we are moving into your cousin's guest room; it's the right thing to do. You need to learn to trust."

"Gillian, it's going to take months till the house is done. Once you leave a house in this state you can't move back in. If you try, the city will condemn the house, which in turn will create other problems."

"Alan, I know you hate being obligated to anyone, especially family. They're insisting we use their guest room and guest bath."

I instantly refused and fought with Gillian over going out on this brittle, weak limb of my family tree.

"Alan, let somebody give to you. Your cousin is extending a hand to us. Give them the opportunity to do something loving for you."

"Gillian, you don't understand, I don't have a good feeling about family."

"You'll just have to trust me Alan."

"I'm not going to do it," I said. I felt guilty though, and gave in.

One month later my other cousin, her younger brother, was separated from his wife. They needed a place to have him stay, unbeknownst to me.

My cousin, who just a month ago insisted we move in, now cleverly came to me and said, "Alan, we would love to see how the house is coming along." I took them to see the roofless, plumbing-less, electric-less construction site. There was only a temporary electrical pole for power tools. Since we were no longer living in our home I had decided to expedite things. We had totally gutted the house and left only things that were thought to be needed to finish it. My cousin looked at me and said, "All you need is a hot plate and you can move back in. My cousin's husband took me aside, and in his embarrassment, said, "You don't need to move out; she just gets that way when it comes to her brother."

I talked to the plumber and the carpenter and we started to figure out a way to make it livable again. It was going to set Gillian and me back in time and money, but the real problem was having moved out. The city could condemn the house; it would be then impossible to move back in. Our bank loans on the house would then be called in, and we didn't have the money to immediately pay them back. We didn't have money to rent a place and finish the house at the same time. I wondered what we were going to do.

My parents had a large house, but they never offered a room. I knew better than to ask. If Gillian ever saw what types of people my parents were, she would never have had anything to do with them. It's easier to think about the coldness and the wrongness of my mother and father when it hasn't involved me. I will always feel flawed and in some way find justification for their cruelty towards me.

In a midday downpour many years ago, my sister brought her newborn son to my parents' business to show them their first grandchild. As the rain came down, my mother locked the old wood and glass front door to their business, almost slamming it in my sister's face. Then my mother glared through the window and rain at my sister and turned and walked away deep into the store. It's too easy to say it was, "all because my mother didn't like the color of her new grandchild's skin." It goes deeper than that. She treated me the same way, and my skin was the same color as my mother's.

I was angry when I left my cousin's home. As Berrigan and I walked on Beverly Boulevard that night, a man wearing newer and cleaner jeans than I, came up to me begging for money. He didn't let Berrigan and me pass. I said, "We are homeless, too." He got mad, and we almost came to blows.

Gillian, on the phone a day later, commiserated with our friend Miriam Swift about the cousin leaving us with no place to live. Gillian shared with Miriam that I was looking for something cheap for us to rent. Miriam told Gillian that her sister Ellen had a room for rent in her house in the Hollywood hills. I remembered meeting Ellen years before at her house. Ellen's house had three bedrooms and two baths, simply decorated with a large rustic rock fireplace. She was one of the only good things that happened during our rebuilding.

We lived with Ellen for a year-and-a-half as our house went from total destruction to being habitable once more. While at Ellen's we rode out the Northridge earthquake. Our house, at the stick stage of construction at this point, was tweaked out of shape by the earth's dance.

Through the entire rebuilding I still managed to take Berrigan to every hockey game and all his practices whether they were at four in the morning or midnight. On a few occasions Ellen, who was a camerawoman for NBC News, filmed Berrigan's games with her professional video camera.

I don't believe people who say they have no regrets. Do they have a crystal ball? I regret that I did not cook more at Ellen's house, that I never lit a fire in her fireplace, and that I didn't make it my home. Ellen made us welcome; I felt akin to the way she lived her life. The beautiful photos she took when on assignment somewhere in the world for NBC hung in her hallway. Ellen's wisdom always masqueraded as a wealth of common sense. At the end of construction we were totally out of money and could not borrow any more until we had the final inspection signed off. We waited for the bank to go through its labyrinth of paper work till we could get a new transfusion of money. Gillian explained to Ellen what was going on with our finances and asked if it would be OK if we waited to pay our last three months rent. Three months later at dinner at the restaurant down the block from Ellen's, we broke bread and paid the remainder of the owed rent without a pause between the salad and the main course.

19

CROSSES, WOOD STAKES, AND GARLIC

Martin requested that we hire his friend, Sam. Sam was about 5'6", brown hair, but not much of it. He weighed 160 pounds, the same as Martin. Sam was not overweight, and Martin was not underweight, although Martin was six inches taller. Sam had mentioned that fact to me at some point during the time they spent with us. Sam's intelligence came to light in the form of his knowledge of facts on unique and interesting topics, such as, "Aardvarks weigh up to 145 pounds, and their diet consists almost entirely of ants." Together Martin and Sam made a good team.

Next, it was time to address the fact there was no foundation under our wonderful home. Louis suggested a man of integrity to do our new foundation.

Poor Bill. The first day on the job, before he could get his truck up past the skirt of the driveway, he ran over one of my hand-wrought iron functional art forms that adorn our house to this day. He got an instant flat tire. When Bill ran over this so-called art piece that kept the gate's bottom end closed, he unleashed my rage. My face turned red as I told him, "I don't know you, but one more thing happens like that, and I will fire your ass."

Bill was a good person and having been told a little about our construction history thus far, he gave me a wide berth. In a short time, he showed me he could be trusted.

I have mentioned that my family thinks I have a temper and I think they are right, but within the laws of western civilization most of the time I've found safe harbor from my rage and knee-jerk reactions to situations. There are those other times: once I dove with no hesitation into an electrified swimming pool (due to an electrical light short) to save my son from being electrocuted. My conscious being is cinched to my body's impulses. In the same way, my anger has driven me.

It is not fair for me to be writing this section of the story, but once again I am the writer I can afford.

It has been said that I have three speeds: "real nice," "leave me alone," and "you are playing with fire." It has not been in my interest to use only this limited range of behavioral patterns. Resentments, lost opportunities and black eyes probably could have been avoided.

A new reality was to unfold. Yes, I knew our house had no foundation. What I did not know was that the hillside our home slept on was in need of over $60,000 of retaining wall. This new wall would hold the hill behind our small backyard from sliding into the house. Bill's men worked hard, so I forced myself to get used to the fact that they didn't know how to use the Andy Gump. I used the dog's pooper scooper for more than just the dogs. The last person to do interior work at our house was germ phobic and wouldn't use our new bathroom. I think I've said enough on this subject.

Mr. Plot was his name; he represented our city government as a building inspector. Is it an arbitrary process the way an inspector works? Yes. The last stand a man can make is defending his house from carpetbagger bureaucrats who do the bidding for the sweet trough of the city coffers. Nowhere in their charter or rulebook is it written they are supposed to be helpful. They could be, but they do not have to be. For us it was too late. The house was uncovered with all its 1920's weakness in construction.

Do or die, I don't die well so we didn't walk away from our house but went forward. There were days and nights that seemed to go on forever.

Later, in the next phase, the plumber would keep me waiting all day and then berate everyone's work except mine; he was no fool. The electrician tried to save money by running the Romex electrical wire through the house as tight as possible. If he could have gotten away with it, he would have just run the Romex wires through the rooms instead of through the walls. He'd tell us we didn't need a clothes dryer: "Just hang your wet clothes on the wires." His real excuse was, "By doing it tight it will hold the house together better." I learned too late to have the plumber do his work first and then bring in the electrician. Plumbing takes up more space in the walls than wires. These bloodthirsty tradesmen from Hallows' Eve were invited into our house by Gillian and Louis before I was involved with the rebuild. Why would I call them that? Because no one knowingly invites vampires in, but once in, they suck you until you're dry. It's no accident that these two children of Nosferatu asked for permission to enter after all the wood two-by-fours had been safely secured to other potential wood stakes.

The house was going through a metamorphosis, but instead of a silk cocoon, the house was wrapped in bank loans and construction purchases made on credit cards. The falsehoods of loans forestalled our insanity, but a few months later I felt the world crash in on me.

My dream home since adolescence has been to be on my back under the archetype Snow White. Like the Dwarfs, I kept going to this metaphorical mine (my house) day and night in hopes that my true love (Gillian) would notice me, but she had no love to give. Gillian made empty promises of love, and I retreated into deep frustration and silent screams. I checked myself into a mental hospital for an hour or two and then checked myself out after a phone call from my dear friend Somerset Brown, who simply said, "I love you Alan, and I trust you know what you're doing." With that I went back to work twelve hours a day, seven days a week without the only kind of love I understood. I died but still lived.

A hard-on, woody, power stroke, "the tool"– how could I not confuse female bidding; it seemed to be all the same to me. I did use all these tools on command, but I was confused. Fixing things never led me to the sexual expression of love using the one tool I enjoyed the most.

In the remote mountainous township of Volcano, in California's Mother Lode, I write these next few pages. It was long after the last particles of sawdust had been swept from the floor of our house construction. I sat in Glen and Jean's guest room with the window wide open, laptop on my lap. The temperature in the room was the same as outside– forty-five degrees– while Glen and Jean kept the rest of their new house warm and cozy. Their house's interior over halfway done, I noted what I saw. A truly finished house is finished in name only, by declaration but not by form.

My dear friend Jean, while giving me the exterior tour, expressed regret at the lack of a larger room, telling me, "We should have continued this wall to here, and the room would have been bigger." I came unglued like an old piece of plywood.

"What! How big a house do you need, Jean? It will never end. Clean up what you have and call it finished! People sweep dirt floors, live in cardboard boxes and only look for needles in haystacks when their bare asses find them. Stop it!"

"Gee, Alan, I didn't know you felt so strongly about this! Did I touch a nerve? I think you make a good point, Alan, but my goodness!"

Jean was right about my touchiness, but I didn't want them to suffer through what Gillian and I went through. Unfortunately, I am certain that not one less nail was used on their house because of my outburst. Seeing our home's construction lived out by their need for space beyond what was affordable ignited the fury of my memories that day.

After dinner, reclining by their new fireplace with Gillian, Glen and Jean, we talked late into the night, finally retiring to our guest bedroom, where I continued to write about the building of Gillian's and my house till shortly before sunrise.

Martin, Sam and Bill with his happy crew were working out well. I kept the subcontractors Ned, the plumber, and Emil, the electrician. They knew the lay of the land, and Louis vouched for their competence, even though they continued to be pains in the ass.

I had no regrets in the following weeks after losing my temper at Bill. The display of rage at this concrete contractor helped all concerned, and for the rest of the time I said nothing that wasn't clear and simple.

As Sam and Martin worked, they discovered more destruction committed by the previous contractor. We don't know if it was done intentionally or out of plain ignorance. The floor joist from the second floor supported the second floor's balcony, which over-looked the living room. This prior contractor had cut the floor joists at the point where they were supporting the balcony. The ramifications of such an act meant that we could no longer walk on the balcony. Martin and Louis talked, and new blueprints were drawn for the balcony and given to me. Why me? No one else wanted to do it.

After looking at the plans, I approached Martin. Before I could say anything, he said," OK, Alan, I'll do the wood part of the job and you do the steel."

The plans called for a 12"x12" header to be bolted to the balcony with four, 8"x 8" posts to support the header. Martin cut the lumber, and I fashioned new brackets from steel brackets that were already manufactured for bracing wood framing. Martin and Sam put up the header or beam and post, while I fitted and put the steel brackets in place and bolted it all together. The two middle posts changed the flow of the living room and limited where we could place furniture. To this day I don't know if it works aesthetically, but we had no choice. After we finished this work it was stronger than it had ever been. It seemed like it was that way with everything we did to the house.

In this time of framing and retaining walls, on the sixteenth of January 1994 we had the 7.5 earthquake. It shook Berrigan and me into the hall of Ellen's house, where we were living.

Running into each other in the dark, I grabbed Berrigan "Are you OK?" I asked. I checked for gas leaks around Ellen's house. Finding none, I went outside and talked to the neighbors now congregating on this small Hollywood Hills street. It was still dark outside when I went back to our bedroom where Gillian was staying true to her reputation of being a deep sleeper. The only time I have ever seen Gillian wake up fast was when she thought a grizzly was growling and shaking our tent in Alaska. When it turned out to be nothing more than a timber wolf, she immediately fell back to sleep, snoring at such a pitch that it would keep away any bruin.

After getting a few more winks of sleep following the quake, I started to drive down into the valley to shoe some horses. I saw a cloud of unsettled dirt above the valley's floor. I knew nothing would be right in the San Fernando Valley that day.

I figured getting an early start on the scheduled house project would be a better idea. Martin and Sam had already arrived. I could see concern on their faces. The house was in the final framing stages with a large part of the shear wall not yet approved to be put up. The huge mass of framing had shook, flexed and contorted, and lost some of its straight structural lines. In the final analyses two-by-four framing is a kind of large Tinkertoy. The living room, the only room in the house that was not going through a down-to-the-bones make-over, stayed untouched by the earth's baritone voice. The room's big, beautiful picture window had braced itself well against the pitching sea of earth. Not a pane had broken, but the equally old fireplace didn't fare as well. The top half of the 1923 brick chimney fell to the ground. What remained now had its own seismic fault between its mortar and brick.

While Sam and Martin expertly manipulated the unsheared part of the house into alignment, I found a new masonry job for Bill. With the sixty thousand dollars of retaining wall finished, I thought that I would not see Bill again. Now the earthquake had given him the job, if he wanted it, of building a new chimney.

The hearth had remained intact. Everything above this, though, had to be rebuilt. We agreed on a price, and work was started. Bill gave his wiry group of energetic men the simple assignment of tearing down what was left of the old, now dangling smoke stack. This side of our house is almost within touching range of our neighbor's home.

Perched high above on the roof and armed with sledgehammers, Bill's merry men shattered brick and cement down onto the walls of my house and onto the house next-door. Great, after fixing the fireplace, we'd have to pay to have somebody repair walls, antique stained-glass windows, gas lines, water pipes and anything else that had the misfortune of being under the arc of their tosses.

Here I go again, "*Alta, muy malo,* you fucking assholes," as bricks fell inches from my head. Was I going to have to shoot them off my roof? They kept working until I sprayed them with a hose. I called Bill on the phone. I told him what was going on and how pissed I was. By this time, Bill knew me pretty well. I was surprised when he replied, "Alan, I've started this big project in Pasadena. It sounds like you are able to communicate with them. Why don't I pay you to be their foreman?"

"OK, but I figure it'll take me about three days to finish this thing, so I want seven hundred dollars. If that's fair to you, Bill, I'll do it; otherwise, you have to be here."

"We have a deal, Alan."

The rest of the demolition went fine. The chimney went up without a problem. During this time we were preparing for a re-inspection of the framing that needed some corrections. When Mr. Plot was here to inspect the framing, he took notice of the new chimney. "Oh, by the way, your chimney is not to code. Since the earth-quake we have tightened up the code on chimneys and yours doesn't fall within the new rules." Martin always knew when to be around to watch out for me. As we stood on the roof, Martin whispered to me as my face turned red, "Stay cool, Alan." Then Martin spoke to Plot, "So all Alan has to do is construct a steel brace between the roof and the new chimney?"

"Yes, that should take care of it."

I left the immediate area while Martin and Mr. Plot discussed the rest of the framing job.

After the inspector left, I talked with Bill and Martin about who was going to put the brace up and how it should look. No one want-ed to do it, so the next day I found myself at the anvil with rounding hammer in hand, shaping a six-foot piece of hot rolled bar stock. I bolted this freshly made steel brace to the roof and chimney. When Martin, Bill, Sam and I looked at my masterpiece, one of us com-mented, "If we have another earthquake, it's more likely that this steel brace will go through the roof and hurt someone than this new chimney will fall on someone."

The truth was: instead of replacing the old brick and mortar with the same materials, we had opted for a zero clearance flue that weighs less than forty pounds. We encased it in stucco, which doesn't increase the weight very much. This fire stack weighed virtually nothing compared to traditional brick and mortar chimneys. The zero clearance flue would withstand more shaking than any other part of the house. Plot knew we had chosen the new and improved way of having a chimney, but the city fathers have a hard time connecting the dots. As if this wasn't enough, Gillian wanted me to weld flowerpot holders on to it. Thank god, Martin said it would not be a good idea to have soil leak onto a composite roof, and we had framed the house to hold a composite roof, not a heavier tile roof.

Plot passed us on the rest of the framing and the chimney inspection. Now we were allowed to finish the shear wall, finish the rough plumbing, rough electrical and heating. These things became our primary focus.

Shear wall is the name given to the sheets of plywood, or composite wood used to unify and strengthen the wood framing, similar to the way sheets of paper hold together stick frames of kites. Just as the solidarity of wood and paper catches thermals, the sheer strength of plywood sheets nailed to the exterior sides of the wood framing holds together a home to keep it strong against gravity, wind and earthquakes. But not so rigid that the structure isn't able to flex with changes in temperature and the movement of the earth. I prefer plywood over composite wood for shear wall. I feel it is the stronger and less toxic of the two, and that is what we used.

Martin and Sam did not miss a beat with their hammers and saws. In a short time we did all the things that needed to be done. The wood sub-floors and shear wall shimmered in a light yellow glow.

When the framing was completed, we were ready to go forward with rough plumbing and rough electrical. "Rough" means that the wires for telephone, stereo, intercom and electrical are strung through holes drilled in the frame's two-by-fours. Much later, the phone and other electrical appliances are installed as one of the last acts in construction. It is the same for the plumbing: faucets, toilets and sinks all coming into the house later; in our case, much later.

As I mentioned before, the electrician and plumber were carry-overs from the original group, whom Gillian and our architect Louis had hired. But they were not affiliated with the old contractor. The plumber had done some work early on, laying down a sewer line under the cement sub-floor in the kitchen. Later, we found that the new kitchen floor, thanks to the original contractor, had been dug down eighteen inches less than the plans called for. In terms of the feel of the kitchen, I am sure the lack of height diminished the airiness, and for my taller friends the eight foot ceiling does seem a little low.

Now it was time for the plumber and electrician to actually start to do their jobs. There was no doubt in my mind that Ned, the plumber, knew his trade. But he never showed up when he said he would. When he did turn up, he would pull me aside to tell me that one of the other tradesmen was doing something wrong. I listened for two reasons: number one, he might be right, and second, it kept him thinking he was being helpful, in the hopes he might be. Maybe I could elevate his ego to a point where he might become proactive at his job.

Ned, like that first contractor, did look at the blueprints, but plumber Ned said not a word about the loss of eighteen inches of ceiling height in the kitchen. Ned was the kind of guy who promised things to make himself feel good. He must have promised the nephew of his girl friend a job as a carpenter, tile man, or concrete man. He assumed that by badmouthing one of the other tradesmen's work, I might fire one of them. Then he'd have a great suggestion for me. On a regular basis Ned would plant the seeds for this transition, "You know, Alan, my girlfriend's nephew can do everything in construction." Ned probably thought whatever this jobless moron of a nephew lacked in skill wouldn't be noticed. If he did run into trouble, Ned could help him lie, or god forbid, maybe even try to help him figure out the problem they'd created. It always amazes me what men will do to score in bed, and I know his girlfriend was harder to maintain than the plumbing job at our house. Ned was in his late fifties and his persona was that of being "just one of the boys" with a peppering of fatherly ineptness.

Emil, the electrician, was from Israel. He reenacted his country's victorious six day war against its hostile neighbors with our house as the battle ground. Emil's challenge was how fast he could get paid, and how fast and tight he could pull the wires through our home. In the kitchen area, Emil had done such a messy job with the wire placement it looked like runs in a transvestite's nylon stockings after a night of participating in the tractor pulls at a county fair. I told him it was unacceptable, and he asked me, "Why?" But it was such an ugly mess I didn't know where to begin. Finally, I said to him, "I have no idea what you have done here, but it looks like shit."

"What do you mean? It's good."

"These wires are not covered properly and they're packed into a space too small in the framing."

"What do you mean? They're fine!"

"Look, Emil, this isn't going anywhere. Stop what you're doing, and let me think about what isn't to my liking."

The next day I had a talk with Louis and asked him if he wouldn't mind interceding on my behalf with Emil. Louis agreed, and the issue became history. There would be other jobs in Emil's future with Louis if he behaved himself on this one.

Emil's hope was this; if he got to the electrical before the always late plumber Ned, he'd get the opportunity to put the wires wherever he wanted, without any consideration for the plumber's piping. Emil did succeed in getting all his work done before Ned ever turned a wrench on our property. The zealot electrician and the always tardy plumber never worked as a team. They ended up costing us in materials and time.

After I realized my mistake of not having the plumbing done before the electrical, I felt the only way to get the plumbing done was to take on the job of holding the plumber's hand. Ned's girl friend, I'm sure, had softer hands than me but a tighter grip on the things that counted.

I called Ned. "We need to get the rough plumbing in so we can pass the rough inspection. When can you start?"

"Next week."

"Which day?"

"Monday."

"What time?"

"8:00 a.m."

Monday at eight o'clock in the morning, there was no Ned. I was hoping I'd get him started and be off to work shoeing horses by 10:00.

I called my customers from my studio phone, the only wire contraption still intact, and let them know I would be delayed. Months before, when Martin took on the job of carpenter, he had taken our house down to its bare bones within a very short time. All of its ancient plumbing and wiring made its way to the dumpster. A temporary power pole was put in place of the old electrical weather head, which had once attached to the no-longer-existing roof of the house. Next to the front door and connected to the Department of Water and Power's power pole, our rented temporary power pole now gave us our daily electricity for power tools and lights.

I waited until noon for Ned before I finally gave up and went to work. He never made it on Monday. Sometime later in the week,

he started to work with his helper. In the rough plumbing process
the outside pipes are welcomed in using wrenches, torches and pipe
cutters. Copper pipes for water are joined with the aid of a gas torch
to do what is called "sweating pipes." Black, steel pipes for gas with
their female and male ends are married together by threads going in
clockwise directions with the turn of a wrench. We hoped that sinks,
faucets, toilets, showers, tubs, the electrical light fixtures and outlet
covers would soon make their entrance before the final act of the final inspection. The rough inspection of the electrical, plumbing and
heating comes early on in the construction of a house. The three of
these inspections take place at the same time. If all is not ready and
the inspector comes out, chances are he'll be angry. Then, god only
knows what will befall you in the form of nitpicking.

The rough plumbing usually goes quickly. Ned trying to appear as if there were no consequences for coming in after Emil had
finished the roughed in stage of the electrical. Ned silently sweated
out the struggle of making a place for a two-inch pipe in a one-and
three-quarter-inch space. Poor Ned, if only he had spent less time
bad- mouthing everyone else except Emil, who hadn't looked out for
Ned's best interest. Ned got it done, but he perspired more than he
was probably used to. Around this time the ducting for the forced-air
heating was installed.

20

GHOST

The group of men who installed the passageways for heat did their job and left. They did nearly all of it in one day with hardly a word spoken. It would have only taken a day if only our ghost hadn't gotten upset.

On that particular day, Sam, Martin, Emil, Ned and the heating guys were all at the house at the same time. Martin and Sam were hammering and sawing; Emil was cleaning up his electrical mess; Ned was at his job of drilling holes into the framing, screwing and nailing plumber's tape to secure the pipes. And now with the added sounds of the heating guys, it was apparently too much activity for our house's apparition. I was not around that day, but that night I got a call from Louis. "Alan, we have a problem, Martin called me and told me they, meaning he and all the other men working on the house, were chased out by a ghost. Tools flew through rooms, the house made a low pitched moan and the temperature dropped. Did you know you had a ghost?"

"Yes, I'll take care of it tonight."

I have always led with my heart, and the only experts I know in the spirit world are all dead, so I ventured in on my own. Inside the front door, the house took on an old church setting, simply because it was empty and hollow. Now I was going to communicate with something that was not from this world.

"Look, this is your house as well as ours, and whatever we do in it will be for you, as well as for us." I said. "We share this house. It is more your house than mine. You will be here long after my family and I are only memories. I know you are tender and loving and that you watch over the house. I apologize for my fear of you, but I will let no harm ever come to you. I don't care to look for proof of your existence or where you come from or why you're here; I just accept."

Is there such a thing as a ghost? Is there such a thing as love? There's no answer to either, only my belief manifested through my fear and passion.

Yes, I avoided looking in different parts of the living room at night, and words off my lips are monitored so in no way can things be misconstrued as conjuring. In the middle of the night I skip stairs to get above the living room quickly.

The next day things were back to normal, but what crossed my mind is: did the ghost see an injustice perpetrated in our house, and was she protecting it?

I know of two instances when fires were stopped inexplicably in the house. One happened while Berrigan, Gillian and I were living at Ellen's. In the middle of the night, I would go alone up to the house to work on it. A workman had accidentally knocked over a high-intensity electric lamp. The plywood sub-floor was singed about six inches around the lamp. The floor was not damp, but it was cold. It had been several hours since anybody had been at the house. The lamp had also been turned off but was still turned over and was cool to the touch; the room was about twenty degrees colder than the outside temperature. When doing the initial tear down of the house we noticed a spot under the floor where a fire had started and in the same abrupt way had stopped. Both of these circles looked as if the fires had been frozen to death.

WARMTH

Architectural designs of interior walls in houses include soffits to house heating ducts. I thought forced-air heating made no sense for our three-story, split level house, but Louis and Gillian were insistent.

On the first floor we had a very good but very old floor furnace in the living room. It never gave me any problems, and it kept our friends warm. We never put the heat on for ourselves. I became aware of this fact when Berrigan brought his first girl friend home. There sitting in a tee shirt and shorts was my son, while his friend sat in a parka, the hood covering her head and gloves on her hands. I walked into the room and wanting to make a good impression, I said, "Berrigan, what do we do when we have guests?" As I watched, my warm breath entered the cold room.

"Turn on the heat, Dad."

"Right, Berrigan."

Now it was time to spend more borrowed money on something that we only used when friends came over. I thought forced-air heating would be less efficient than what we already had. I pled my case to the impatient stares of Gillian and Louis. "This doesn't make sense. This old, beautiful heater keeps the house warm. I always put a kettle of fresh, filtered water over the furnace on its floor grate, and we have clean, moist heat. That's something you can't do with forced air. Let me also mention there is no whooshing noise with this old friend, as there would be with a new furnace."

I took a deep breath because I was on a roll, "Plus, the old furnace uses the hallways and each room as a heating duct. Since heat rises, a ceiling fan in the master bedroom on the third level would circulate the warm air back down to the lower floors quicker than the constricting labyrinth of heating ducts and noisy heat registers of the so-called new and better (forced-air) system. Furthermore," I said, "A few drops of eucalyptus oil, in the kettle on top of the heater's old, wrought iron grate does the same good that it does with my horses in the winter. Applying a small dab of Vick's Vapor Rub in their nostrils at the first sign of winter and a dash of apple cider vinegar in their water troughs keeps the chill out of my horses and human friends."

My concerns were directed toward Louis. Gillian listened, hoping Louis would agree with her, and he did. "You need the new heating system." To me his words were sullen tones for wasting money and more nonsense.

I then asked, "What do we do when the heat rises? The ducts upstairs will get more than their share of the heat. How do we keep the living room and new kitchen downstairs warm?"

"Simple, Alan, just close all the registers upstairs."

"Then why do we need them upstairs?"

"We need it, Alan."

"Louis, can we leave the old furnace in, so at least we have a back up?"

Gillian chimed in, "Alan, why can't you just go along?"

Looking at houses for sale in the neighborhood, I noticed that the list of features included an array of many less-than valuable enhancements used as selling points. For example, intercom systems which fulfilled some weird idea of what kind of communication a family needs for their 2,500-square-foot house. You'd think that those who came up with the intercom system for houses had read "1984" or too much Ayn Rand and missed the point. The invasiveness of speaking and listening into rooms that you're not in is unsettling to me.

I caved in so it wouldn't look as if I were obstructing the project's progress like one of our tradespeople. It's been noted by others close to me that there is a part of me that feels as if I am only a visitor in my own home. I have thoughts that if I don't handle myself in a prescribed way I will be asked to leave. Before that would happen, I would leave on my own accord to avoid the humiliation.

At least now we can say we have a list of useless things in our house, such as forced-air heating, an intercom system and recessed lighting.

Flash forward to ten years later: Gillian and I are in bed. She utters words in my direction, "Alan, the heater makes so much noise and dries out my eyes something terribly. Is there anything we can do about it?" I don't answer but I think, "Yes, you could have left the old furnace in the floor, you stupid asshole."

I've given no homework with this book, so I hope you'll indulge me in this small request. Starbucks is now almost everywhere; enter one and look up. There you'll find electrical conduit, big heating ducts, water and gas pipes, all exposed and painted the same color as the ceiling. Starbucks doesn't seem to need soffits to conceal all of the pipes and wires, so why should we? Soon, I'll be entertaining the possibility of building still another house, the next time in the Sierra Nevada Mountains or in the Coast Mountains of British Columbia. This house will have all its mechanical plumbing exposed, just like a Starbucks, where my family spends most of their time anyway.

LIGHT

The insulation people came and went as fast as the heating duct guys did, and the house seemed warm except for the chill of the ghost in the living room.

The only chance the tradesmen had to manipulate anyone was to seek out Gillian.

Our electrician was smart at discerning what he could get away with. He had not finished his job, but he wanted his money in full so he could go on a trip to Israel. Our son would do the same thing to get his way – seek out Mom. Years later, our son acted out an Emil moment on the phone. "Hi, Dad, can I talk to Mom? Hi, Mom, I hope you and Dad are having a wonderful time in Catalina. See you in a couple of days. I love you. Oh, by the way, could I have my cousin and a few of his friends over to drink the remainder of the beer from Dad's fiftieth birthday party, all eight six-packs?"

"Sure, Berrigan, and I love you, too."

Our second "son," the electrician, was good at manipulation and got the rest of the money from Gillian with the promise that he would leave us in good hands with his apprentice and that he would be back. The electrician's apprentice did nothing to gain my negative attention so I don't remember his name. He'd fallen prey to the same manipulation by the electrician that we had. The apprentice came equipped with not much more than what was needed to change a light bulb; Emil had told him the job was ninety-percent finished.

As we got closer to the time of the final sign-off on the electrical, certain things had to be completed. Switch covers, faceplates and light fixtures all had to be secured over exposed electrical hardware and wires. All this was accomplished by the apprentice. Whatever else needed attention electrically to make the job look complete was now supposed to be done.

We couldn't afford all the light fixtures needed to finish the look of our 1923, Spanish vintage Hollywood home. Cheap plastic light fixtures were substituted for wrought iron sconces and chandeliers. It gave the house an electrified mine or cave quality, which was comforting to me. The light bulbs just hung or stuck out from the walls and ceilings with nothing covering them.

With orgasmic excitement, we began to witness the electrical juices surging through the Romex wire toward the living room's individual light bulbs. The apprentice manned the switches, as if he were the only one qualified for this task. How could it be any other way? He was the one wearing the electrician's belt, with all its assorted tools, pliers, connector-nuts, and battery-operated screwdriver.

The first light went on under the bent index finger of the electrician's apprentice, who was now promoted to electrician status by virtue of one illuminated 60-watt light bulb. The first bulb lit was in the living room. Now he flicked the next switch in this same room using the same finger in the same bent manner, but nothing happened. No lights went on.

For the previous two years of construction we've been subjected to the use of a temporary power pole outside our front door. We would be unable to get the sign-off from the city if the pole remained our direct link to the Department of Water Power's high tension wires. With construction, there always seems to be insult with injury. For each month during most of the remodel, we paid rent on this simple old, green painted, 6"x4"x15' wood post that stuck in the ground. It was the most expensive piece of lumber on the property. For some bureaucratic reason (bottom line, I am sure, some city official makes money from it) the rule apparently is, you are not allowed to have a qualified person make the connections to a post you got from a lumber yard that you only paid for once.

What had happened to our bought and paid-for electrical sperm? Gillian and I went through the rest of the house, self-promoted to electrician's status by virtue of also being able to flick un-electrified light switches.

Sixty-percent of the lights did not go on. The scenario for the wall plugs was the same. The apprentice said he had more notes from the electrician at home. I envisioned him waiting at the beach for a note in a bottle from Israel. The next morning, the apprentice showed up with a small piece of paper, which served no purpose. He shrugged his shoulders and didn't know how to say he was sorry. In some almost undetectable way, he said he was lost without saying it. The apprentice looked cold, small and tired, like a young child at an amusement park when parents are nowhere to be found.

When all else fails I go into survival mode. Water flows in rivers and electricity flows on wires. So I followed the shores of Romex alone. In my young adulthood, I roamed the Sierras and later the Brooks Range in Alaska. Understanding topography is what always got me to my destination and to shortcuts. This will probably be the last time I'll admit that my shortcuts aren't short.

In this landscape of stucco, drywall, milled wood and the scars made by other men's hands on my beloved home, I was a trespasser and trespassed on. The malfeasance of these tradesmen's souls helped me lose my way. Lost, hopelessly lost, I searched in the dark of midday. Why didn't the lights go on in my house?

When I was the raw age of eleven, I made a promise to God that I did not keep. Now, as I write this childhood experience, I have tears in my eyes.

I prayed to God, for no one talks to God; spiritual conversations are always prayers. The degree of transparency in the veil between God and me is in my ability to believe. I know the reality of conversation, but how could I know the reality of prayer?

"God help me off this mountain." I was lost, separated from my friends on Mount San Jacinto. I walked all night and into the next day. God's spirit inside of me must have carried me to where my friend Ted's mother was supposed to meet us in her Jeep the next day. She arrived at the prearranged place, on time, a few hours after I had gotten there, and a few hours before Ted and the other boy arrived, tattered and torn. I was without a scratch. I promised God that I would always believe. I thought at the time I would keep this promise. Unfortunately, I got so much praise at the meeting place from Ted and his mom for my hiking skills, I never admitted to the fact that I had help and later was embarrassed that I would partake in a belief in God. Feeling that it showed weakness or a lack of intellectual sophistication, never would I admit, "I believe," but I do – deeply.

Now with prayers, I went to the headwaters of our electrical source, the "power pole" and stood at the foot of this false patron saint of energy. Clarity came to me: "Find a new electrician." It might sound obvious to anybody else but for me it wasn't, since Emil had already been paid and I didn't want to go deeper into debt with a new electrician.

We had no kitchen at this time, so my adopted kitchen was a café where I'd been going for my coffee even before construction. The coffee at this cafe was my lifeblood for staying awake while sculpting. During this period, I was starting to work more hours as a sculptor. The change from shoeing horses to writing and sculpting found me doing what a well-trained quarter horse does: when not chasing bovines, they rest. Some quarter horses will lock their front legs and fall asleep. I've even had them sleep while shoeing them.

My lids became heavy, it was impossible to stay awake in a seated position while sculpting or writing if not for this coffee. The warmth of the textured ochre and sienna walls, food and caffeine made this café a home. The owner of the café became a friend.

I became friends with many of the people who served me there. These people saw more of me than Gillian did. Lorne, student and server of food and giver of precious coffee, became a confidant. She gave me the bolstering that, along with the coffee, made my work easier and my belief in myself a little stronger when I had so many doubts.

On the day I realized that my house was only semi-electrified, I brought my metaphorical tears to the café. Lorne was there; I told her of my electrical plight. Instead of the normal, wonderful support in the way of phrases, such as "You can do it," she said, "Why don't you call my dad?"

His name was Ron. The highest compliment I can give someone is to describe them as a breed of dog. Ron reminded me of an

Airedale, curly coarse brown hair and biggest of all terriers. Airedales won't think twice about going after a mountain lion and will take abuse from a young child without a whimper. They've been used as Seeing Eye dogs, also in police and military work. In our case, all of these disciplines came into play in dealing with my house. Ron's other qualifications were that he was an electrician and general contractor.

Wires were missing; the drywall that had recently been put up and paid for now had to be eviscerated to get to the wires and junction boxes inside the wall. A junction box is exactly what it sounds like; it's where wires come together inside a small, steel, galvanized or plastic box. This is where switches or plugs are also connected to the wires.

Men who put up drywall are notorious for covering over electrical outlets in their frenzy to get all the interior walls up, so they can get to their next job. Big deal, if they forget to cut a hole in the drywall for light switches, outlet plugs or even the plumber's pipes, that one day hopefully we will have faucets attached to. All this added to the confusion of the electrical problem. I did not remember where Emil had placed these junction boxes. It was like mind reading, trying to figure out where all the wires in the walls were. To call on his apprentice would be useless, since he never worked with Emil at our house. Also, my fear was that if I had the apprentice over one more time he might want to charge for just looking pensive.

Gillian and I began the always necessary step of spending additional money on work that had already been paid for. Ron was not free, but the task of tracing the wires with him was going well and worth every dime we spent. At this time, we let go of any thoughts of buying expensive light fixtures.

During this period the stove was delivered. We took it out of the box immediately after it was in the kitchen while the delivery men were still there, I'd learned to inspect deliveries before signing anything. The appliance looked undamaged; more than that, it spoke of the future: "Yes, we will eat here again someday." I looked all around the stove and admiring it, for it was one of those built-in types. Black and streamlined, it begged you to turn it on.

I noticed there was no plug at the end of the wires coming from the back of the stove. "Where is the plug at the end of these wires?" I asked the delivery man. "It looks like this stove is wired for 220." My biggest fault with the whole construction job and life in general is making assumptions that people know what they're doing; yes, it would make sense, since I'm paying them, but it doesn't work that way. Is this my way of avoiding getting involved by thinking someone else is thinking so I don't have to? The delivery men looked at me with blank stares but did confirm that they delivered the right appliance, and, yes, it was wired for 220.

Apparently the city inspector's perception of our kitchen area was that there was less ventilation than what would be acceptable for an all gas stove. To get around this problem, the stove had been ordered with a gas cook top and underneath an electric oven and broiler. The stove had been paid for early on in the rebuilding. Outside of telling Gillian that the kitchen appliances should be black, I was not involved at all with the construction during this time. It turned out that the kitchen had more than enough ventilation for an all-gas stove, but I found that out only after we were again living in the house.

Unfortunately, none of the house was wired for 220. I guess Emil in his haste overlooked the call on the plans for 220 for the stove. Now Ron and I were stuck trying to figure a way to run more wires behind the wall.

I was getting good at making holes in the new drywall and was slender enough to squeeze into the new cabinets and under the living room floor. I cut a hole in the old hardwood floor while Ron fed me conduit from the other side of the living room wall from the newly installed breaker panel. I was under the floor for about three hours drilling, chiseling and prying my way through to the kitchen closet. There was no simple way to get to this closet.

With Ron coaching me, I ran the flex tubing or electrical conduit from the circuit panel, through walls and the virgin kitchen cabinets, securing it with conduit brackets every couple of feet. After going around more than half of the kitchen wall's perimeter, inside the cabinets, under the kitchen sink and the living room floor on my belly with conduit in hand, I found myself finally behind the backside of the stove.

Now, with the electrical veins carrying the blood of two hundred and twenty volts, the oven worked. Yes, Emil had put a plug in the wall behind the stove, but it was only a 110-volt outlet, and, unfortunately, it was done with Romex wire. Romex is similar to a heavy duty extension cord except it is flat and very water resistant and there is no way to increase its voltage. If we had run the wire throughout the house in conduit like I wanted to, whenever we wanted to change or alter anything, such as in this case, all I'd had to do was pull new wire through the conduit.

To our shock, pun intended, Emil, who left us high and dry, now showed up. Though we had made major progress with the electrical, there was still a lot more to be done. I was hoping it was a good sign that Emil had returned. There was much still unanswered as to where the plugs and switches were under the drywall.

When I told Ron that Emil had come back, and that he'd said he would make everything right, Ron's reply was, "That's great." I paid Ron what I owed him and told him, "I might need some leverage with the electrician to get him to do what he was paid to do. Emil argues over just about everything. Would you be up for helping me in a little game if it comes down to him not taking responsibility for his work? I'll pay you for your time."

"Sure, Alan, whatever it takes."

Gillian had felt she let the family down again by paying Emil in full before anything worked. So she took it upon herself to tell him what needed to be done. The work was moving along but with tension in the air, and it wasn't coming from the electrical wires. Gillian, trying to get the house electrified, always had to confront Emil on what was not working and what he promised he would do.

It was a warm summer day. I was working on the same sculpture in my studio I'd started right before we began the remodel the year before. Shrill sounds of loud anger emanated from the house. "Keep that crazy woman away from me!"

"Yea, I'm crazy all right, and I'm going to kill you, you son of a bitch."

"She's nuts, keep her away from me"

There on the balcony was Martin with his arms wrapped around Gillian's waist, holding her back, as she tried to go for Emil. I ran up the stairs. Both of the combatants settled down. Emil started to talk, "Look, I said I'd run the electrical out over the living room beams, I just wasn't going to do it today."

Red-faced Gillian yelled back, "You're a fucking liar; it's only now that you decided to do what you were supposed to do, and now after I'm at my wit's end with your sloppy work and your lack of honesty. You're a jerk!"

I knew if I didn't say anything they'd be at it again. "So what you're saying Emil is you'll run the electricity along the top of these two living room beams?"

"Yes, I promise, just keep her away from me."

"Alan, two seconds before you got here he was fighting me on doing it."

"I know, Gillian, but he is going to do it now. Let's just let him do it." Without realizing it, Gillian and I were playing out "good cop/ bad cop," and it was working.

I needed to take a different tack. Emil was trying to get out of doing what he said he would do, or at least wanting to do things that were short cuts, which later could make problems for us; I could see it was time to employ Ron in my little game. I'd learned my lessons well; city codes, like bank lending criteria, are arbitrary. There is no truth in either world, but only what is made up in that moment.

The story I fed Emil was that Ron was a construction specialist brought in from the bank. In the charade, Ron was to estimate the progress of the house. If we received thumbs up from Ron, the next stage of construction loans would be released. Of course, the only thing holding it up was Emil, the electrician. Bank rules always seem to be intimidating, so Emil did exactly what Ron told him to do. Emil started to look like he actually enjoyed being honest. Wires that before had no electricity running through them found light and power at the end of their journey. Emil even found all the electrical outlets that were covered over by the fast moving drywallers. For the first time in a year I saw real progress in the electrical part of the rebuilding of my home. We were now moving past using kites with iron keys dangling from string during a lightning storm.

REDEEMED

Ned finally got the rough plumbing done weeks after Emil the electrician had made the corrections to his job.

We filled the natural gas lines and attached the gauge to the line outside to see if there were any leaks inside the house. There were none, so we moved ahead.

Insulation, dry wall, roof and stucco were next. At this time the windows and exterior doors had all been installed by Martin and

Sam with no fanfair, other than that our first contractor directed Gillian to buy the exterior, wood-framed French doors. These doors opened the master bedroom to the intimate yard. Months had gone by, and the doors were now warped from sitting in the house from the start of construction, though not enough for them to be replaced. In these days of almost totally air-sealed homes, it is nice to be able to see the outside world through the door's edges that never quite meet the door frame. I am sure that within these imperfections of our unsealed doors, mold will never find a home.

Stained wood is nice but increase the maintenance of the house. Unfortunately, that was not one of Gillian's considerations when she picked out the windows, even though I made a plea for an alternative. Why should she worry about it since I'd be the only one concerned with maintaining them?

Sam, who worked side by side with Martin on the framing and much of the interior wood work, was now laying tile. Sam reminded me of a cross between a yellow Labrador and an American Staffordshire terrier.

When I speak of dogs, I'm talking about the ones that have stayed true to their original breeding. This change from wolf to dog, didn't happen overnight and wasn't driven by aesthetic whims. It was based upon the survival needs of man. Unfortunately, in recent times some ancient physical and mental standards have been thrown out the window. There are those who sing the praises of exaggerated angulations in the hind quarters of German Shepherds, lowering their hips to the point that the hind legs no longer serve the heart and breath of this loyal breed. Due to bad breeding, how many Irish Wolfhounds can still run after wolves these days or live to a ripe old age? The answer: few or none.

As with Sam, yellow Labs are kind and can handle cold nights and hot days with calmness, and Staffordshires don't quit.

Sam had done the tile work throughout the entire house until, instead of snow blindness, he had tile blindness. He worked slowly. I could have found someone faster, but I was comfortable with Sam, and if something was wrong it wasn't a big deal. There were a few times things that weren't straight. He fixed them right away with no fanfair. When I think about it, he worked alone and finished tiling the whole house himself. He had tremendous patience with Gillian's eye for detail, which could be exacting. He was also intelligent, and with communication at a low point for me it was really good to have him as one of the men working on my house. I only spend time with people I like. All I have is time, but it's fleeting and borrowed, Sam was worth my time: I hope he'd say the same of me.

The kitchen floor was made of one-foot square terracotta pavers and the counter tiles were handmade, green four-inch squares; the backsplash tiles were also handmade. These backsplash tiles were beige two-inch squares, interspersed with artistically placed accent tiles. Martin and I made the hood for the stove. Martin did the wood frame during the day; that night I covered it with chicken wire and tar paper. The wire would hold the cement, which I mixed with water and troweled on. It had a similar look to that of adobe, which gave the hood a look and feel of an old Spanish kitchen. While still wet, I placed accent tiles artistically into the white mud. It was a large hood; it took me from seven o'clock at night till four in the morning to finish it.

In those days of construction, my schedule was exhausting and lonely. During this time the cracks in my self-confidence widened, and the imperfections I saw in others were magnified. At this point in my life, a normal day would start at seven in the morning when I'd shoe three to five horses. At two or three in the afternoon, I'd go to our rented bedroom in Ellen's house. There I would nap till five, then I'd pick up Berrigan from day care. Later, we would meet with

Gillian for dinner. After dinner, Gillian and Berrigan would go to our bedroom at Ellen's while I'd go to the construction site, formerly known as our house. I'd work on what needed to be done, sometimes staying as late as three in the morning. Every night I worked alone. On the weekends, Berrigan had ice hockey. Practice could start as early as just after midnight or as late as six in the morning. Ice time is a scarce commodity, and boys and their parents have no influence on the scheduling. On Sundays, there would be a game. I never let Berrigan know that I hate hockey, and it gave me no pleasure watching other young lads hit Berrigan or see him hit them while on the ice. I was depressed during this time; it was safer than feeling anger.

I was tired from three years of twelve- to sixteen-hour days working on the house and horseshoeing. I had given up on my agreement with Gillian to retire from shoeing. My tank was empty. The hardest part of the whole deal was that Gillian and I were both physically and emotionally distant, and with now no time for sculpting or writing, I wanted to be insane.

As I mentioned before, I checked into a local mental hospital. The puke green walls and people who had given up all desire for autonomy so they could wear the label of "patient" showed me immediately this place was unhealthy. For the most part these were intelligent people, who just needed a "time out." Instead they were seduced into an invocation of pharmaceuticals, while others took on an alpha role by wearing a collar of credentials. It reminded me of when I worked in the Intensive Education Unit at Mountain Glen Home for Children and later ran their horseback-riding program. There I saw children who just needed to be liberated from a crazy home situation to regain their sanity.

Two hours later I checked myself out, realizing this was not a place to get help. The prescription I needed was for a horny nurse. My commitment to celibacy, in the name of a romantic notion of letting my wife heal from the men before me, caused me pain. My passion for life and the surge of hormones running through my body caused me to psychologically implode into self-pity. I had passed the line of redemption through emotional and physical relationships, the only way out was to find myself again. I wondered where I could go for emotional support.

Not having any money for therapy but being a strong believer in Carl Jung's theories on how one can recover from alcoholism, I chose to follow Jung's route of possible redemption within Alcoholics Anonymous. I didn't have enough money for gas to drive to an AA meeting where issues like mine were discussed (don't ask me what classification my issues would come under), so I went to the closest group I could find. It happened to be a gay and transvestite AA meeting at a church in West Hollywood. There I heard inspiring stories and felt a kinship with the group, although booze never was a problem, and I'm heterosexual. At the close of my first meeting during the serenity prayer, for the first time in a long time I didn't feel alone or different from others. Until that moment, I hadn't realized how alone I was – shoeing horses in silence during the day, then working late into the night alone on the house. Within this Tuesday night circle, I was flanked by a six-foot-six transvestite and a hunchback who was barely five feet, palsy stricken and also a transvestite. Holding their hands in this affirming circle while my lips whispered, "God give me the strength to change the things," and so on, I found a home.

The romance of building a house for my family seemed noble in my mind's eye. Instead, I found myself in the middle of the night with no one around. Even the ghost respected my aloneness. To make matters worse, Gillian often left our bank checkbook in her car, parked on the street in front of Ellen's house. A thief broke the window in her car twice and stole checks from the middle of the book each time, so it wouldn't be noticed. From this, the thief stole my identity. This unconsciousness on Gillian's part would have continued if each night after work I didn't go into her parked car in front of Ellen's house and clean the car of anything valuable.

As a camera newswoman for a big network, Ellen had an uncanny sense for good and bad news. She said, "This guy is most likely into drugs, and things could get worse because he knows a lot about you now." Off the record, the police concurred.

So in the middle of the night I found myself working on the plumbing, electrical, cleaning, making and plastering a kitchen hood or putting accent tiles into the adobe- looking mud with the comfort of a loaded, Ruger .357 magnum on my hip.

As with everything, there is irony if you're ornery enough to live long enough to see it. Fifteen years later, a woman went to jail as the ringleader for the theft of my identity and others. Before she was caught, she had not only used my identity to procure incidental trinkets to fill the void within her but made purchases at a Bible store, trying further to tarnish my good name.

BAPTIZED

We spent thousands of dollars on tile and its installation. The second floor had its share of tile; so did Berrigan's bathroom. His shower area was made of handmade cobalt blue tiles. The floor was tiled with terracotta twelve-inch-square pavers; one of the tiles had a coyote paw print in it. This tile was put in the middle of the bathroom's small floor. These terracotta, or saltillo, tiles as they are sometimes called, are made in the traditional way by forming a huge wood border on the ground, pouring the local clay into this large framed-in area and then cutting it into squares of popular sizes. Most common are 12"x12"s. During this part of fabrication, animals sometimes walk on the not yet dried field of tiles during the night.

After the pavers dry, they're stacked like a log cabin or pyramid. A bonfire is made in the center. This takes the place of a giant kiln. You can see the discoloration in the tiles where they rested on each other while stacked.

Our master bed and bath are on the third floor. Here in the master bath was where Sam laid the most expensive tiles. This was where our sunken tub would sit after the tile was laid. Ned, the plumber, was to put the stems and faucets in for the tub before Bill did the tiling. As usual, Ned never showed up when he said he would and was sabotaging the tiling schedule for Sam and Martin, who had other things to do. Ned, trying to make light of his absence said, "Yes, I know I was supposed to do the finish plumbing before the tile was laid, but don't worry, Alan, I have special drill bits to drill through tile. So just let them do their tiling. I will make the holes in the tile for the tub's spout, the shower and the tub's hot and cold water valves."

Of course, a few tiles were broken as Ned drilled holes into them. You could hear him yell, as if it were an unimaginable surprise that tiles would break in the process of drilling into them. Later, Ned paid Sam to drill holes in new tiles before they were put into place.

Ned installed toilets, bathtub, showers and sinks, but it took forever. Not willing to wait any longer I installed all the other things that seemed like one-man jobs, which would bring the plumbing job closer to completion. I installed all the faucets and faucet handles. They all worked well; they spoke a language that made it clear we were one step closer to the final inspection.

Agreements made with Ned in the early fantasy stages of the remodel led to too many things being taken for granted. For instance, Ned said he *could* put the master sunken bath tub in, but he didn't say he *would*.

I waited for Ned to put in the sunken tub, which was the last thing to be done. "Ned, when are you going to put in the tub?" I asked when I called him.

"Ah, Alan it's the carpenter's job to put the tub in."

"What, how the hell is it the carpenter's job?"

"Alan, the tub is cantilevered out and over the walkway. They know how it will structurally fit. I'll do all the pipe connections in the crawl space under the tub after they've put in the tub."

My mind whirled: Was Ned afraid to install it, or did he want more money? If he had never done this type of thing before and was afraid to, did I really want him experimenting on my house? If it was more money he was after, I'd rather hire another plumber to do the installation, one who would at least show up when he said he would or call if he had to change the appointment. The other thought I had was that I had truly gone crazy, and what Ned was saying was legitimate.

Just to make sure that I wasn't going nuts, I went to Martin. "Ned said the carpenters are supposed to put in the tub." Martin looked at me. Both of us started to laugh and shake our heads. "Martin, I don't get it. What's the problem with him? Why doesn't he just come and finish the job?"

"Alan, finish plumbing is the hard part; it's where everything is supposed to all come together and fit." I didn't want Ned to put in a bath tub when he was scared to do it. If something went wrong, all I'd get from him would be a cistern full of excuses about how everyone but him screwed up.

I called the neighborhood plumber; he took one look at the job and quoted me a price which was more money than the tub, faucets and tile cost altogether. I took his estimate as an unverbalized, "No, I don't want the job." When all else failed, I looked in the yellow pages. There in bold type, "Over forty years in the plumbing industry, no

job too big or too small for our experts." Yes, I thought, these guys
will have no problem with the tub.

Two young guys showed up, on time, in clean uniforms and
with confidence gleaming through their grins as if they'd used Tidy
Bowl on their teeth. Given what I had gone through with Ned, I
thought their quote of four hundred and fifty dollars was fair. There
would be two of them, which meant I didn't even have to help carry
the tub up the three flights of stairs. Everything was included in a
neat, professional contract. The appointment was made; they said
they'd return in ten days. The next day I got a call from the plumbing firm's secretary, "Sorry, we'll have to decline on your project," she
said.

"Why?"

"It's not the kind of work we do."

"Your men came out just yesterday and gave me a bid, and I accepted it."

"I know Mr. Claymore, but they were mistaken. We are very
sorry for the inconvenience."

I told Louis the architect, who came up with the idea of putting
a sunken tub on the third floor in the first place, that there wasn't
anyone who seemed to want the job.

"Alan, why don't you put the tub in? Ned said he'd do all the
connecting after the bathtub is in place."

"I don't understand what the problem is. The framing and rough
plumbing inspections both passed with flying colors. The hardest
part looks to be carrying the tub up the stairs. All that has to be done
is to build some sort of cradle to hold the tub secure. Am I missing
something, Louis, or am I right?"

"Yes, Alan, you're right."

Never having put in a bath tub, I sought out Martin. "Martin, I apologize for taking you away from your work on the house, but what do I need to do to get this sunken tub in?"

"Alan, take two-by-fours and make a frame for the tub a little bigger than the bottom of the bathtub. Then make struts every few inches and nail them within your frame. Then set it in place where the tub will go. I'll help you carry the tub upstairs, and we'll gently rest the tub on it, making sure not to crack the tile. After you have done that, take the tub out, buy some ready-mix mortar, mix it and pour it into the frame you made, and then yell for me. We'll put the tub back in and let it set. That's it."

The frame building went well; it resembled a wooden grate that could keep out the demons of hell. When I showed it to Martin he said, "Wow, Alan, this will more than hold the tub."

I followed Martin's instructions to the letter. I started the final steps – mixing the mortar and then pouring it into the frame, which was now sitting in its permanent place in the area where the tub would spend the rest of its life.

Ned and his helper came in unannounced. "Hi, Alan, you're mixing the mortar too wet, put more mortar in," Ned said.

With the mortar at a consistency that met with Ned's approval, we lifted the tub carefully on top, avoiding damage to the tile.

"It's not setting into the frame, goddamn it. You made it too dry, Ned," I yelled. There was no way to add water to the mortar in the frame. I got in the tub and used my weight to sink the tub into place. I got it to within about a half-inch from where the lip of the tub was supposed to rest gently against the tile. I started jumping up and down; it was moving slowly, but time was running out. Within a short time the mortar would be too hard. When Ned saw that my frantic jumping was a safe thing to do, he and his helper joined me. Now, all three of us were jumping up and down inside the tub.

Finally, the bathtub sank into its resting place without a crack in the tile.

Ned immediately started in with his self-acknowledgement. "Boy, we got that in and it looks great. I'll see ya' later Alan."

"Ned, where do you think you're going? You're not leaving until the tub's plumbing is connected, and I fill the tub with water to really set it in."

"Oh, yeah, Alan I'll get right on it."

Soon the tub was filled with water. Our house's plumbing was completed.

21

THE FINAL

The lack of internal accomplishments haunted me, even though I had completed so much. Finishing this house never gave me comfort from the unexpressed love between Gillian and me, or relief from the stalking shadow of a life not lived to its fullest. I continued the A.A. meetings for a short time but never got a sponsor to help guide me through the twelve steps. I was able, though, to foster enough self love to go forward.

Things were back on track. The fragrant aroma of what is known as the "Final" was wafting over our land. This is when you have had each phase of the building process inspected from first getting the plans approved to building the house.

I was elated with the prospect of the sign-off on the Final. While down in the hollows of the empty living room preparing for the last inspection, I got careless. Full of joy, I told the ghost that I didn't care if she showed herself to me. She dropped a tool off the fireplace mantel; as usual I ran out of the room, and in the safety of the outdoors I started to laugh. From outside the house, I apologized. "I'm very sorry for being scared. I am going to walk back in and finish getting ready for tomorrow's Final. I promise not to disturb you."

With the aid of a horse, I have pulled other horses out of deep snow and mud. I have dug out trucks mired in snow and mud with the use of vehicles, shovels, winches and, at times, my own back. My body has been stuck in both mud and snow. Frozen white death

I fear less than the slow, dark death of mud. These thoughts run through my mind in bed on rainy nights in Laurel Canyon.

As I said before, "In the construction business, lumber, rules and men are not necessarily what they say they are."

Inspectors are men who, in the trade of construction, are sometimes considered those unable to make the grade as contractors. I don't know if this is entirely true. Maybe they just aren't willing to get their hands dirty, or they may like seeing things done right. It's possible they're just looking for a job where they can tell people to do things over and over again. Perhaps it just comes down to feeling good each night after work, coming home and having experienced the exhilaration of being right all day long, even when you're not. If you, as a city bureaucrat, caused somebody great financial pain, and it makes you feel more like a have than a have-not in the small world of uncountable discretionary income, then for one moment you too can feel like the entitled few.

Our original city building inspector was ready for retirement. Not my fault.

What do retired city inspectors do? They do the same thing that retired tax collectors and ex-heroin addicts do. They become consultants and counselors, and that is what Mr. Plot did. I will say this in defense of one action that he took. We spent an unforeseen sixty thousand dollars on retaining walls in the backyard, and I actually thank Mr. Plot each time it rains for his uncompromising need to have things right, especially in this one area. During downpours in the middle of the night, lying in bed, I think about a story I read of a West Washington coastal Indian tribe, which had been living in lodges on hillside banks by the Pacific Ocean. They'd lived here for eons. One year the rain was harder than the tribe had ever known. During one of those nights, the rain came down so hard that the people in one of the lodges were all buried alive when the earth embankment behind the lodge came down onto the dwelling with the vengeance of an avalanche.

Mr. Plot's building expectations had become predictable, but now he had retired, right at the time we were getting close to being finished. Once again, we were saddled with the unknown. Who would be our new city building inspector? The unknown made me over-prepare for the most critical of all inspections. Passing this inspection would be like a thumbs-up that the house was done. We could then move back in. The bank would let us refinance the house, so we could get out from under the high interest loans we were paying.

I know certain things about life and the flushing of toilets, but some things are not known to anyone. Before the city bureaucrat arrives at the front door, the walkway that leads to the door can even become an issue. It is in this spirit that the unwritten laws can play a significant role in the prized signature of the city's bureaucrats.

The plan for getting the final sign-off was to put the architect's plans and the individually-signed cards for each phase of the home's construction into the empty, freshly painted living room. They were all on display in a fashion similar to that of the Dead Sea Scrolls when discovered.

The inspection process goes like this: first, the obtaining of the prized city sign-off of the architect's plans; then, the geologist's report for the grading permits and foundation inspections; next the framing inspection; after that comes rough plumbing and rough electrical, insulation, mechanical or heating and air inspections; and finally, plumbing and electrical. Last, but not least, the Final, where the building inspector looks at the house in its hopefully completed state. These are all individual cards, about the size of my grammar school report card and with the same connotation surrounding them.

I rested a four-by-eight -foot, three-quarter-inch-thick sheet of plywood on top of two sawhorses. On this table, I laid out all the paperwork, including huge stacks of plans, reports, correspondence plus muffins and coffee for good luck. Maybe the inspector would run through the house in a caffeinated frenzy. The art of being a contractor comes into play now more than ever. It's conceivable that a contractor would not know how to use a hammer or a saw. On the other hand, if a contractor can't communicate well with an inspector, you could end up having an illegally-built house. The city could make you tear it down. Even if somehow you didn't get in trouble, which is doubtful, just try and sell it without the "Final" from the city. With the right words, though, spoken at the right time to the inspector a bent nail can appear to be straightened telekinetically.

I could nail two-by-fours together as good as anyone but that wouldn't make up for my lack of experience in communicating with building inspectors. Too much was riding on this sign-off: the loan, our debt and, of course, moving back into our home. When I fired the contractor that Louis and Gillian originally hired, I became the homeowner / builder in deed and in writing. So at the close of this adventure, I was supposed to have the words that soothe the inspector's suspicion that all builders are bad. Once again, I planned a charade. The last charade with the electrician got the electrical finished and working. Why not try it again? I called Ron. He said he was up for it.

Ron stood behind the inspector, and I was in front of him. When the inspector asked a question, Ron indicated a "yes" by thumbs-up or a no with thumbs-down. The new inspector I drew was nice and conscientious. Still, I proceeded with the plan. As the three of us walked our way through the house, I answered all the inspector's inquiries with the poise and knowledge of a builder of castles.

Who knows whether Ron and I needed to do what we did, but I got the final inspection sign-off accomplished. For me, the City's Final meant this was the final thing I would do to the house. It was sanctioned by the city. Who could disagree with that? Gillian could. I didn't realize that as hard as the city was to deal with, Gillian was more of a problem. The tug of war of childhood needs became paramount. Nothing was finished in Gillian's eyes, and I still felt more comfortable living in a tent. Fancy light fixtures, wall treatments, carpets and hardwood floors were glaringly missing to Gillian's eyes.

THE LIST

I had a flash of memory as I stood near Martin on the third level of the house as we both rejoiced about the city's final sign-off. I looked down at the new, large, wooden steps which led up to the still-not-finished, in Gillian's eyes, master bedroom. Just then Gillian came up the steps. I saw her as she climbed the stairs through the eyes that had first brought me to her twenty years before. There might be something more heart poundingly beautiful than Gillian; don't ask me what the hell it is. There have been other women in my life, but my caring for my wife must have come from Cupid's arrow. Cupid is not a gentle cherub.

Gillian's green eyes and the blush of her face framed in curly auburn hair knifed through me. Our eyes met, and I could not speak. Gillian's smile is what I want to see for the rest of my life. As I write this in my fifties, mid-morning in a loud café, I start to get turned on. I am one lucky son-of-a-bitch. I was whelped from a real bitch of a mother; to have found love within my scope of family experiences is amazing. The arrow is tender with its delivery but the arrowhead is still dipped in a concoction of lethal passion, so I went back to work on the house.

There was no end in sight. While drinking coffee at the café across the street, I saw a small sign on a two-story building, "Quit smoking with hypnosis." If hypnosis can help someone stop smoking, why can't it help me put a halt to working on the house? I stopped drinking the coffee before I could see the bottom of the cup. I did not want to be put under when I was totally adrenalin-ed up. I might have the desire to request more energy so I could then ask Gillian if there was anything else I could do. I walked across the street and made an appointment for the next week.

As I entered this barbershop of the mind to have a little trimmed off my unconscious, I was already subconsciously making a commitment to put a leash on the house project. The hypnotist was tall with pretty eyes and a voice that would soothe the savage beast or at least the conscious mind. As I reclined in a comfortable leather chair, I fell asleep allowing her words to lead me into clear thinking. Make a list of home projects, and have a party when all is completed. Then, for once and for all, declare this house done.

My list went something like this: Build a three-foot deep pond with a wall fountain in the master bedroom's yard. Build a privacy fence in the yard off the master bedroom. Landscape the upper level and lower level yards; patinate the garage door. Remove the wood-shed where we did our laundry. Relocate laundry room to the closet in the kitchen. Move the water heater to the outside of the house into a new aluminum water heater shed. Install a new wood floor in the living room. Make a living room closet door. Rewire the electrical from the house to the studio and from there to the soon-to-be remote controlled front gate. Build a dog area. Install fancier doorknobs and locks on all the interior doors. Make a new driveway.

The list went on. I should have kept the list for the purpose of writing, but I never thought to write about this expenditure of my fleeting time on earth, so I burned the list at our first party in our newly-done house. Parties are a great way to obtain witnesses, and I needed witness.

Some of the work was divvied out to different tradespeople. I was involved even in those projects at some level, either as the person who did a lot of the work or just as the homeowner, who paid when things were finished. It probably is one of the few times in my life that I almost completely listened to the instructions of others to avoid over spending and mistakes.

On one of the work intensive Saturdays and Sundays, the digging of a pond became my undertaking. I dug a hole three feet deep and six feet in diameter. The next week, I bought a thick plastic pond liner. I carried the eighty-some-odd pound thing up the three flights of steps to the small yard where the master bedroom's French doors open up to our intimate outdoor space. I indulged myself in the purchase of a large fiberglass level and leveled the bottom of the dirt hole, then covered the dirt bottom with three inches of pea gravel. After lowering the tub into the hole, the fun part of filling it up was mine. The next weekend came the rock treatment. Once again, I learned that rocks are heavier than they look. Two thousand or more pounds turned out not to be much rock. Some were about the weight of my shoeing anvil– about eighty-five pounds– and others weighed a lot more. Gillian had worked hard all week and was now on the bed watching TV. Something seemed quite unfair as I walked up the three flights of steps to the master bedroom and out the French doors, past the reclining Gillian, who was probably watching some gothic romance where the leading man is a warrior, sensitive lover and a virgin.

For accuracy of detail, I counted the steps which I had climbed carrying the thirty- plus rocks up to the back yard. They numbered forty steps. Each rock was between seventy and a hundred pounds.

Strolling laboriously with these boulders while holding them not only
with my arms but also supporting their weight with my thighs and
lap, I looked like a skinny sumo wrestler entering the ring. Sweating
as I passed the bed, I wondered: has anyone ever found Sisyphus attractive?

After placing these rocks in a random manner around the pond
to give it the look of a natural setting, I realized I needed more rock.
Instead, I hauled up many sacks of pea gravel to create the feel of a
natural pond and small stream. To finish off the setting, I did a casting in cement of a sculpture of a wolf's head that I had done originally in bronze. I put a water pump into the pond and ran the water
line from the pump under the rocks, then to the wolf head fountain,
which I'd hung from the back wall. Next, I created the little stream
that meandered back down to the pond. The pond was done but not
finished. In my heart, my obsessive nature never lets anything be finished. It is said that a sculpture is never finished, only abandoned.

I know it's not good manners to luxuriate in a backyard pond
with fish and lily pads, but cool water on warm nights softens harsh
days. I did this for a few months and then the novelty wore off, so I
went back to bathing indoors. The pond's fish soon found their way
to the inside of our neighborhood raccoon, and a few years later the
constant musical sounds of water gently streaming out the wolf's
mouth could not compete with its maintenance. In time the wolf
just bared its now-dry teeth at us.

Saying no to Gillian's wish to patina the master bedroom's privacy fence started a silent fight. Through hypnotism, I had become
a nimbus cloud of strength. The storm of limit-setting in me was
unleashed. Gillian tried to yell at the storm and fight, but like stop-
ping the rain and slowing down the wind, I wouldn't yield to all
her wants for the house. This was where I would let the relationship
die, over this stupid fight. There was stillness and calm in the center

of my storm; my being stood still. No words passed between us for three days. Gillian and I never stay silent with one another; talking holds us together.

She broke the ice with the most incredible story to come from an educated woman: "Alan, the reason it was so important to me to have the fence finished in a patina is that in a past life I was accused of being a witch and buried in a wall. I feel claustrophobic with the fence having no dimension of color to it."

"You're not serious?"

"Well, I tried."

I wish I could say nothing has been said about the fence since that date, but on occasions when there's a need to, I'll ask Gillian, "Is this a patina on the fence request?"

The old electrical wires which ran between the house and my studio were frayed and hung threateningly low. Replacing these wires with safe underground wiring appeared on the house list.

Incredible as it might seem, Emil, the electrician, showed up at our house. With earnest eyes he told us, "I want to make both of you happy. Alan, will you help me and my new partner?"

"Yes."

We almost couldn't believe it. Emil was legitimately in the process of reinventing himself into a man of honest intent. I had a gut feeling that once upon a time he worked from a place of integrity, but through time he had lost the grip on what was right. Some habits die hard, but he wanted to make good on his vows of electrifying the things not immediately pertaining to the house at no extra charge. It was a promise he had made in the very beginning of construction: to do the wiring from the house to the studio and from there to the gate area.

No one can say what changed in Emil to have him show up on our doorstep. I have noticed in some men who build homes a sense of searching, not a boyish seeking, but a forlorn search. Is it to find a forgiving and accepting father, perhaps, in one of the closets yet built?

Emil, his new partner and I, proceeded with the arduous task of running electrical conduit under the ground, beneath the old retaining wall and old terraced landscaping between the house and studio. It was interesting to watch Emil struggle with internal change and become a man of his word. At times, I saw the beginning of frustration on his face, but he never let himself drown in the thoughts of taking an unethical shortcut with the job at hand.

At one point, Emil fell over something, and he looked comical. Both his partner and I started to laugh. Emil joined in. This was so different from the man who before had worn a frown and wanted to race through my beloved house just to make a buck. Gillian and Emil became friends, and her thank you to him at the end of it all was sincere.

Before removing the laundry structure which was separated from the house by a walkway and terraced area, I called in a plumber who worked for a large company that my mother's side of the family had used for many years. Denny was tall and clean-cut. He fit the bill for anyone who was looking for someone competent. If I were a casting director, I could have cast him in anything from an honest lawyer to a vegetarian, though he was too substantial to play a vegan.

The closet in the corner of the kitchen was where the new stacked washer and dryer were to go. Originally, this space was occupied by a water heater. Denny and I hauled up a new water heater and aluminum shed for its new place. Denny made a cement form with some quick kind of mix, which did not hold up well. Fifteen years later it had to be replaced. Other than that, everything functioned as expected. The job of bringing the water line to the outside wall of the kitchen and then to the water heater was another story. Both of us ended up working on drilling through the cement wall. After burning up his drill and nearly mine, we finally bored through, making space for the water lines. Later, we realized that if we had made the holes only two feet higher we would have been drilling into drywall, stucco and plywood, instead of going through solid concrete. That would have only taken three minutes instead of the two hours we spent. The rest of the installation of the water heater went well. The hot and cold water pipes and gas line for the washer and dryer were right there. There was no problem in hooking them up.

At the top of the driveway, against the rock wall was a well-built eight-by-twelve foot wood structure with a wood-shingle roof. Years ago we plumbed this quaint structure for a washer and dryer, and it served us well. Unfortunately it didn't fit the squeaky clean concept of today's homes. Even if the style is old Spanish, everything is expected to be new, even if you have to pay extra to have it look antique. Under the direction of the Taste Police, I smashed it apart with a sledgehammer.

CONCRETE

The driveway was asphalt. It was old when we bought the property a decade before, and now with construction's ugly rage of steel-wheeled dumpsters and other things resting on it, you could say it looked like the surface of the moon. Also the old retaining wall I had fortified earlier with rocks, using the dump truck that I couldn't stop, no longer looked right. The rock wall and driveway was now not up to par with the rest of the house in the eyes of you know who.

When I pictured myself breaking up what was left of the asphalt with a sledgehammer, putting it into a dumpster, having it hauled away and then making a form with two-by-sixes, plus lay down re-bar, I started to feel overwhelmed.

Early Sunday morning, on our way to Berrigan's hockey game, in a heavy rain that had gone on all night long, Gillian drove down the freeway as the water pounded the road and our truck. On the narrow bench seat in the back of the cab I slept and dreamed about wet cement trucks. At that moment our pickup came almost to a full stop in two-and-a-half feet of water under a long dark overpass. I was thrown onto the floor. The next minute we were whacked from behind at fifty miles per hour, bending my truck's frame. The sound of ice cubes shaking in a glass were the sounds my anvil, vise, drills, drill press, grinders, two hundred pounds of horseshoes and hammers made as they echoed from the truck's shell and bed.

The motorist who ran into us was hurt and needed major medical care; his car was totaled and he took full responsibility for the accident. Berrigan, Gillian and I were stiff, but we claimed no injuries. The insurance company that represented the other driver covered the repairs on my truck but fought with me over replacement of some of the tools that were ruined.

This was how my conversation began with Sadie, the pretty owner of the auto body shop where the repairs to my truck were being done. Nothing gets by Sadie and she asked me; "Alan, why were you dreaming about cement work?" I told her about building my house and that my wife now wants me to make a concrete driveway.

"Alan, I have a wonderful cement mason, and he's honest." I called him that day. Maybe I had to be hit at a high rate of speed to let someone else work on my house.

Kumi was a Tongan and far better built for heavy work than I. If he needed to stop an old, overloaded, twelve-ton dump truck filled with stone, he could. Kumi and I agreed on a price and a time line. Work commenced.

Kumi's crew was his family and friends. One of the people was someone's mother in the group. Her job was to do the cooking for the men while they worked. She came equipped with a barbeque and everything else needed to make great meals. They even fed me. It was the first home-cooked meal I'd had in a long time, maybe years. My property had been transformed into a South Sea paradise. The studio's garage door opened onto the driveway. My studio became a lanai for all of us Tongans. My friend Jeff Reynolds used to send me slack-key music from his recording company. Over the years my collection has gotten fairly large. I played the music on the stereo in the studio as we worked and ate.

It was a warm summer day. Kumi, his friends, family and I watched from my studio-lanai as large cement trucks poured their loads into the wooden forms they'd built, covering the rebar like muddy seas covering the bones of some prehistoric whale.

Gillian's desire was that stones would intermingle with the driveway's cement. When the pouring of cement reached the right level, all of us tossed pebbles into the waters of cement. As the music from the islands played, I felt the kind of contentment I'd feel if I were tossing flowers into a lagoon. This was the most calming moment in all my time involved with construction.

On October 31, 1996, friends and family came to the house. With a 12-inch bowie knife, I posted the three page list on one of the timbers in the living room that support the balcony.

The presence of the ghost by the closet under the living room steps was apparent to some of the party goers, mostly those from the horse community; I got comments from different people in the following weeks about their experiences with the ghost during the party. One woman friend who owned a Clydesdale horse avoided that section of the room, while another horse friend tried to have a conversation with the spirit. Horse people in general are a different lot; through the love of horses we squelch our fears of them, as we quiet theirs of us. It is with horses we find peace, a type of stillness you can't find anywhere else. I wonder if there is a relationship between ghosts, people and horses. On that Halloween, I am happy to say nothing happened to get my faded lady upset or scared.

Around 10 p.m. in the presence of these witnesses, I tore the list away from the post and burned this manacle of words in the fireplace. The large knife remained in the wood all night. While the cheers of costumed friends drowned out the silence of my not yet satiated bride, I rejoiced as the manifesto burned.

A week went by and the knife remained stabbed into the timber; it would still be there today but Gillian requested it be removed. "Alan, when are you planning on removing the knife?"

"Gillian, it's not on the list."

I pulled it out. Was I taking the cane away from the door that kept the gates of hell closed?

A year before the house list was created there was another list. This one had a date, "January 1st." The list was taped next to a dental mirror I put up when Gillian requested a mirror in the master bathroom. Both tiny mirror and list were within a four-by-eight foot border of overpriced tiles on the bathroom's wall. At some point an equal in size beveled mirror would fit in between these borders.

This is a glimpse of what was on that list:

Finish sculpting "Dly-Le-En"

Complete two more chapters of my novel (not this story about my house).

Cast a wolf's head in bronze.

My friend Jim Smedley was visiting from New York at the time and happened to notice the list with the date taped to the mirror. Some of the items had already been checked off.

"Wow, Alan it's only February and you've already finished almost half the things on your list. That's amazing!"

"Ah, Jimmy, that's my list from last year."

"Oh."

We both started to laugh.

It's a life's list that now guides me instead of a house list. In those days of construction when I let Gillian, who had very little common sense, lead me around by the nose, I felt that I, at least, was the one with common sense.

An artist's list can spell out things that make no sense to the rational mind. Who in today's world as a husband and father would dare say, "I'm a writer and sculptor of non-commercial things" and not feel as if he were irresponsible? Thank you, Gillian, for your support by way of your uncommon sense.

NO REST

I took a breather from listening to the house and Gillian's voice and let my guard down. A well-known plumbing company was called in to unplug our clogged sewer line. The man arrived, and I showed him where the line and cleanout was. Pulling out his rooter machine, he stuck the rooter down the sewer line and turned it on. It seemed as if he was not really letting it find its way down but holding it back like a hooked piranha.

"Um, I can't clear your line."

It really looked as if he wasn't trying. I am pretty much off guard when I take a break when letting someone else do something that I could do. This was the case when he said that he could not unclog it. I responded by saying, "I've used one of those things before. Let me give it a try."

"My insurance won't allow me to have you do it, but I'll try once more."

Once more, he went through what I perceived to be a contrived attempt. He said the only thing he could do was bust the cement up and put in a new sewer line; he just so happened to have an opening this week. I had been lulled the few weeks following the party into a calm of apathy.

"What, you can't be serious. There couldn't be anything wrong with my sewer line!" I yelled.

I had a wrenching feeling in my gut, no pun intended, and I almost started to cry. These weren't sympathy pains for my sewer line. Thinking about paying someone thousands to bust up the new cement or doing it myself, I only had the strength to tell him I didn't need his services. I called out another rooter service and the line was cleared with no problem. I now do my own sewer line most of the time, but not too long ago another rooter gentleman said he needed to tear up my driveway and put in a new sewer line when trying to free it from a clog. I looked him in the eyes and said, "I've killed people for saying less than that." The rooter guy's eyes got wide. He left quickly.

We wanted yellow pine floors on the second level where we didn't have tile. The floor installers came early in the afternoon and stayed late into the night. Screams came from upstairs as a pounding on my studio door brought me into the present. One of the installers yelled in Spanglish, "How do you shut off the electricity? Help!"

Looking up at the house from my studio door, I saw blinding lights flashing through Berrigan's bedroom window in the dim light of afternoon. For a moment it was as if I was one of the towns-people looking up from the village into the midnight lights of Dr Frankenstein's castle laboratory.

I ran upstairs. In Berrigan's bedroom I saw the belt sander push-ing and ramming up against the wall in the corner next to the window all by itself. An electrical arc from the opposite wall's outlet whipped across the room to the sander's plug. Dark shadows were strobed away by the pulsing, bright current energizing the power tool as it continued to crash into the bedroom wall. I stepped out of the room into the doorway to avoid the volts slapping me. I spoke to our ghost as I had done in the past. "I apologize, these guys are not good men, but let's let them finish and we'll be done with them. Nothing will happen to the house." The ghost has been the best judge of character in the house. With that, the arc of electricity pulled back into the wall. I told the men, "The rooms are sanded enough. Just stain the floor now, and come back tomorrow to urethane."

Gillian had decided on a color stain and was out of town. Probably not having anything but a light-colored stain in their van, the leader of the floor people told me this was the stain Gillian wanted. I was sure she wanted a darker stain. As all good children do, once again I was being manipulated.

"Your wife wanted this color stain."

"I think my wife wants a darker color."

This went on for a while, then with the reality that it was taking way longer than it was supposed to, and with the fact that I don't listen to Gillian as well as I used to, I gave in. Sure enough, it should have been darker.

When Berrigan goes up north with his furniture to finish college, I'll re-sand and re-stain the second floor with a dark stain.

Jim Smedley was back in town and had a conversation with Gillian where she shared her frustration with me. "Jimmy, I don't get it. Alan doesn't want any furniture in the house," she said.

"Well, look at how he was raised."

"What do you mean?"

"Well, you know."

"Know what, Jimmy?"

"Maybe you don't know. Alan grew up in that big house with no furniture in it."

"You're kidding!"

"No, I'm not, they had beds and not much else."

"Jimmy, Alan's parents owned a furniture store."

"I know."

Later that day, Gillian came to me. "Alan, you never told me you grew up with no furniture in the house, and that's why you're fighting me now on buying any furniture."

"How did you know that we didn't have furniture?"

"Jim told me."

"Oh."

FINISHING TOUCHES

Only a few chapters away from the end of the first draft of this memoir, I've decided that I'll soon put my house on the market. I need to move back to the mountains, where once more I can ride a horse out my back door and make noise sculpting in the middle of the night without worrying about neighbors.

Sometimes I wonder: will I be judged as crazy as Old Lady Winchester, who struggled for an afterlife within her world of fears and hopes? Mrs. Winchester endlessly built onto her house in an attempt to keep her imaginary demons at bay. She was haunted by the legacy of her husband's firearms company. I am haunted by the fear that no matter what I do, it will never be enough and that I must always move on, looking for home.

In the dark of a Sunday night, I wander the halls and rooms of my three-story home. I turn lights on and off as I enter and leave each room, performing perfunctory chores while on the phone with Jimmy in New York. Within this late-night conversation, I'm transported to our young adult years, not by the subject matter, but by other things: Jimmy's voice and those unspoken memories within almost every sentence. Although Jim and I have been friends since we were five, literally meeting in the sandbox, the unconscious choice in these late-night conversations is to feel the blood force of our late teens. During this time my strength, energy and possibilities were at their most unbridled.

Phone wedged between my shoulder and ear, I turn on the light in the master bath, and see a stranger illuminated in the now full-sized beveled mirror. I'm startled, to see how much I have changed. I am no longer a young man. Thinning hair, lost flesh, lost sight of youth, forgot to hold on at the right minute and lost my grip.

Another friend once wrote, "Having children is as close as we can come to immortality." We live on within them in the hateful or loving conversations they remember. The art we create also remembers our name.

THE VOICE OF MY HOUSE

I bought Minwax stains to treat and finish the wood trim around the outside of the house: Golden Oak, Olive Green and Dark Walnut. I waited, but Picasso never showed, so our gardener Enrique and I stained the fence without Pablo.

Enrique is methodical and soft-spoken. He walks gently. Five feet, two inches of stout and strong frame, Enrique can do things that a man twice his size can't. A full head of short jet black hair, an open, gentle face adorned with silken lines of sixty some-odd years, this is an honest man.

Enrique goes back to Guatemala each year to be with his wife and family. He sends all of his money to them. Years ago I was gruff with him, and, I imagine curt, when trying to tell him what I wanted.

Though we hardly speak, we show each other much respect now. In almost a whisper we talk, "Hi, Alan."

"Hi, Enrique, how are you?"

"Good."

Enrique hears what our garden wants and gives it to her. I never know when he'll show up; sometimes once a week, and then months can go by without seeing him.

At the forge, I hold wrought-iron with fire tongs till it's orange-hot, then pivot to the anvil. With striking blows from my rounding hammer, I turn and shape the steel into two large fire screen door frames. I sculpt sticks of steel into wood branches to make handles for the fire screen doors. After I mortar the fire screen into place I can almost hear the house say, "I'm finished, and now enjoy me."

Gillian looked at it and said, "It's beautiful Alan, you really out-did yourself, I love it!" Berrigan has taken on the family trait, "Well, Dad you could have made more steel branches."

"You really think so, Berrigan?" I answer, knowing all along that I could have.

"Dad, I'm just giving you my opinion."

"I think, unfortunately, you are right, Berrigan, but I am done."

The attempt to find meaning in this life is fraught with demons. It's been said, "What you love, you kill." George Plimpton turned it around. "What you love, kills you." At the time, Mr. Plimpton was referring to Mohammad Ali. It could be extended to Martin Luther King, Jr., Sitting Bull, J.F.K., Gandhi, and anyone trying to bring substance to this life. The question isn't, "Should I or shouldn't I love?" but "What do I choose to love?" Do I embrace a two-by-four, or a legacy of something more? I can, like many men, become totally obsessed with things, situations, art, horses, women, architecture and probably almost anything. The important question is, do my choices sever me from my humanity? The closest I will come to understanding water, stars and the earth is by self discovery.

At some point, I made a fire behind the new fire screen with wood from the half cord I'd bought from Ivan Holt. Ivan is an old friend whom I only see when I shoe an Arabian stallion named Robert that's boarded at his place. I have shod Robert for years. Ivan's small ranch is landscaped with old saddles, plows, water barrels, an old forge and a hundred other things that harken back to days that are alive only in old Westerns. He has a good place to shoe horses: a sufficient number of shade trees and a large, level, cement slab with a good strong hitching rail made of thick steel pipe, which extends the width of the slab. I back my truck up to the hitching rail, making sure to leave plenty of space between the rail and Robert in case he pulls back.

Ivan is a big man, about six-foot-three, large-boned, ruddy complexion with a big, auburn mustache and long, terrier eyebrows. His views are straightforward with a strong odor of political incorrectness. The topics of conversation reach sometimes no farther than the tires on my new truck, or at times to life and death. I enjoy disagreeing with him.

"Hey, Alan, how could they sell you this big heavy-duty truck and give you these small shit tires?" Ivan was a mechanic for many years, and it was kind of a blessing that while I was shoeing Robert, Ivan was under the hood and in the driver's seat and all around the whole truck. Normally, I don't like anybody touching my stuff, but this is different. Honest men who work with their hands relax the part of me that seems to be alienated from the rest of society.

"Well, Alan, this truck will last you a long time, but it is a shame you have to use it for work." With three nails in my mouth I didn't say anything. The rest of the nails I keep on an old leather band snapped to my wrist with a large magnet bolted to it. Ivan continues his exploration of my truck.

"Alan, they even gave you a transmission temperature gauge. I covered the one in my truck with tape; it drove me nuts while pulling a four-horse trailer and a big camper. With what you carry, I wouldn't worry though."

Ivan sat part way on the tailgate of my new truck as I finished shoeing Robert. "Hey, Alan as far as you and Gillian leaving L. A. and living somewhere in the country, all I know is that if you wait too long it gets harder to make the move. The next thing you know, you're too old to do anything!"

When my hands are immersed in the work of shoeing a horse, I can't lie about the things that are obvious. The fragility of the hoof and what God asks of these fibrous-horn encasements boggles my mind. Many times I've held up a quarter or more of the horse's weight while holding up the horse's leg to nail on a shoe and pad. A horse can need all four legs to abate, for example, the torturous pain of laminitis. At those times I become the horse's fourth leg and more. I know that without the shoe the horse won't be able to stand. If it can't stand, in a short time it could die.

A time will come that I won't be able to bear it anymore, not the physical part of shoeing but the burden of not being able to do more for horses in pain and to see them in tiny stalls.

When I was a young child I pretended I was a horse, I got all the other children in my class to play along. We ran free around the one-acre grass field chasing each other.

When older, at first I was shocked that horses were kept in small stalls, where they could not play. My life has become like those horses, sad and confined.

Now I fear I will wait too long, and old age will prevent me from moving to a place where I can run free.

22

CLAYMORE CHARM

As I write this, I am sitting in a café with Berrigan. He is now twenty-one, and I fifty-one. He reads, while I struggle with my spelling. The women come to him now and strike up conversations with him instead of me. I wonder, "What were the thoughts of my grandfather for me at this age?" My hope is that Berrigan's looks, mental prowess, and social graces lead him into the arms of a woman with love in her heart. I pray she'll be blessed with a strong gentleness, which some women have in abundance.

My grandfather lived into his late eighties. His cognitive abilities were never blurred by age but by the wear and tear of life. Wars, angry parents, bad governments and in general, unkind life, gave him a perception of living that might differ from mine. As I think about my life, maybe my grandfather's life was not any worse, just different. Toughness served Grandpa Will. At 85 years old, while he waited in his hospital bed for one of Odin's Valkyries, he grabbed me by my tee-shirt, pulled me to him and told me, "I am tough," not knowing at the time that I was also living out this Claymore legacy. Whether I like it or not, I am a throwback to the past: I love horses, dogs and sometimes show no caution in the face of death. Like me, Grandpa Will had no home at sixteen. He gave sage advice within stories about his life.

Grandpa recounted to me his proposal to my Grandmother, "I took her out on a date. We went out onto Lake Superior in a row-boat. When we were about a half-mile out I told her if she didn't marry me I would tip over the boat; she said 'Yes!'" My grandmother didn't know how to swim.

Grandpa Will was not a tall man but was extremely strong with very large arms and a huge chest. A big mustache covered his upper lip completely and about an eighth of his cheeks. By the time I was born, he sported a bald head without the need of a razor. Grandpa's left thumb was cut off at the second knuckle. He had the most beau-tiful smile for me but no one else that I know of. Will liked to gross people out by spitting his teeth out. I loved Grandpa and I still do. Is it OK to say, "I love you?" Yes. I like to talk to the dead and feel they answer back through my skin.

At sixteen, he embarked on manhood by sailing on the last sail-powered freighter's last trip to leave Aberdeen, Scotland. Trained as a cabinetmaker, Will was hired on. It was around 1900; the destina-tion was Nome, Alaska around Cape Horn and up the west coast of the Americas. There he looked for gold and then traveled down to San Francisco, where Grandpa rested his weary young bones. I don't know why, but he traveled to see his brother John in Minnesota where Will met my grandmother. He used to describe her to me. "She had the tiniest waist I had ever seen and the bluest eyes."

After that Claymore-type romantic courtship they had four kids, my father being the youngest. Before his birth, my grandmother's sis-ter, who was somewhat of a coquette, made it known to Will that his manliness was pleasing to her. There were no real words or passion shared between my grandparents for a long time afterwards, and my dad became the foil for Grandmother's displeasure. My grandfather would say, "She never let me spank your dad or have any real contact with him." Swatting one's child in some families is still seen as a form of caring, although my son has never felt that kind of affection from me. My Grandmother said on many occasions, "He was always such a good boy, he never did anything wrong. Your dad never needed a spanking." In contrast, from the age of five to eight, a night did not pass without the violent caress of leather or a hand on my behind.

23

ANCESTORS

Only now that I'm in my fifties do I acknowledge the experience of Carl Jung's synchronicity.

Events once ignored or shrugged off as coincidences seem to haunt me. An ever-maturing new reverence for friendship overwhelms me in these years of my late forties and early fifties. Is this the stage of life where I begin to reflect?

Having been confronted with my heritage through people, places and tragedy, I still discounted my roots. It did not conform to my image of who I should be. Maybe this denial of the truth has caused me to go in the wrong directions my entire life, if there is such a thing as a wrong direction.

I have finally learned to respect the signs that are never given in word or text, but through experience. Whether it was my mother's insistence when I was seven that I only own a dog from Scotland, or my physical appearance, the truth has always stood still long enough to let my mind discover what my soul already knew. My life is shared with the ethers of others who came before. As I get closer to death, the voices from the other side tell me I come from a place, and I do belong to a people. This path to my awakening has been crooked at best.

I take this time to chronologically acknowledge my synchronistic truth.

ONE

Duncan Macgregor, shaped his words with a thick Scottish brogue, wore his kilt and fought in the Scottish military in World War I. He was my maternal grandfather's best friend. I first felt Duncan's intense warmth through a glance, more than from a word, a half century ago before I knew how to speak.

TWO

My paternal grandfather, "Grandpa Will," drove down dirt roads in new Cadillacs at seventy miles an hour while singing old Scottish songs to me when I was five. One of his songs, "Rolling Home," was about sailing around the world and back home to Scotland. Maybe my grandfather learned the song on the steam freighter from Scotland to Nome, Alaska. I rediscovered this musical tune my grandpa sang while listening to a current Scottish band called Old Blind Dogs. I picked up the CD because of its name. Anything with a title having to do with dogs attracts me.

Grandpa Will had talked of two breeds of dogs, the ones from his youth and a dog he owned as an adult named Curry, the namesake for my Little Curry.

Curry Senior was huge, over a hundred pounds of dog. Grandpa called it an "English Coach Dog," now called a Dalmatian. He was a dog with an attitude. Will was the only one who could get near him when he ate. At this time, in the 1920s and 30s, the family lived in Texas. Will followed the oil strikes and thought nothing of, on a whim, packing up my grandmother and their four kids to move to Tyler, Texas, from Hobbs, New Mexico. At one point, he decided to move the family to Pomona, California, in their Model T. There was no room for Curry, so he was sold to a farmer. As they packed for California, Curry ran the ten miles back home. Will brought him back to the farmer, and this time Curry was chained. He broke the chain twice, each time running home. On the third go around,

Grandpa said, "If Curry breaks this new, bigger chain, we'll take him with us." Unable to break that chain, the family left Texas dog-less with only grandpa's fists and pearl handled Colt .45s to protect them.

The dogs of my grandfather's youth were of a standard that were bred as a family tradition in Austria. I never gave it any thought at the time when Grandpa and I talked "dogs" that this family breed of dog was named MacNab, and that it didn't sound Austrian. I was told my family is from Austria. But who thinks about where your family comes from when you're young, and you are just trying to fit in where you live? My ancestors' stories are not happy ones; why else do people change their names and stories? Forty some odd years later, I visited Scotland only under duress at Gillian's insistence.

THREE

I've always felt safe and warm in plaid and wool. After the bus ac-cident when I was eighteen, I searched for solace and understanding. First I sought healing in a Protestant church, then a Catholic church and last, in a Jewish synagogue. I realized then that employing reli-gious establishments for dealing with grief would always be in vain. These establishments and their inhabitants were cold, suspicious of my intentions in wanting to talk to the clergy. With no spiritual help, one night I started to thumb my way out of California with my dog Curry. My first ride was with a black man, who was friendly and conciliatory in the way he phrased his sentences. Wisely knowing warmth of the spirit can spill over one's lips within the realm of a weather-related conversation and the world, or, at least I, was better for it. I felt blessed by his words.

That night I slept on Sea Marigold at the cliff's edge, overlooking the Pacific Ocean's pounding surf, thirty miles north of Sausalito in a place called Inverness. I felt safe and at home, not knowing this first place I had chosen to sleep was named after a city in Scotland.

The noise of the waves could not drown my sadness. Waking up the next morning with nothing on my mind but death, I watched the coastal morning fog reflect the sun's light onto the green plant life that held Curry and my grieving soul all night long. Rolling up my sleeping bag, I took out one of Curry's packaged dog foods and a peanut butter and honey sandwich for myself. I ate with a stomach full of sorrow before heading north.

Numbly sickened by life, I stood up. We walked to the road. Looking at the broken, gray asphalt, Curry and I walked north. When late afternoon arrived, I put my thumb out for a ride. Before dusk, I got a ride in an International Travelall, just like the one that I spent my youth in as a passenger with Laird Macgregor. This time, it was with three merchant mariners all older than me, from Scotland. The three of them instantly started up a conversation with me.

I thought I was stumbling through my words okay. An hour later, at the top of Coleman Valley Road, we all got out to take in the ocean view, looking ten miles down the rocky, green sloping mountain we had just snaked our way up. One of the men, the oldest one in his fifties, was once probably lean. He now looked like a thick anchor. He took his eyes off the scenery, turned to me and asked me in a deep Scottish brogue, "What's troubling ya, mon?" My young eyes got weak and filled with tears.

"Let it out, mon."

I told my story. They listened. My tale fractured their half smiles. Bent over, groaning sobs came out of me. "It's all right, mon."

The three men stood halfway around me, hands on my back, all of us facing northwest, as I bled tears. Then I was quiet. The four of us and Curry stared off down the ten miles to the ocean. The older man took his eyes off the sea, looked me straight in the eye, "You're welcome to join us on our travels."

"I think I'm going to stay here."

"Are you sure you want to do that?"

"Yes, but thank you."

I shook their hands, and the older man gave me a hug. Before they drove off, one of the men called back to me; "Take care of yourself, mann."

The view was framed by winds, native grasses and a fast-moving, cloud-covered sunset. It was all that was left of the day. The world was my room.

With Curry's head on the sleeping bag at my feet, I fell into a deep sleep in the mist and loud night wind.

In the company of these men I found the peace of belonging. It brewed within me, a mixture of tragedy and kindness. The Scotsmen showed me the beauty of each moment with their compassion. Somehow then, I understood that death is part of life, and life is part of death. And to this day, when looking into another's eyes, I see it as a flash of a miracle and try not to leave loving things unsaid.

The next day Curry and I walked back down Coleman Valley Road and hitch-hiked up the coast. Eventually, we ended up in Alaska.

FOUR

Writing this all down in my fifties some thirty years later, the lure of bed tries to find me, so I find late night places to write. The Cat and Fiddle pub in L.A. seemed to be good for one night's worth of writing. The name of this bar got me thinking: it makes no sense that I have had such bad luck with cats, except for one named Agamemnon. They all met their fate by way of coyotes or something equally horrendous. As for thoughts on the fiddle, quite a few years ago I got the idea to take up the violin. A distant relative of mine is a famous violinist; therefore, why couldn't I play? With a gentle genetic push, I drove to a professional musician's music shop in Studio City over the hill from L.A., the name of which escapes me. The proprietor was known to be the quintessential fitter for famous and soon-to-be famous musicians.

The story goes that with uncanny preciseness he can fit anyone with the right musical instrument. I have heard that lips wrapped around a horn or fingers laid across strings of this shopkeeper's choice is what a first kiss or hands touching desirous flesh feels like.

I walked through the quaint old doorway of the music store. I couldn't wait to get my hands on a violin. Within the low ceiling of this cottage-style store, I looked at the walls. They were covered with new musical instruments. Violins, oboes, tubas, guitars, cellos were all so raw, beautifully real. Inside this silent womb of notes, I knew the violin would bring sweet joy to me in the mountains inside a cabin somewhere. In between sculpting, writing and sex, I would make warm, soulful music from the wood and strings.

Introducing myself to the owner of the shop, I told him who my famous distant relative was. "I think there might be a drop of his creative violin blood in me. Maybe you can pick out the right vessel for my musical destiny."

His old hands held one of mine and gazed at me through clear eyes. His ease of evaluating was piercing.

"I hope you are not insulted, but the violin is not for you."

"Then what is?" I asked, thinking cello or viola.

From under the counter, he brought up a poorly-bred cloth animal, one half elephant and the other half octopus, dressed in plaid. He looked at me and said,

"The bagpipes are for you. This is who you are. I hope you're not insulted."

"Of course not, thank you for your time." I had lied; I was insulted. I walked out empty-handed. Knowing what I know now about Scotland, even if I never learned to play the bagpipes, I should have bought them and at least hung them on my wall.

FIVE

I had shod Colleen and Adam's horses for many years. When they brought Duffy the Clydesdale home as a young colt he was more than a handful. Colleen described her perception of my first encounter with Duffy, "Alan, the minute he saw you, he started to tremble, then stood still, and literally did not move a muscle the whole time you were working on him."

When Colleen shared this with me, I instantly felt that I had done something wrong. Was Colleen inferring that Duffy could sense something demonic in me? To me, nothing unusual had occurred that first time I came to trim his feet, but Adam and the vet who was there also were astonished by Duffy's transformation.

I don't have this effect on horses in general. The first words from Colleen this day with all seriousness were, "Duffy must have known you in a past life." In all the years I've known Colleen, never has she said anything that could be the least bit construed as exaggerated or mystical. She was one of the sanest people I've ever met. I still blew it off as no big deal and was just glad that they weren't implying there was something wrong with me.

I don't know if I'm reaching here, but Clydesdales are from Scotland. Is there a connection here also? How could Duffy and the musical store owner feel so strongly about me, although now I do sense the ancient vapors of Alba (the old name for Scotland) around me? It is hard at times to see this welcome to Scotland in the form it comes. Have I been living the life intended for me?

SIX

Ten years ago, I ventured into the realm of psychotherapy for the first time. The therapist was an army ranger with a PhD. He taught Shakespeare from a psychological perspective to graduate students. There are many things he said to me, and most were right. Whenever he would refer to roots which I didn't know I had, he would talk of Scotland. Such as, "Mr. Claymore, do you know what is meant by the old Scottish saying, 'Don't give a sword to a man that can't dance?'"

"To really know when to fight and when not to, a man must know joy first," was my reply. When I told the therapist months later that I was taking a trip for the first time to the U. K., he seemed overjoyed and only focused on my going to Scotland. Did he see what everyone else, including Gillian, saw, but I couldn't?

SEVEN

"Gillian, I don't like England; it's too well-used. Let's go to the Globe, see a play then leave this crowded country. I want to go home and hike in the Sierras."

"Alan, trust me, you need to see Scotland. If you don't like it, we'll go home to the Sierras." In Scotland, I found myself in a place of deep emotional and physical understanding. Feeling my blood in the ground and in the sky, I saw myself in everything dark and cold. I keep this part of me hidden from the rest of the world. Desolate, hued in black is Scotland; unlike me, there is no pretense of something else there. I don't care to find out what my family did after the break-up of the clans in 1745.

Now, years after grandpa's death, his talk of dogs, horses, guns, single malt and song make sense.

The way I understand it, a true MacNab Shepherd is an amalgamation of Airedale, smooth-coat Blue Merle Collie, a pinch of Deerhound, and Smithfield Collie.

As a child, hiking in Griffith Park with my little Curry from the Shetland Isles, on certain days there was a man playing the bagpipes. Curry and I would just listen with ears far beyond our youth. I will always well up with tears when the bagpiper blows, but will no longer discount the tears.

On the plane with Gillian from England to Scotland, I got nods from old-looking rustic types in tweed. I always feel uplifted when skies are dark and rainy with the sound of wind; Scotland was the antidote for crowded England. While walking the streets of old, beautiful Edinburgh, Gillian and I came across a group of very old stone sarcophagi with human figures sculpted in them. I turned to Gillian as twenty or so Japanese tourists were taking pictures of these coffins, moving out of the way to allow them an unobstructed shot. They quickly motioned me back into the frame. Perplexed by their bowing and thank you's, in my embarrassment I turned to Gillian as she motioned to me to look at the faces of these sculpted figures.

"What? I don't see anything."

"Alan, look at the faces of the sculptures."

"Yeah, what about them?"

"You don't see it?"

"What?"

"You look just like the sculptures."

I did a double take. Gillian and the Japanese tourists were right. Staring back at me in stone was me. Barely able to stop from yelling the word "Whoa," it whispered past my lips. I did look just like an ancient dead Scotsman – wizened, sharp features, a wiry Pict. But I was alive with the coloring of a calico cat. To the other tourists I was the breathing part of the stone coffins.

In Edinburgh Castle, following the sparse crowd through the exhibits, a young girl pointed at me and laughed as I stood once again in front of my likeness. This time it was in the form of an ancient Scottish fighter. Even in Los Angeles at a Scottish restaurant called the Tam o' Shanter, a better groomed, younger version of me hangs on the wall, among other two hundred year old, Scottish pictures.

EIGHT

A day later, Gillian and I rented a turbo-diesel VW before going to the Isle of Skye. It was fast, and we drove north. Gillian offered to drive at one point, but she wasn't able to drive out of the rural church parking lot we'd pulled into.

"Alan, the gear shift is on the wrong side. I can't do it. I am so, sorry, you'll have to drive. "I got back in the driver's seat, and we drove to the Isle of Skye where we stopped in the town of Broadford.

"I need a little time to myself," Gillian said. She didn't tell me how much time, nor did I ask. I looked for the art community in this small town.

Walking down the east side of the narrow street which ran through the town, I saw a very old, single-story art store next to the little bank. A woman in a shirtwaist dress was working the money machine. I noticed the backside of her beautiful calves. I walked past, making sure that I didn't stare for legs are my weakness. Focusing on my objective of the art store, I found the door to the old, white-washed building was locked. While viewing notes, flyers and an array of cultural advertisements on the outside of the door, I felt a tap on my right shoulder. Turning around, I stopped breathing, seeing the front of this woman I had turned my eyes away from before. Her beauty caught me up short. I was lost in her face, brownish-blond hair, beautiful eyes and slender athletic body. The pause became electrified with her looking at me more intensely than I felt I was looking at her. She cut the silence with her words after a minute. "You are looking for the art community, and you're a sculptor."

"Ah, yes to both, but I think you have the wrong person." Her smile got bigger.

"I am going to take you there."

"Great." We walked and talked. I normally don't feel comfortable with my heart in my throat, but she seemed so familiar to me.

"I feel I know you."

Her reply was, "I know." With that, she grabbed my hand and squeezed, too hard to be gentle and not hard enough for me to think her crazy.

As we got to her car to drive the short distance to the art community, I noticed a box of books in the back seat. She told me she was a school teacher. I had mentioned to her I taught horseback riding and animal care. She said she also worked with and loved horses. I told her when it rained, I read stories to the kids in the tack room. In this box in the back seat of her car were the same books I carried in my truck to read to the children, held in the same kind of cardboard box.

There are things that form haunting feelings of familiarity. If revisited in thought, they cause disorientation and an experience of a state of limbo. I refuse to remember or think about that box of books in her back seat for fear this might slip me over the edge to move to Scotland. Those childhood books hold my youngest and truest dreams.

Belonging has never been my strong suit. I know that living in L.A. is a place of not belonging, but the promises I've made in Los Angeles have created more a place of belonging than Scotland might be. I do wonder if everything in my life is a mistake. Could it be that the stork made a time and place error?

As I got into her car, I saw Gillian running full bore towards us. I never saw her run that fast. She got in the back seat.

"Oh, this is my wife, Gillian."

"It's nice to meet you."

As we drove, even with Gillian in the car, the conversation didn't change; it was dark with warm familiarity. These were like the quiet words shared after love has been explored.

Arriving at the art section of this small town, I looked straight into her eyes and said, "Thank you." Normally, I don't look people directly in the eyes.

She again grabbed my hand, looked straight at me without hesitation and said, "We will see each other again."

After we got out, Gillian's comment to me was, "She has beautiful calves, and she looks like the actress Julie Christie, but prettier." Nothing else was said.

The warmth I felt that day has not been broken by the four years that have passed since we met. The words that were said have faded, but I do dream of her at night when I sleep alone. I have searched my soul for what to do with this encounter that laid me open. Wrapped within her beauty was something deeper. Yes, she was as beautiful a woman as I will ever see, but that was only an introduction to a relationship, or an opportunity to a different way of life, a life that could have been, maybe no better than what I have now. It might be a foretelling of the future. She and others in an unconscious way might be securing their destiny while showing me mine. Could it be that the fabric of this unconscious rendezvous is to be looked at through the looking-glass of art? A fellow horseshoer and writer, Arthur Gilchrest said to me, "Take this energy and put it into your art," and for now this is what I do. I found out later that Arthur's mother happens to be from Glasgow, Scotland.

Gillian and I found the art community down a small gravel drive that emptied into a small boat launch to the open Scottish sea. The art community population turned out to be one painter and a weaver. We visited both. Gillian bought a brown sweater that was thicker than a Komondor dog's corded coat. The wool was shepherded, sheared and woven by the same pair of hands that sold it to Gillian.

I sat with the painter in his studio. He had a quiet demeanor. His dark hair and stocky build seem to fit as an added piece of art in his studio gallery. Watercolors on his brush stroked the canvas to form a wren. I'd have bought it if I had the money.

He was willing to rent me space in his little studio to sculpt. It seemed as if he was expecting me. I purchased one of his boat scene postcards and said goodbye. I walked across the dirt path to meet Gillian, where she was paying for what looked like wool armament in the name of a sweater. The thought of how it would be to live and work here entered my mind.

We didn't see too much more of the Isle of Skye that day. We had planned a hike, but where we decided to walk was far off the beaten path and infested with sheep. At a car rental place near Fort Williams I overheard an unsettling conversation between the owner of the establishment and an Englishman returning a car. Charges were being racked up for little scratches that in the States would not have been noticed, or at least would be considered normal wear and tear. I told the rental man that I overheard his conversation with the guy returning the other car. He confirmed it, "Yes, you get a ding in it or a scratch, you pay for it."

I have sheared sheep, trimmed their feet and castrated a ram or two. During these times, I watched sheep rub up against things such as my truck with their thistle-laden coats. That day they all looked like dirty-white steel wool on four legs.

We were running out of light, and we didn't have a map of any other areas. Gillian asked me, "Alan, do you really think they'll damage the car?"

"I'm sure the sheep don't have insurance; if you want to ask one, that's fine, but what I've heard is that they all lie."

Later when we returned the car I told the man who rented it to us how we felt restricted, having to protect the car from sheep. He apologized and said, "If you want at anytime to rent again I'll rent you my old Land Rover for cheap, and you won't have to worry. But I wouldn't have given you the hard time I gave to the other man when he returned his rental." The man's face was kind, and I believed him.

NINE

The second visit I made to Scotland was with my son Berrigan the next summer. I needed to go back. He wanted to join me. Berrigan had read that the mountain-biking was some of the best in Europe, and he just wanted to be with me. We brought our bikes and cycled over some of the highlands.

It hailed and snowed on us while we biked over Pitlochry's soft low mountains; I was in heaven. It seemed all my wishes came true in Scotland as we finished our descent from the mountains, which hover over the small town of Pitlochry. I felt calm in the cold air, seeing the curve of the earth so far away. Too much of the time I spend thinking about what I should have done, or what I should not have done. On this day, nothing got in the way of living for the moment. On the mountain above Pichlocary, I filled my lungs with happiness, for my soul was at peace.

Once again on level ground, the wooded path followed a small river back to town.

"Berrigan, what would make this a perfect ride would be to see a Scottish deerhound." About ten minutes later as we biked towards town, a bounding deerhound ran past us. The movement of a Scottish deerhound is a sight that I'll never forget. Its torso is long and flowing like a wave before yielding to surf. They move like greyhounds that are rich; wealthier in size and strength, they can afford to make visual music when they run.

We ended up talking to the owner and stealing a few pets from this shy hound. He then jumped the twelve-foot ravine where we stood on the edge. Now on the other side he gave a bark and a sideway gesture of, "Let's play, but stay on your side."

Farther down the path there was a little building, smaller than a croft, selling pastry and coffee; we got both. I pulled off my riding gloves and noticed my ring finger was bloodless white the other fingers were not even cold. The restroom had running warm water and was able to bring my digit back to life. On top of the mountain where we had been it had been hailing, but I bike and shoe horses in colder weather than this and ski on days that are below zero.

The truth is that somehow my hand laid across the handle bars in such a way as to stop my circulation.

But was there a deeper truth? My relationship with Gillian had no blood running through it. Beauty and love for life surrounded me in the Highlands. I needed to let Gillian go or steal her away from her flabby, abusive work life which she blames for everything. With us, it's always been a fight between her job's golden handcuffs and romantic love.

At every turn, Scotland asked me to look at my life. Are all these experiences a coincidence?

Einstein believed that there was no such thing as probability. The throwing of dice, if one was able to calibrate the relationship of the spin of the earth, and the gambler's toss to its nth degree you would find the formula for snake eyes, or any other combination of thrown dice. No longer could anyone be called a gambler.

Is life a bet placed on a green felt table of destiny? And just like all betting palaces the fix is in, even if it looks like there is chance involved.

Was the pull to Scotland a calculated toss toward introspection prompted by forces in my life or the will of god? The choice seemed to be mine, to let things ride or pick up my chips and move to Scotland. The world's axis swung my heartbeat to Scotland but not to stay there. Was I afraid of losing more than I gained?

After Berrigan and I biked the last few miles to our B&B, we showered and rested. That night we walked up the mile and a half to the lodge and brewery that we had passed on our bikes when going up to the top of the mountains. The heart of this three hundred year old lodge was its pub. Its essence and the fact that people ate inside with their dogs brought back memories of being in a bar with my grandpa in Chatsworth, California, when I was about six. It was my first introduction to a MacNab shepherd.

"Alan, go sit down on the floor by the dog and pet him," grandpa said.

I sat down at the foot of the bar next to this large, wire-haired dog, petting him while my grandpa had a drink and talked. Then Grandpa turned to me and said, "Alan, watch the dog's face."

As my grandfather walked towards me and the dog, the dog started to show his teeth and growl at him. Then my grandfather yelled at the dog as he turned sideways to us, his right hand now in a position to give a back-handed hit to the dog. This dog, bigger than me, backed up almost onto my lap and growled even louder. I could feel the vibration of the dog's warning and a deeper fragrance of horse sweat and dirt in his fur. Then Grandpa smiled one of his loving smiles that he had only for me, the only smiles I knew from a family member when I was young, and said, "Now, Alan, that is what a good dog is supposed to do."

This Scottish pub brought me back to the age of six, but there were no MacNab shepherds here, not even a Scottie. Only a yellow Lab and a few small, mixed terrier and shepherd types lined the bar's floor and seating area. Whatever history I've learned has come my way through the study of dogs, whether it was the Roman's conquests with their large mastiffs, or how the Turks have lived for thousands of years tending sheep in the Anatolian mountains with their Anatolian shepherd dogs. The truth is that when an ancient people disappear or mix with those from foreign lands, the original dogs become rare or disappear. Occasionally, breeds will be born again, find their way to that ancestral origin, but it is only for a visit and as nothing more than a pet. In a way, they never go home. The Scottish deerhound became scarce after the break up of the clans, and now he'll never know the chase and the cracking of a deer's tibia in his jaws on a cold, foggy morning.

The food was good at the pub on this hill, and the beer took me up short. I was a third of the way through it when Berrigan, bless his heart, slid the brew to a contemplative distance from my hand and said, "Dad, you're getting drunk."

"I am? You're right, how could I get drunk off not even a half a schooner? Berrigan, I'll be right back, I'm going to take a leak." At the porcelain trough, the guy next to me said in a Scottish accent, "It's a good night and good food; no one could ask for anymore." I replied, "I can't argue with that, but one glass of your beer has gotten me drunk. Just between you and me, I am ashamed to say, I didn't even drink half of it."

"Your secret is safe with me, but that is no shame. You know, our beer has twice the alcohol content of our whisky, so don't feel too bad."

Berrigan and I, with bellies full and I a little drunk, walked back to our place down in the village in the chill, wet night's air.

TEN

At the end of the trip, in Inverness, waiting a couple days for the plane home, I took lessons from Berrigan on how to just hang out. But on the day before we were leaving, I told him I needed to go back to the Isle of Skye. "Berrigan, stay in Inverness for the day, or come with me; do what you want."

"I'll go, Dad."

The train travels over beautiful country, along the green coast, jagged rocks and ancient worn mountains that look like the teeth of an old bear.

Midway through the train trip to Skye, an older, casually-dressed but stately-looking married couple sat down in the seats facing Berrigan and me. The man was a retired structural engineer from England. I don't recall what the woman did, other than the fact she was from Scotland, as were her ancestors. After a few minutes of light conversation between the four of us, she turned and pointed her index finger at me while she looked straight into my eyes. "I have something to say to you," she said. Her boldness had warmth for me, but didn't take away from the passion for what she had to say. Berrigan sat deeper in his seat, adopting the posture of one on the uphill part of a roller-coaster ride, and her husband's eyes got wide. He sat at attention as she started to speak. "I want to tell you a saying and I don't want you to forget it."

Here's to us,
Wha's like us'
Yuy few'
Ar'they're all deed!

{English version,}
Here's to us
Those like us
Are few
And they're all dead!

"Don't forget it, for that is who you are." Then she proceeded to write it down for me. A tear escaped from the corner of my eye. She turned to her husband and said, "I told you he would understand."

It touched me in an area of my psyche that I did not know was empty and wanting.

I am lost to another time. Old impulses beckon me to a life in the cold and rain. Fighting but never dancing, these emotions sit in me and wait.

I write this thinking that I should have been dead long ago, long before I was born. I feel that I have been left behind. I do have a legacy that has never been spoken of. It lives in the cold, dark, wet Scottish days of the ancient past. It lives in three hundred year old sculptures on the tombs of the dead. To see my reflection in the mirror is to look at a phantom. I have always felt that I wandered into the future and left my kind hundreds of years ago. I'm lost in this life which never seems to fit.

ELEVEN

On the bay in the small town of Kyle of Lochalsh, the tracks end. We asked the conductor if the timetable was right; if we didn't make the last train back to Inverness we would miss our early morning flight to London, then the connecting flight to L.A. We got off the train, walked out into the open, wet sky of Lochalsh, went up the hill and caught the crowded municipal bus for the eight miles to Broadford.

When we got to Skye I froze. The reality of a fork in my life's road was in front of me: to reconnect or not? Something older and more passionate than me is contained here and waits for me. Berrigan, knowing something was not right, asked me, "Dad, I thought you were going to visit somebody here."

"Berrigan, do you want some pie?" With those simple words, the town appeared to change, to be almost abandoned, and the spectrum of colors that showered this Isle faded into black and white. Sounds of the seagulls and the wind were taken away from my senses. I was no longer anywhere, only tied remotely to my own son's voice.

Beat-up and torn apart, I am very old in my blood; it's something that this life only hints of. Easy to anger, easy to cry, easy to kill, easy to be stricken with great remorse, easy to risk everything on actions not thought out, to belong to things that have no members. That is my nature.

After the pie, I called a cab. The owner of the cab was a warm-hearted, older attractive woman. She allayed my son's questions, of "What's wrong Dad?" while seeing something was paining me. "It's all right, laddie. Be patient with your father. He loves you." We rode the seven and a half miles to the bridge. Then this gentle soul of a woman said, "It costs another eight pounds to take the cab over the bridge, happy to do it, or if you want you can walk over the bridge. It's always a nice walk." So we paid and got out, then raced the half-mile across in the 45-degree rain. Berrigan at eighteen is built for speed and I for endurance.

Back at the Bay of Kyle of Lochalsh, I sat in the rain with my legs hanging over the edge of the dock, waiting for the train that meets the sea to take us from Skye back to Inverness. Feeling empty, between two worlds, I try to understand these emotions. I stared at a beautiful old fishing boat moored almost within reach and thought of choices that I needed to make. I prayed for wisdom. I gazed at the carefully painted wooden vessel's name written on the side of her bow: Gillian. There and then, I recommitted to my wife.

Do I turn around and look back and wonder? Am I more than just a man? Promises to the heart mean more to me now. The ones made to others and to myself I must keep. Maybe someday I will live on the Isle of Skye or maybe not.

Gillian travels frequently for work, and on those nights I sleep alone I dream about this woman from the Isle of Skye. It is always the same, I awake in the morning with this muse in the shape of her straw gold hair, lean warm body and beautiful face. Not many words are said between us. We smile, knowing this is the right way to spend our lives or deaths. It truly seems to be another me living there, but from what I can tell my flesh is in America. Sometimes I do awake from these dreams and think I'm still in Scotland. For a brief moment, after I realize I'm not, I don't know where I am. In fleeting moments I wish I would die and be buried on a desolate cliff overlooking the ocean in Scotland.

TWELVE

Berrigan and I boarded the day's last train headed back to Inverness. About halfway into the three-hour ride, a man in his thirties, tall, angular, with a hooded rain parka covering his face, rolled a bike onto the train. Soaking wet, he looked around. I made a comment when he faced my direction, "Looks like you just took a shower." He grinned and said, "I think I'll sit here." With that he sat down next to me, shedding his soaking wet jacket and getting me a little wet.

"My name is Alan."

"Glad to meet you. I'm Michael. You don't look like you're from the States but you sound like it."

"I'm from California, third generation. The fourth generation is sleeping over there." I pointed to Berrigan's semi-slumbering, solid, 185 pounds of muscle and his thick mass of curly blond hair. Berrigan stirred, half sat up, attempted a wave and then went down for the count.

"That's your son?"

"Yes."

"What brings you to Scotland; it's more than just a vacation, isn't it?"

"Yes, how did you figure that?

"There is something else about you, something familiar, maybe a little bit of the look of my grandfather. So if it's not a vacation, then what brings ya here?"

"It is kind of a strange thing; I never wanted to come to Scotland and almost didn't. A year ago, my wife wanted to come to the British Isles, more for me than for herself."

"Why is that?"

"She had traveled all over Europe, and when we met I instantly reminded her of Scotland. I asked her what it was about Scotland, and why it was so important for me to come here. Her answer was, "The nature of you and Scotland are one and the same: somber, wild and gentle but not tame, you're happiest in the rain. The gray complexion of Scotland's sky keeps you at peace not bright lights or city life. They sadden and confuse you."

"I said OK to the trip, with my usual provisos: number one, we see a Shakespeare play, but instead of some non-equity theater called the Globe, it would be at The Globe in London. The second thing on my list was to take a long hike and camp at least one night."

I began to tell Michael some of what had happened on that first trip to Scotland with Gillian.

"Yes, this trip is not just a bike ride through the highlands with my best friend, my son, but a journey towards a voice, a calling, a search into the earth of my being. What is in the land here resonates to something in me – a quiet warmth of the earth, and sky. I've come home, but like going to a loving childhood home, you can maybe only visit and nothing more. I just don't know. Michael, what do you do for a living?"

"I'm a nurse and an organic farmer."

"What kind of nursing?"

"I do hospice work, and on my off days I tend my garden, out here on a plot of land. The vegetables that aren't shared with my friends get taken to market. I live in Inverness with my girlfriend. Where are you and your son headed? "

"We're also going back to Inverness, and then tomorrow we fly to L.A. from Gatwick. The type of nursing you do, I imagine it's pretty intense. Dealing with the dying, do you ever get the feeling that you see a side of these people that their families don't and are then able to help with the family's grieving?"

"I don't know if there is another side to see, but I feel I've gotten a deeper understanding of life, and how important every moment is. For instance, this moment with you in this conversation I appreciate far more than I would have if I weren't doing this work. I don't really get involved with the families and friends. I try to leave their privacy intact for whatever time they have left. The process of death is invasive enough. The understanding for me comes from taking on the things that free up the families and patients to just share the

silence and stillness with each other and to see what comes forward
from that.

"Alan, what else has brought you back to Scotland?"

"Well, it's beautiful here, and I like the rain." A little laugh gave
away the fact that I was here not just for the weather.

"What else, Alan?"

Berrigan was fast asleep a few rows in front of us across the aisle
on this well-kept, fairly empty old train. Rolling through the early
evening rain, with the train's interior lights flickering, I shared my
plight with Michael.

"How do I find peace with the promises and life that I've created in the United States? There is this love at first sight for the land,
the people. There's a familiarity and comfort which breathes here
in Scotland for me. For the first time I feel that I belong. I went to
Skye to see if the woman would reappear and tell me more. But I
didn't take the little steps needed to make contact with her. I did
not seek out the liaison between the two of us. I've left the ghost
of my soul here on the Isle of Skye." I told Michael about the boat
with Gillian's name on it and about making my vow to go back to
the States. "Scotland is left unanswered for me. The real crunch for
me is that I have fallen in love at first sight with somebody I have
spent less than an hour with and a land that only harbors my dead
relatives." Michael looked at me. We said nothing, as Berrigan slept
out of hearing range.

"Alan, what are you and your son doing for dinner?"

"We have no plans."

"Why don't you come to our house?"

"Won't your girlfriend mind two more people at the last minute
coming to dinner?"

"No."

Stepping off the train, we followed Michael through the old
town of Inverness. Many steep, stone steps brought us up to a quaint

residential street. Small two-story homes lined the street and touched each other. Stately in appearance, with roofs of dark hand-broken slate and walls of hand-cut stone, they would remain unmoved in rough weather.

As we walked, it drizzled. Berrigan confided in me later that he was concerned who this person was we were following through the dark, hilly streets of Inverness.

Berrigan and I have appetites that a cook for sumo wrestlers would be accustomed to. My second horseshoeing partner was named Ted. He was a full 6'10' and broad. Ted's wife was also tall, at least a good head taller than me. Ted, knowing that I was single, would invite me to his house for dinner. His wife served up ample portions from their organic garden and delicious egg dishes from their chickens. She would place a serving platter of food in front of me that was equal to what was on both their plates. Sometimes, I would get a little embarrassed by their blatant gesture of hospitality.

"It's OK, Alan; we like watching you eat," Ted said.

Berrigan, Michael and I rounded the corner and walked another block up to the front of Michael's house. Inside we were introduced to Kate. She was slender with an open face and gentle disposition. We all walked into the small kitchen area that became large with the four of us inhabiting it. Berrigan and I sat down at the kitchen counter on stools and watched Michael and Kate cook. We talked, ate and never got full of conversation or the steamed, brilliantly colored, exotic and tame vegetables that were touched with cheese instead of dew. I felt once again that I was at Ted's house. Michael and Kate cooked everything in their kitchen; unlike dinner at Ted's I did not let on how big my appetite was, and neither did Berrigan.

The conversation did include Berrigan this time and was less personal than Michael's and mine on the train. Philosophy, politics and psychology seemed to be the dominant themes; the dialogue took us into the night. At around ten p.m., Berrigan remembered we had an early flight home and suggested we make our way to the hotel.

"We'll walk you home," Michael volunteered.

The dark, wet streets and sky reminded me I was still in Scotland, but it felt more like home with every minute that passed. A maze of streets leading to many steep stairs took us down to more streets that finally led to the River Ness and over Ness Bridge across to the river's other bank and our lodging. Is the reason I'm going back to Los Angeles the same reason a bird flies back into its cage? Does Carl Jung's synchronicity exist, or is my nature just quixotic?

The hotel was an old building, about six or seven stories, made out of stone with a slate roof. The lobby's decor was formal from bygone days. I imagine today's guests no longer are dignitaries, but the hospitality was ever present within the stately, tall, white walls. The large bar was tastefully elegant, with comfortable seating. It was too good to pass up, so we sat in the lobby, drank good coffee and continued to talk. The conversation sailed off into psychology once again. Michael talked about his hospice work and I about my work at Mountain Glen Home for Children.

I started thinking of conversations with my friend Cheryl, who was also a nurse and who worked with older patients in a hands-on as well as a supervisory position. Cheryl and I share an appreciation for the psychologist Carl Rogers and his work. Clear within all of his writing is that the answers to our individual dilemmas exist inside of us. In Rogerian terms, therapy is the art of creating a safe, introspective place for a person to discover himself. I was about to ask Michael if he had ever read any of Rogers' writing, in particular, "On Becoming A Person," when at that moment he said, "Alan, I think you would enjoy a book called 'On Becoming a Person,' written by psychologist Carl Rogers. His writings have played an important role in my thinking."

Nothing was clearly answered for me that night. Perhaps I was not, and am still not, ready to see the message of what to do next in my life. But it is clear, and I agree with Rogers, the answer lies within the individual.

"Dad, we have an early morning flight. Thanks for dinner. It was nice meeting you and Katie. It's two in the morning; I'm going to bed."

Michael stood up from the lobby chair and shook Berrigan's hand.

"Berrigan, it was great meeting you. Be sure and bring your father back, and cut the old man some slack; he's a good one." They smiled at each other, knowing that sons never give any slack while their fathers are still able to walk.

"I'll be up in a minute, Berrigan."

It couldn't have been this late, but it was. After Berrigan left the lobby, Michael, with adroit sensitivity, brought the question up that was left unanswered on the train. "What are you going to do? Are you going to move to Scotland or go back to the States?" Still without my answer, we exchanged numbers and hugged. There was energy in his hug and warmth, the way he might hug the dying or the grieving. Maybe I am the dead, and I do grieve for things unknown to me. I climbed the stairs to my room, pulled the sheets over my tired body and fell fast asleep.

An hour later, I awoke to the sound of water rushing into the room. Maybe someone in the room above us left the tub running? Our room was dry, though. I looked out the half closed window and saw curtains of rain, and thunder, illuminating and graying the night's sky. "Dad, what's going on?"

"It's just the rain."

The phone rang; it was four a.m. The man at the front desk suggested we leave at five instead of six to catch our seven o'clock flight to London. Waking Berrigan up is always a pain in the ass.

The rain was still coming down hard at 5 a.m. when we loaded into the Škoda taxi.

"You lads might not be able to make it to the airport. Some of the bridges are washed out, but I'll do my best." With that the driver did: the little four-door Škoda was driven on sidewalks, bicycle paths, and forded deep intersections. Back-tracking when we would hit a washout, we kept driving in the predawn rain.

Traveling on an overpass for sixty yards and around a bend, we found the overpass now was going under the road it was supposed to be going over. We were passed by another motorist hell-bent on denial as we backed our way off this defunct overpass. With many of the routes we tried that morning we would have to turn around, but the taxi driver always found another way to go. Finally, the airport was in sight a mile away, with a long, flooded road separating us from it. "Maybe you lads should ride your bikes from here?"

"Our bikes are dismantled and wrapped in plastic for the trip back to the States. By the time we put them together we'll miss the plane."

Readjusting his cap, he drove the cab into the two and a half feet of water and then the last quarter mile on a sidewalk.

At the airport, right on time, we waited with a few others. An hour later the airline employees showed up. They left their wet shoes at the front door and wore just their socks.

Much later, while on the plane going to Gatwick, I looked at Michael's address and along with it a note, "The facts are friendly here."

I know what Michael meant in his note. The facts are that Scotland opened its heart to me, as one would for a lost but not forgotten son. I'm learning to trust this acceptance. Michael's note touched me.

THIRTEEN

When Berrigan and I returned to the States, Gillian met us at the airport. "Hi, Alan, hi, Berrigan, I missed you guys!" Gillian's face will always look fresh to me, especially when her skin is flushed.

"How are you doing? It's great to see you, Gillian; you look beautiful."

Eye contact came easy for me. I always forget how beautiful Gillian really is.

"Berrigan, I missed you, how was the trip? Something came in the mail for you from school. You should read it as soon as you get home."

"Mom, I just got off the plane, and you're already doing it."

"What?"

"You're already telling me what to do, and I haven't been on the ground for twenty minutes. Leave me alone!"

We walked in silence to the truck. When Berrigan and Gillian go at it, I become quiet. The feel of us all being together was less than happy. Decisions made while not trusting our own resources have taken a toll on Gillian and me.

Years ago, Gillian made a decision I opposed: to work with a man that I thought would only pull us apart. He demanded long hours and an unrealistic work load from Gillian, and it has stayed this way.

The slack in Gillian's golden handcuffs are what California's restaurants, mortgages and new vehicles are made of. There always seems to be freedom between the end of the chain and a bone not yet chewed.

I forget that I have an abundance of creativity, and failure is not in my vocabulary. Thoughts of why my little family relates to one another at times in such a petty way flashed by me as we walked to the truck carrying our gear.

Driving home, the streets were soured by the glare of L.A.'s sun. Up the steep driveway at home in the midst of unloading, while Berrigan carried one of the bikes up to the house, Gillian turned and made gentle but strong eye contact with me.

"Alan, did you see her?"

I am bound by the truth, which means I can think anything I want, but not do anything that would cheapen me into a lie. I did not ask dishonestly, "Who?" I just said, "No," and the air stood still between us.

There was relief in Gillian's face but no feeling to move closer to me. Looking at each other with our electrical switches off, the day ended without passion. If I were to leave, it would be because Gillian will never find the raptures of lovemaking with me. Maybe she would be relieved not having to deal with what she calls, "my perpetual hard-on." It's not the truth; I 'm not always aroused.

Is it cruel to both of us to be together?

The next day, I told Gillian about the boat with her name on it, and how then and there my commitment to her was renewed.

With time to think about it and Gillian saying that she would move to Scotland, if that's where my soul needs to be, I now understand that Scotland will always be there for me.

FOURTEEN

A year after my trip with Berrigan I returned to Scotland a fourth time.

In Edinburgh, Gillian and I picked up the train to Inverness, a six-hour ride. Knowing we would get in late, Gillian made prior arrangements for lodging at a bed and breakfast.

Early the next morning we walked back to the train station and caught the train to Kyle of Lochalsh.

This time something was wrong with the tracks right outside of Inverness. So at the train station, everyone going towards the Isle of

Skye boarded a bus for the first forty-five minutes of the three-hour train ride to Kyle of Lochalsh. Gillian and I shared the same row with a fellow who was a graphic artist in Inverness. We talked about life and work. I told him that if I found a job in Scotland working with children, teaching them sculpture and horseback riding, I might move here.

His reply was, "My wife is one of the administrators in just such a place and they are looking for someone like you." I was glad Gillian heard what he said; I would've thought it was my imagination.

I felt God was saying, "It's your choice but as your father in heaven I would like it if you took Scotland up on its offer." Unfortunately, I hadn't had enough of Los Angeles yet.

Forty-five minutes later, we got on the train bound for Kyle of Lochalsh. At the tracks end, at the dock, we walked to the City Link bus stop as I had done with Berrigan the summer before. This time, we didn't stop in Broadford or on the trip back, run across the bridge as I had done with Berrigan in the cold rain. Instead, we went on to the small beautiful town of Portree.

In an amused way the bus driver said to Gillian, "I remember that man you're with. He was here last year with his son." When he saw my face get red, the driver started to falter through a partial explanation. He told Gillian, "At the time, I had just returned to work after recovering from a car accident, and that is why I remembered him and his son." This time while on his bus we rode everywhere for free.

How could he remember me on a crowded bus from a year ago? I'd like to know the answer without asking the question. Mark Twain said, "Man is the only animal that blushes and needs to."

I've been told, "Close your eyes and your inner voice will know." I can see the woman's face from the Isle of Skye looking at me, the way I had wished Gillian could, with raw wanting.

Throughout the Isle of Skye while on City Link buses, we were introduced almost like family to the other drivers. Whatever kind of impression Berrigan and I made, at least it was not a bad one.

FIFTEEN

Not having a strong interest in castles, we only visited two during our four trips to Scotland: Edinburgh Castle and a small one on the Isle of Skye. The stately manor of Dunvegan on Skye was nice, but the grounds of this castle were beautiful. The lush green trees and plants met the languishing old growth on winding, narrow footpaths. These paths veined their way behind, over and around waterfalls and followed the old brook's journey faithfully.

We walked in the cool drizzle for a few wonderful hours. Then we rested and ate in the estate's rustic, single-story, workmen and visitor's cafe. An older man in a tweed jacket sat down next to me. We started to talk.

It was a conversation that was lightly framed, but something deeper inside his words suggested more than just a friendly chat. I enjoyed the conversation.

It was getting near the close of the day. Gillian and I finished our food and drink. The man got on the last bus home, back to Portree with us. In this nearly-empty bus, he sat down in the seat in front of ours and turned around. He asked us if we had any children. We spoke about Berrigan and family in general. The pain I felt coming through his body when we first started talking in the café now made its way to his lips. His eyes got teary as he talked of the love he and his wife have for their only child.

"My son married a Belgian woman. We didn't care who he married, as long as there was love between them. She's taken him from Scotland; maybe he'll never return. He only calls home when his wife is out of ear's range. We're denied visits with our grandson, either to go to Belgium or to have her spend time here. My son apologizes to me and my wife for not letting us know our grandson.

"Her rejecting us is one thing, but the way she treats our son is another. He has told us that she had planned to have his baby, and after that to stop all affection towards him. All she does is demand that he work more, so she can buy things for her other family members. It appears it was our daughter-in-law's plan all along.

"She is a fashion model first and foremost. Nothing comes before her reflection in the mirror. To say anything would only make the situation worse for our son. Hope is all that is left for me that someday we will be together again. Until that day, we love him from afar."

I replied, "I love my son deeply. It would break my heart if this happened with us."

"Yes, my heart is breaking."

I believe the heart knows the deep, mysterious reasons why it pumps blood, and all it needs to continue is hope.

The home inside me is filled with love for my son. This closeness is enriched by the uncluttered modesty of my external world. Making sacrifices for Berrigan is easy. If he were drafted, I'd go in his place, or if he were to fight for our homeland, we'd be side by side.

Another man in his fifties, who'd been listening off and on to the conversation, now shared that he was today reunited for the first time with his twenty-year-old daughter. "I haven't seen her in fifteen years. I know things are the way they are, and it would be nice if things were different, but they're not. I am an outsider to my own family. My ex-wife has shut me out as your daughter-in-law has. I had an affair, and my wife never stopped hating me."

My ears have probably never been put to better use than hearing these two men's stories. On this day, I did something rare for me: I just listened.

Within this conversation, I saw clearly what was at risk by choosing to leave my home.

My nature is to push things past their limits, over-tightening jar lids and nuts onto bolts. Men have offered me torque wrenches; I refuse thinking when the wrench indicates it's enough, I should do more. Tasks feel unfinished if I cannot take them to the point of stripping or breaking. I fear things falling apart or coming loose.

Other times I will just leave without a word. Not one who stays on trails, I look for landmarks in the distance, thinking I'll be guided toward some unknown destinations. Instead, for the most part I'm left dirty with my boots worn, wondering if I can back-track toward the people and places I've abandoned, hoping to change the past.

I've tried to leave Gillian many times, but a fever, not in my flesh but in my skull keeps me from running. Like a retriever with a duck in his mouth, I wouldn't let go of Gillian. I softly bit her with words, plans, and then she brought me to my knees by having our son.

Gillian and I love each other, but if I left, the fog between us would quickly become thick. The memory of her voice and touch would soon leave me. I believe god would not let our paths cross again. In the first few months of our relationship if we hadn't spent almost every day together it would have fluttered away like a seasonal butterfly.

Under all of this crap of how Gillian feels about me, it's simple. I wanted to be ravaged and always will.

With the same stubbornness I hold onto everything I desire, I've held onto Gillian. I took Berrigan and a friend of ours on a horseback ride while Gillian was at a national sales meeting for her work in Vancouver, British Columbia. We rented horses about an hour north of Vancouver. The wrangler who rented us the horses said, "We don't need guides. Theses horses know the trails; they won't let you get lost."

Knocking on a door, a woman came out. I said, "Hi, we seem to be lost. Could I use your phone to call the stable?"

"Yes, but how did you guys get all the way over here with those horses?" The wrangler was also shocked at getting this phone call two hours past our one-hour ride time from the hilly, neighborhood home, miles away.

I had forced the sweet mare to go the way I wanted her to go. Even though she reared and backed up as did Gillian in our relationship. I backed the mare into a tree, and when the horse's front hooves came off the ground, I whispered in her ear, "Stop it."

I've taken this beautiful woman Gillian on a ride in a direction she didn't want to go. For months I told her, "You love me, why else would you want to spend every day with me?" Finally, she said, "I love you."

"No, Gillian. It's, 'I love you, Alan.'

By this time, I didn't believe her. I'd worn her down, forcing her toward intimacy. I wanted to jump creeks and run in the surf with her not take her back to the ranch. As with that mare in British Columbia, I wish I'd let Gillian take me where she wanted and then dismounted. Along with wearing Gillian down, I wore a hole in my belief that anyone would find me attractive.

This universe does conspire. God gives me little doses of death each day, and I don't want our relationship to die. I love the wind; what holds this relationship together could be lost because of a breeze, a whim, hurt feelings or infatuation, so I hold on too tight for it's easy for me to leave.

Would my wife be better off with someone else? She does hold her emotions in check with me, and she spends time with better educated men, not ones rough around the edges like me. She talks about how great they are, adding fuel to my negative thoughts. I've said to her, "Gillian, it's all right to leave." But that's just part of a game to see myself as someone dark and alone, fulfilling a childhood mindset of a destiny which kept my young ego intact. I'm angry – pissed off that I need to be perfect to deserve love. In this constant state of imperfection I, at times, see a hermit's life as my only option.

SIXTEEN

One last Scottish encounter, and then I'll let it be. A Scottish art dealer asked me if I would be interested in doing a small sculpture of William Wallace. Not knowing what William Wallace looked like, my answer was still, "Yes." There was one stipulation, which we simultaneously agreed on: He would not look like the actor Mel Gibson, who portrayed the Scottish hero. After some research, the visual was still not any clearer to me about what this patriot of Scotland looked like.

While standing in line at a café in Venice, California, I sandwiched between two men talking. The one behind me sounded as if he had a Scottish accent. Turning in his direction I asked him if he was a Scot. He replied, "Yes."

"Is it possible you might know something about William Wallace and statues of him in Scotland? I have been given the opportunity to do a sculpture of him."

He turned a little white and said, "Yes, my father, who died last year, was responsible for discovering the largest sculpture of Wallace in Scotland and single-handedly organized the successful endeavor of restoring the huge statue to its original luster. And you're in luck I'm going home to Scotland in a few weeks. While I'm there, I'll take pictures for you."

I received the photos. The sculpture resembled a Roman soldier. It was not what I envisioned but it gave me permission to go in my own direction. William Wallace is patient with me though. I have half-finished sculpting him twenty times, then destroyed the sculpture. I need to listen to Wallace's spirit.

This connection with Alba is about more than the crumbling of old flesh and blood, then recycled and used in my name. I feel like I always have to pretend I have good manners – overly polite, held back from living.

I can only be patient that on the other side of death it will all become clear to me why I'm living in the twenty-first century instead of just being bones in Alba. Most likely I'll be born again and forget it all until I trust to let the intuitive self lead.

24

LACK OF INTIMACY

In 1970, at the age of eighteen, I hitched north with my dog Curry. In Oregon, heading towards Alaska's Arctic Circle, I got a ride a hundred miles southwest of Mist, Oregon in an early 1960-something, Chevy pickup truck. We were all young. There were three in the front seat and I was one of three in the back, in the bed of the truck on a mattress, elevated on a sheet of plywood. We watched the forest go by under the protection of the truck's camper shell. We drove deep into forests owned by the toilet paper empire Crown Zellerbach.

We got to know one another while picking up and dropping off other hitchhikers. Curry and I became residents of this truck – going who knows where. The intimacy slowed me down. For three weeks my dog and I were mainstays, as the Chevy rolled over Oregon's dirt roads. The companionship was good; nobody ever asked me where I came from. No one seemed to mind that I didn't smile or say much. We were five men and one woman, all unshaven, long-haired and lost. At times it was musical chairs: someone was always leaving and coming, and most were young men. Two of the mainstays were a boyfriend and girlfriend. She was an attractive Janis Joplin type who fucked everyone who came on board, while we all cruised down the road.

On a quiet night, all of us just sitting around a camp fire, she looked at me and said, "It's your turn. Come on over here, or do you want me to come over there?"

"Thank you for the offer, but I don't think so."

"Do you mean you don't want me? You don't like women?"

"I like sex when I feel like I'm the only one. Besides you already have someone who loves you; I don't like hurting people."

Later that night, the boyfriend came up to me and thanked me and petted Curry while I said nothing. I was fearful of touch and I wanted it so bad. When people petted Curry, I always felt like I'd been hugged.

While her boyfriend spoke, I was thinking. The mandate for life is strong but fragile. I don't know why I didn't die in infancy while being left in that makeshift cage by my mother and father, but like puppies in pet stores who seem to survive alone, I found happiness once released. One careless act of a parent can mean death to a child, or this boyfriend might start a family with this nightmare of a woman in the back of a pickup.

2

In a bar in White Horse, a big Native Canadian woman said, "I want to fuck you, hippie, and your dog, but first I'm going to beat you up." As I turned to leave the large, old, crowded bar, she jumped on my back. I spun around ramming her backside against the door jamb. She let go and sank to the floor. I've run from tenderness and withdrawn from brutal overtures at times.

Though I had long hair and a beard, you could not consider me a hippie. I've always been unkempt. Even today, somebody has to remind me to get a haircut. I really don't see the purpose in cutting my hair, other than it can get in the way when welding a sculpture or using the nippers while trimming a horse. To save money and time on warm days, I wouldn't waste the day getting dressed if it weren't a law and didn't offend so many people.

3

Once again back in Oregon a few weeks after leaving Alaska, my dog Curry and I got a ride from Tacoma down a small two-lane road to the Oregon coast, in an old van driven by a woman. I was almost nineteen and she was sixty-something. She told me, "I was once a dancer, and now I teach it." Her legs vouched for it as her left foot depressed the VW's clutch. The gray in this woman's red hair seemed to calm her down, and the freckled, weather-beaten, tanned skin slapped youth across her face with a sensuous hand.

We got drunk on red wine in her large, one-room cabin in the forest. At some point she tossed me a towel. "If you want to take a shower, the bathroom is over there. The bathroom has no electricity, but there are candles on the shelf in flower pots above the bathroom sink, and another on a shelf in the shower." All the walls of the house were cedar, including the bathroom, but the shower's long and tall exterior wall was made of mosaic tiles —coke, wine, beer and whisky bottle bottoms, glass blocks and things that were indiscernible but handsome. There was no need for a shower door; the entrance was offset on the other side of the bathroom's cedar wall. Feeling my way from the bathroom through the maze to the shower and finding the second huge red candle, I lit it with a long wooden match from the bunch in the second flower pot. The full moon draped in storm clouds beamed through the shower's glass wall, making a faintly shifting glow of greens and ambers onto the shower's mosaic floor.

Over the sound of the pounding surf, I heard her say something, then the creak of the bathroom door opening. She was old, but her body wasn't. She held me and kissed me; it felt good, but the space of the years between us made me lonely inside, like making love to a ghost.

4

While attending horseshoeing school during the day, I got a nighttime job on the Sunset Strip at a striptease club as a part time parking lot attendant and cashier. I was also supposed to tell men not to make a mess in their seats. A few times I was asked by one of the dancers to take my clothes off and, so to speak, dance on stage with her, and Curry and I did.

After work, early one morning at this stripper's house, she made it with her girl friend after she asked me to watch. I wasn't interested in watching. I only stayed with the hope of being next, but sleep found them first.

Watching them did nothing for me sexually. Leaving them sleeping on the bed, Curry and I walked back home in the shadows before sunrise. I felt unsettling quietness in my body. While watching them I perceived them to be tied to a more stable force, which didn't need to impose dominance in order to will pleasure. The sexuality between them was as tender as a slow dance. They were holding hands with their whole bodies and then shivering into a climax.

The following night at work the stripper apologized.

5

While hiking in the Sierras, I came across a woman in her thirties who was crying. I asked her if she was OK. "Yes, but I'm lost," she answered.

"Where do you want to go?"

"I was on the Muir trail, and I don't think I'm on it any more."

"You're still on it, just keep going north or south and don't be so distracted by the beauty that you lose sight of the trail," I replied.

"How did you know that's what happened to me?"

"Cause it happens to me all the time. I've learned over the years to look as far ahead as I can on the trail, mark it in my mind, and only then look at all the beauty around me."

"Would you mind if I walked with you and your dog for awhile?"

"No, not at all."

Then she looked at Curry and back at me and asked, "By the way, where are you going, if you don't mind me asking?"

"Um, I don't know, but I know where I am. If you tell me where you want to go I'll set you in that direction."

"OK."

"Where is it that you wanted to end up?" I asked.

"I don't remember."

Looking straight at her I asked, "How did you get here anyway?" She started to cry again and finally said over her weeping, "He was my friend, and then he attacked me."

I said, "You need to go home as quickly as possible. You need to be with friends."

"Yes, please get me out of here!"

Trying to put her mind at ease I said, "There are a lot of trails which intersect with the John Muir trail; we'll take the next one out. It will almost drop you off, down into Bishop, were you can then take a bus home or call a friend. I'll hike with you till it's all downhill and switch backs. At that point, there will be a lot more people on the trail, and it will be impossible to get lost. Do you want to tell me what happened?"

"He was a friend. We've known each other since we were kids. On our fourth night into the trip, we went to bed after a long night's conversation. In the middle of the night he jumped on top of me.

I thought he was just kidding. I couldn't get him off of me. He was yelling at me at the same time."

"You were just friends?"

"Yes, only friends, it was totally out of the blue. We'd been, or should I say, I was trying to broach the subject of his homosexuality, which he denied all of his life. Something I said set him off. He told me he was only attracted to women, which I knew was a lie. Soon afterwards we turned in for the night, without another word said.

"I felt him not desiring me, but his anger instead: needing to prove to me he had this overpowering need to have sex with me. It was such a bad acting job that I almost wanted to console him after his feeble attempt at being a 'brutal heterosexual.' Then he apologized and said he didn't know what came over him, and it wouldn't happen again."

"He left you here all alone?"

"In the morning, I told him I wanted to hike by myself; he left me my part of the food and then went on ahead."

6

To a wolf, a limping animal is a meal. I watch all of us yearn to limp in safety. While Gillian was lecturing on the positives of nutraceuticals for women's healthcare to doctors in London, I walked the city's streets.

Museums are my weakness and after spending the morning gazing at works of art I took a break for lunch in the museum's restaurant. I was led to a window seat by a pretty hostess with a Belgian accent. I passed by a woman in her thirties, who was being seated at a table I had refused. It faced a bare, white wall and was isolated from the rest of the restaurant's patrons in a place that could be considered not even part of the restaurant.

The view from my table looked down onto the city square, with other museums and an opera house surrounding it and a magnificent fountain in the middle, which made the area come alive.

All the tables on the side where I dined were up against this window, so everyone ate side by side, while viewing the square.

I thought about the woman accepting the table that I hadn't. It led to a painful question—what will people accept in life? Why does one person take a last hunger-weakened step and lunge into a bus, leaving his or her poverty behind, while others die in their own despair?

My drink was served to my table. As my food request was being taken, the woman I'd noticed being seated at the less-than-desirable table was now being seated to my immediate left.

I thought I wasn't in the mood for talking, so I didn't speak to my new lunch time neighbor. The tables being close together with the seating focused on the scenery of the courtyard below gave subtle permission to converse without having one's space truly invaded.

My silence didn't stop her from starting a conversation with me.

"Are you an American?"

"Yes, how did you know?"

"I heard you giving your order to the waitress. What brings you to London?"

"My heart."

"You've fallen in love with someone from England?"

"No, my wife is lecturing here in London. I don't care for England. It seems a little over used, I'm just here for a day, then to Scotland." I explained some of the events which led me back to Scotland.

She then said to me, "I knew when you passed me on the steps in the museum that you were one of us."

"I passed you on the steps?"

"Yes, you smiled at me as you ran up the stairs. You're an open person. "

"I am?"

"I'm from Ireland. Scotland and Ireland have a lot in common."

"I've never been to Ireland, but a plan is in the works to go there next year. I hear it's beautiful there."

"Yes, it is beautiful and you'll love the people."

"What do you do in Ireland, if you don't mind me asking?"

"I'm a psychologist at a school for emotionally troubled girls."

"Many years ago, I worked at a home, or what you call a school for emotionally troubled children. It was the best job I ever had. Do you enjoy your work?"

"Yes, very much."

"What do you do there?"

"My job is to help the girls who are dealing with self abuse, pregnancy, and in general are in emotional distress. Sometimes I can make inroads and see change, but most of the time if they do have a breakthrough, it has been a long uphill journey. Molestation victims are the hardest to help. At the school in the states you worked at, did you see these problems?"

"Yes."

"So you understand the struggle these children go through."

"I understand about molestation: they hide out, overachieve, over compensate by being tough, sexual, or anything to hide from the guilt and pain of not being in control. The pain they go through is unbearable to watch without feeling sadness and rage at the same time. Their youth, freedom and love for life seem to have been stolen from them. They walk at times with their heads down, hair covering beautiful faces, only acting strong when it doesn't count while they move through the day."

Looking out the window she took a taste of her white wine and said, "So you know."

With both our meals finished and plates removed, we both just stared out the window.

After a few minutes of shared silence she rose from her seat. I stood up and we hugged with no words spoken.

From my seat a few moments later I watched her enter the stream of people in the city square below.

7

I have always been attracted to tomboys. The ones who hike, speak real thoughts, and used me to get themselves off. Gillian and I were like that for a while in 1974. Then, we found other things to occupy our time: making money, building a home and surrendering to our memories of childhood abuse. Being married changed me; like trickling water down the side of a road, all of a sudden, it was a ditch. Gillian used to complain that I was dogmatic and never would apologize for anything; now, she complains that I'm too apologetic.

It hasn't just been me who has discredited my gender; I know others. I saw my friend Robert collude with his wife in his own emasculation. Following his wife's lead, he gave over the mentoring of their son to another man who was far less qualified. Intuitively my friend knew it was the wrong thing to do. So much of the time male intuition is misinterpreted as paranoia.

Robert was undermined by anti-masculine sentiments. Sensitive, questioning every thought, he later developed a full-blown chronic case of self-doubt. The truth is this probing and pushing of men into self-awareness by women is that they're not in touch with their feminine power. The lie is that women and men's strengths reside within the same silhouette. We aren't women without breasts.

My friend gave the reins of his son's mentoring to a self-professed spiritual guru. Robert's reward for choosing this path of not believing in himself was divorce, distance from his son and perpetuating this legacy of the lie that men are a lesser kind of woman.

The most unattractive woman I ever met was Robert's wife. The ugliness was what came out of this so-called enlightened mouth and the behavior that followed. She was always pointing out her husband's inadequacy and his lack of masculine attributes; nothing ever passed her scrutiny. The fact was he had a good heart and a brilliant sense of humor. His wit showed off great intelligence, tenderness and kindness, which he had in abundance. But to avoid taking a stand in the family, he had employed self-doubt, and that was his mistake. Self-doubt is seductive. It starts off as almost a recreational academic endeavor and then it becomes the reason that things of a challenging nature don't get done.

I retrieved my manhood by firing the people that Gillian and the architect had hired to build our home. With the kind of drama that only real life can bring, I rolled up my sleeves and saved the day, the house and my family's financial situation. What an inauthentic game, or is it?

I had a hard time believing such a good couple could give their son over to the creepy guru.

This spiritual phony put together a curriculum for their nine year old boy, which would be any middle-age retiree's dream. The son was being taught the deeper meaning of life through the ancient traditions of tennis and golf. This cardboard mentor was actually getting paid a lot of money for hanging out and playing golf and tennis with their beloved son. This so-called spiritual mentor was so out of shape that a young boy was just perfectly weak enough;

he could win against the child at will, but at the same time, this preteen was energetic enough to go chasing after all the tennis and golf balls. At one point, the guru had even conned the parents into giving him access to their trust fund; you knew they had to have one of those things floating around. Looking for gurus to live with you instead of the reverse is what people do with large amounts of what is called discretionary income that's not earned. This way of pursuing enlightenment is like asking a sculpture teacher to do your work of sculpting for you; never developing the talent or enlightenment that comes with putting your hands in the clay.

My son's best friend at the time was this child. The guru forbade Robert's son from having any contact with other children, unless they were part of the guru's small enclave, "for our son is on a higher path." At one point there must have been concern that this guru's coffers were beginning to dry up. So with a heartfelt fear he sought out Gillian and I with a "once in a lifetime opportunity." Because he could see "a glimmer of spirituality in us," he invited Gillian and me to become part of his group. The wife was emphatic. "Just meet with him once, Gillian; you'll see what I am taking about." Gillian has always been a tripper, and she said OK. I declined the wife's "once in a lifetime opportunity."

Gillian is a medical anthropologist. In addition to her knowledge of western medicine, she has studied traditional approaches to healing from different cultures. She has counseled some big names in guru-dom. When she met this so-called guru, to use Gillian's words, "He isn't one of them. He's just an angry, old fart, who's a con."

I went to Robert's fiftieth birthday party years later. It was celebrated within the context of a Quaker meeting. Forty people sitting in a circle; on internal urges individuals would get up and speak. Is this a good thing? If you were anyone but Robert's now ex-wife it might be a good thing.

She, like an erection that couldn't help itself, got up and spoke.

"When I met Robert, he was so unattractive that I wondered who would ever go out with him. Then, of all people, me, I'm the one who starts dating him. Can you imagine that?" There were other "flattering" descriptions that she showered on him during his birthday ceremony. All of her impromptu moments were equal in their childish forms of hostility towards him, and in this same breath she skillfully filled the air with complements for herself.

I am really good about behaving at parties and I did. My tongue stayed still, but my mind started to whirl with retorts to her backhanded compliments.

In my twenties and thirties, the popular thinking was that men and women were the same. My need to be in a relationship led me to at least give this fallacy lip service in the hopes of finding pleasure for my lips. Finally, it became obvious to me that the pretense of this philosophy - *we are just like you females, so go to bed with us* - didn't work. What this thinking did, though, was make us look weak and displaced. It also left women frustrated. We were unable to be men who stood up for ourselves and our loved ones. The denial of manhood taken to its extreme truly leaves me defenseless against the social ills perpetuated by unsavory men who rape, beat, and make slaves of women and other men. I think mankind's past proves this, but tragically, history is more of a practice than a study.

Before I met Gillian, I had never incorporated this kind of thinking or questioning. Looking for a second meaning in everything I do and being sensitive, I did what I needed to do and didn't look back to see if I hurt someone. They would tell me if I had, and I was willing to make things right. But I wouldn't spend time on what I should not have said or what I wished I'd said. Things expressed in a rage were let go of soon after the fever of that moment left, never to be lamented.

In the early 1970's, Raul was in his mid-twenties. He was working on his PhD in psychology and had a supervisory position at a mental health institution. Being a very capable young man, he gained the respect of a young attractive gay woman colleague; Barbra felt safe enough to be free and honest with her compliments for others. They were very bright people and both were quite inspiring and altruistic.

Admiration and friendship began to grow for each other. Raul was straight; it was only a matter of time before he would fall in love with this wonderful woman. They talked about intimacy, but no amount of conversation could ever yield a change in desire for Barbra towards Raul. She was just not physically attracted to men.

The heart will make us do things at times that our sensible judgment would not allow and take us places that we should never go.

The argument Raul's heart gave to Barbra was that he was just like any of her women friends: warm, sensitive, and deeply caring. "So what's the difference?" They finally made an agreement to go to bed together with one promise: he would not touch her, unless she made the first overture. Above all, he was a man of his word.

With deep passion and desire for her, he tortured his way through the night without a touch. They remained friends even though he did truly have all those attributes that good women hold so dearly. He was still just a man. If he had not given into the lie that "underneath it all we are all the same," he would have saved himself the pain of that cold night.

8

I have learned to feel safe and comfortable with women and to love being around them, though to this day I don't feel comfortable in my mother's presence.

My love of women continues because of the wonderful women in my life: my wife, my sister, women friends that I shoe for, my sculpting group, writing group and the women who showed me their hearts before I knew how to receive them.

After writing this chapter I realize that though it is said men are less complicated sexually than women, I have to disagree. I leave this chapter unfinished.

25

HEART IN AN ICE CHEST

I accompanied Gillian this winter to an alternative medicine conference in Aspen, Colorado. The emphasis at the conference was on the things that are beyond the scope of medical science — why acupuncture works or why does prayer help, and looking at biochemistry under a different light. I had the opportunity to have a conversation with one of the top cardiologists in the United States. At first, I didn't understand why a heart specialist would lecture, or for that matter, attend a group of seminars where the focus was so far removed from the kind of work he does.

After talking to him for awhile, it became clear. He was here to understand the things that can't be understood through the eyes of western medicine. Then I recall the famous heart surgeon, Dr. Michael DeBakey, being interviewed by a talk show host. The host asked DeBakey, "How is it that you can get off the airplane with an ice-cooler containing a heart, and hours later in another person's chest the heart beats on its own?" All the other questions the doctor was asked, he had answers for. But when it came to this one question, his reply was, "That is a question for God."

HOPE

Through the years when I find my attraction to Gillian is waning, I'll sit someplace where there are no distractions and write about when we first started dating, and then my desire for her is there again. I put on the page memories of my initial attraction to Gillian, what she wore and where we were, but not what was said. In this crazy world of psycho-babble, Gillian's tongue was a poor messenger for her heart. I remember her gray and pastel tee shirts and overalls, loving the way she moved underneath them, as her French braid gently swung while riding one of the horses.

I don't know, maybe the search for the right woman is in vain if I think I'll ever find peace between a good pair of legs. But being a man who wrestles with love is far better than being a man who doesn't.

I've been asked why and how it is that we've stayed together all these years. I do believe I have found help from above. I would have fallen into the poverty of loneliness and would never have known what a family could be if not for Eros.

26

NO IMAGE

"It sounds as if you're in the dark night of your soul." My friend Luka Maxwell said these words to me over industrial grade coffee at a café. His words would have gone down better with single malt whisky.

I met Luka and his wife June through Gillian over two decades ago. They were sitting in our row at the Ram Dass lecture on Gillian's and my second date. They all met in graduate school. During my twenty-five year relationship with Luka and June, we've watched each others' angst over career mistakes, marriage struggles, loved ones' sicknesses and now the attending of friends and family members' funerals: the inevitable curse of middle age.

What brought on this "dark night of the soul" comment was that I said I was having a hard time finding a manly image of myself to hold onto. I thought by the time I was in my fifties, I'd have it all together. Most of my adult life, there's been something that isn't working and a counterbalance of something that is. But now most everything I do is eclipsed by self-doubt. In the morning, I can no longer effortlessly paint a picture of myself as a blacksmith, horse-shoer, sculptor, writer or builder of my own house. I'm left with one truth: I am. I'm not the imposed standards of manhood I've worshiped all these years. In my mid-twenties, I exchanged my title from being just "Alan" – this culmination of childhood loves of nature, animals and sculpture – to husband, father and man. No one asked me to exile me from myself. I just did it. My actions were that of a salmon going upstream, thinking my loves were only childhood notions. As a young man, I thought I needed to take my place, to fling myself towards shallow headwaters, to grow pale and die.

But now, the struggle to make my mark or lift more than my weight doesn't hold a candle to those childhood truths. At the same time, it's painful to let go of the things that held my pride together for so many years.

Under all this manly work stuff, what has washed up onto shore is a sense of never belonging, mistrust of others and shame. There are moments when, just walking down the street, I need to reach out to people, not to be friendly but to make sure that I haven't done something to get myself ostracized from the world of humans. At other times I don't even want to be part of this world.

Gillian and I have adopted what has turned out to be a kindred soul for me: a Great Pyrenees, from a Pyrenees dog rescue. He was found in Tulare County with broken ribs, pneumonia and the pads of his paws scorched from walking on hot pavement. The Pyrenees rescue named him Tulare Tim as they lovingly watched him heal. We call him Tulie. I love him.

Gillian and I joke that we should have named him Spooner. Each night, all one hundred and thirty-five pounds of him gets on the bed to spoon with whoever is in bed first. And during the day, in some fashion, Tulie does the same with Rosalind, our extremely confident thirteen-year old Great Pyrenees. But the times in between haunt him. He shies from children on bikes, cowers when I have a rake in my hand. There are other times though, when he leaps a four foot wall to attack a red tail hawk that has found a perch in our yard. He reminds me that even though he is one of God's brave and majestic creatures, the pains of puppy hood stay. Like Tulie, I must remember to spoon.

I told Luka, "There are fragments of childhood remembrances emerging: things I cherished in childhood, friends, art, dogs, horses and the written word. Maybe I can make this time of my life all about these things."

Luka looked at me with a smile and said, "How interesting, Alan. It's amazing, we spend so much of our time doing things that aren't our passion, and if we aren't following our passions, what are we doing?"

Not long ago, in the mountain resort of Mammoth Lakes, California, I met a man from India. We talked while we gazed at the sunlight balancing on the ripples of cobalt blue waters of a high Sierra lake. He told me, "I find that after a short time I need to go to the city. I can spend months in New York and London, but somehow I don't think it's that way for you. You seem to feel at peace here, but I need the electricity of the city."

I replied "You're right. I need the quiet. I get lost in the clutter of city noise. In the mountains, I can hear my inner voice. The dictates of society scatter like cockroaches."

"But you said you live in L.A. How do you manage that?"

"I found a community within L.A., West Hollywood, which is home for me, where men prefer to hold hands rather than fight, and aesthetics plays a part in almost everything. The chance to be myself, do my art, write, and smile for no apparent reason is fostered here. True, it isn't being in the mountains, but at least an individual can find his own voice."

Then he asked me, "Have you ever read Carl Rogers's book, "On Becoming a Person?"

I replied, "That book was a lifeline for me when I was young. I'd always felt different, but Rogers made me feel okay about being me. 'On Becoming a Person' was the how-to book for Shakespeare's words, 'To thine own self be true' The fact that you keep Rogers's work in the back of your mind must make it hard for you to see the poor in your country, witnessing the limits of their existence and just working to stay alive."

"No," he replied. "It's the opposite. It's because of 'On Becoming a Person' I can understand that the individual is much more than a bank account. A person walks into Roger's office not understanding who he or she is, influenced by social dictates of what he or she should be. But if a person knows his station in life the focus can then be about the internal process. My appreciation has grown for my country's cultural wisdom. The facts are there are more millionaires in India than in the entire population of Canada, and India's middle-class is larger than the entire population of the United States. You should visit India. It's beautiful – the glass-making, clothing and the food; it's unlike anyplace else in the world. We are a civilized people. India is the only country that peacefully got the English to retreat. Ours is a culture that sits on ancient wisdom."

"But how do you justify the caste system?" I asked.

"All men live within a caste system. In the United States, it's where your house is, what kind of car you drive and, of course, the clothes you wear. Even the Amish in Ohio have distinction in quality of fabric and stitch in their clothing between communities. In India, we have no pretense of equality which leads to envy."

Soon after those words, we parted. I watched him get into a twelve-cylinder, eighty-thousand-dollar Jaguar, thinking how temporary his life is with no place to call home. As he drove away, it became clear to me that I should only visit Scotland rather than live there. The family I've helped to create here would be destroyed, even though at times I feel empty and dead inside. But my being adds to the welfare of my wife and son's lives and theirs to mine. I do wonder, though, if I have outstayed my visit, that the powers that be are telling me to move on. Since I've been a child, I've been outstaying my welcomes.

I shared this conversation with Luka. His reply was, "It takes a year to no longer feel like a visitor in a place. How interesting, this guy from India just travels, but it sounds like he never stops long enough for the honeymoon to be over. You're the opposite."

"You think so, Luka?"

"Sure, man. You're staying with work that for the most part wasn't what you wanted to do and living in the city instead of the mountains, which give you peace. The question always remains: 'What does Alan want to do?'"

"Yeah, Luka, finally now in my fifties, I'm starting to do what I love to do: make love, ride horses, write, sculpt and be with friends."

"Bravo, Alan."

Wrestling with these thoughts, I've come to understand that my blood and soul, which are tied to this earth, belong to Scotland, but my life is owned by the commitments that I have made to family, to friends. My home is in America and Canada. I will keep visiting Scotland to remember the ground I come from, so I can remember I belong.

My son will leave for college in two months. He'll never return home in the same way, as a child. But the things that bind us together will remain: dogs, nature and love.

Echoes of my days with my son Berrigan are all that will be left in this house I made. It shouldn't be any other way; there is solemnity in time passing. But, as with all old dogs who teach puppies the ways of the world, if and when, I'll help with my son's litter, so a healthy legacy can take hold.

I have two promises to this wonderful home that has kept us dry. One is to have an arborist check the health of our two redwoods, and the other is to have a conversation with the ghost, whom I will always be scared of but love.

I feel a little lighter after writing all this down. I wonder how I'll soon feel when rolling these pages up and placing them within the staircase banister I made.

This house I built has framed my thoughts into a tangible evocation of me as a man, while the healthy voice in me is what sustains and tells me I am.

Closing the fire screen, I'll sit alone and listen for Her to speak in flames, wood smells and heat, as men have always done. I no longer wait for things to be the way they should be but never are.